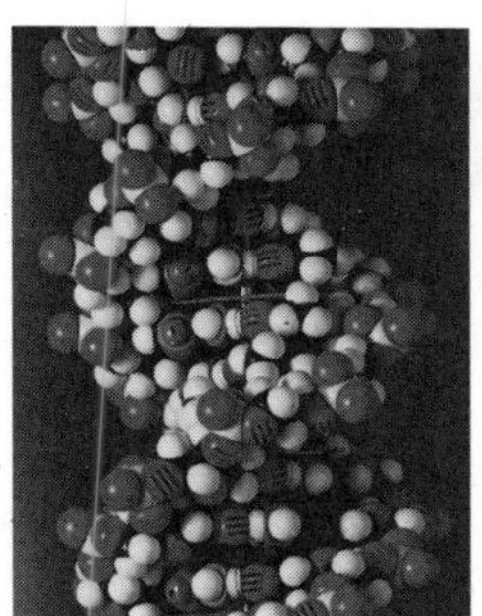

Exploring Chemistry

General, Organic, & Biochemistry for Lecture

Tenth Edition

Eileen Delgado Johann
Dorma J. C. Gottlieb
Ana Alejandre Ciereszko

Department of Chemistry, Physics, & Earth Sciences
Miami Dade College–Kendall Campus

Tenth Edition

Printed in the United States of America

10 9 8 7 6 5 4 3 2 1

ISBN 978-0-7380-5605-0

Hayden-McNeil Publishing
14903 Pilot Drive
Plymouth, MI 48170
www.hmpublishing.com

Ciereszko 5605-0 F12 (Exploring Chemistry–Lecture)

Acknowledgements

The authors sincerely appreciate the contributions and dedication provided by the faculty and students of the Chemistry Department of Miami Dade College. Special thanks are extended to Professor Larry Bray for his suggestions and valuable input in creating many exercises added at the end of each chapter, to Dr. Marta E. Pappas for her many hours of effort assisting in this project, and to our families for their patience and unwavering support.

This book is intended to be used by students in the health professions enrolled in a one-semester course in General, Organic, and Biochemistry. The sections in biochemistry are combined with organic chemistry to accelerate the pace of the course. If the user elects to do so, the order of the chapters may be modified.

Table of Contents

1

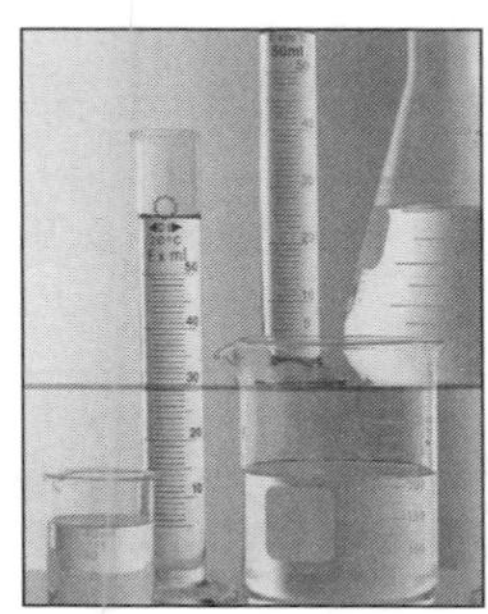

Measurements

Measurements are essential in science. In the field of medicine three systems of measurement are used: the English, the Metric, and the Apothecary systems. Conversions within and between measurement systems are necessary. The concepts of density, specific gravity, and temperature and their applications are also in common usage in medical sciences.

I. Conversion Factors in Calculations

To convert from one unit of measurement to another, conversion factors are used. Since there are 100 cents in one dollar:

$$100 \text{ cents} = 1 \text{ dollar}$$

Conversion factors for this relationship are:

$$\frac{100 \text{ cents}}{1 \text{ dollar}} \quad \text{or} \quad \frac{1 \text{ dollar}}{100 \text{ cents}}$$

The form of the conversion factor used in a calculation is the one which allows for the cancellation of units.

Example A: How many cents are there in 5 dollars?

Known equality → 1 dollar = 100 cents

$$? \text{ cents} = 5 \cancel{\text{dollars}} \left(\frac{100 \text{ cents}}{1 \cancel{\text{dollar}}}\right) = 500 \text{ cents}$$

Problem 1. Perform the following one-step conversions:

a. 6 yd = ____ ft (1 yd = 3 ft)

b. 12 ft = ___ yd (1 yd = 3 ft)

c. 120 sec = ___ min (1 min = 60 sec)

d. 4 min = ____ sec (1 min = 60 sec)

II. The Metric System

The metric system was developed to simplify conversions among units of measure. The French Academy of Science proposed the system in 1790. Antoine Lavoisier, a prominent French scientist, participated in the effort to develop the metric system although he is better known for his experiments on gases. He gave hydrogen and oxygen their names. In 1794, Lavoisier met with an untimely death. For his connections with the French monarchy he was guillotined. Lavoisier is one of the better known victims of the French Revolution.

Basic units of length, volume, and mass were established. Other units are multiples of ten larger or smaller than the base unit and prefixes are used in conjunction with the base unit. The base unit for length is the **meter**, for mass is the **gram**, and for volume is the **liter**. A ruler can be used to measure length, a balance to measure mass, and a graduated cylinder to measure volume.

A. Base Units

Length	Mass	Volume
meter = m	gram = g	liter = L

B. Prefixes

Prefix	Abbreviation	Examples for length
kilo	k	1 km = 1000 m
deci	d	1 m = 10 dm
centi	c	1 m = 100 cm
milli	m	1 m = 1,000 mm
micro	μ	1 m = 1,000,000 μm

More examples of how prefixes could be expressed are given below:

Mass:			Volume:		
1 gram	=	10 dg	1 liter	=	10 dL
1 gram	=	100 cg	1 liter	=	100 cL
1 gram	=	1,000 mg	1 liter	=	1,000 mL
1 gram	=	1,000,000 μg	1 liter	=	1,000,000 μL

To interconvert between metric units, one or two steps are needed. One step is needed when converting from a prefixed unit to one of the base units or from a base unit to a prefixed unit.

Example B: Convert 2.73 m to cm.

$$? \text{ cm} = 2.73\,\cancel{\text{m}}\left(\frac{100\text{m}}{1\,\cancel{\text{m}}}\right) = 273 \text{ cm}$$

Example C: 125 μsec = _____ sec.

$$? \text{ sec} = 125\mu\,\cancel{\text{sec}}\left(\frac{1 \text{ sec}}{1{,}000{,}000\,\mu\,\cancel{\text{sec}}}\right) = 0.000125 \text{ sec}$$

Two steps are needed when converting from one prefixed unit to another. This process is as follows:

$$\text{prefixed unit 1} \xrightarrow{\text{step 1}} \text{base unit} \xrightarrow{\text{step 2}} \text{prefixed unit 2}$$

Example D: 100. mL = _____ cL

$$?\ \text{cL} = 100.\ \cancel{\text{mL}}\left(\frac{1\ \cancel{\text{L}}}{1000\ \cancel{\text{mL}}}\right)\left(\frac{100\ \text{cL}}{1\ \cancel{\text{L}}}\right) = 10.0\ \text{cL}$$

Example E: How many decigrams are there in 0.0571 kg?

$$?\ \text{dg} = 0.0571\ \cancel{\text{kg}}\left(\frac{1000\ \cancel{\text{g}}}{1\ \cancel{\text{kg}}}\right)\left(\frac{10\ \text{dg}}{1\ \cancel{\text{g}}}\right) = 571\ \text{dg}$$

Problem 2. Perform the following conversions:

a. 127 cg = ____ g

b. 1.34 L = ____ dL

c. 2030. μm = ____ mm

d. 1512 cL = ____ dL

e. 471 mg = ____ g

f. 0.00268 km = _____ m

g. 3.67 mm = ____ cm

h. 0.0175 cL = ____ μL

i. 0.631 g = ____ mg

j. 163 dsec = ____ ksec

III. The English System

The English system was developed over a period of centuries, therefore it is rather haphazard and confusing. This is the system that is commonly used in the United States. Since there is no consistency, to convert from one unit to another, relationships need to be memorized and tedious calculations performed! This is the major drawback of the English system, which led the British to discard it in 1971.

Commonly Used Relationships

Volume	Mass	Length
1 qt = 2 pt	1 lb = 16 oz	1 ft = 12 in
1 gal = 4 qt	1 ton = 2000 lb	1 yd = 3 ft
1 pt = 2 cups		1 mi = 5280 ft

To convert between units, the above equalities are used and the process may involve several steps.

Example F: How many feet are there in 24 inches?

The following relationship will be used:

$$1 \text{ ft} = 12 \text{ inches}$$

given quantity with unit

$$? \text{ ft} = 24 \cancel{\text{in}} \left(\frac{1 \text{ ft}}{12 \cancel{\text{in}}}\right) = 2 \text{ ft}$$

unwanted units cancelled out

IV. Metric ⇌ English Conversions

In order to convert between metric and English units the following conversions may be used.

Volume	Mass	Length
1 L = 1.06 qt	1 lb = 454 g	1 in = 2.54 cm
1 qt = 946 mL		

Example G: How many liters are there in 2.12 quarts?

$$? \text{ L} = 2.12 \text{ qt}\left(\frac{1 \text{ L}}{1.06 \text{ qt}}\right) = 2.00 \text{ L}$$

Example H: Convert 200. mL to qt.

$$? \text{ qt} = 200 \text{ mL}\left(\frac{1 \text{ L}}{1000 \text{ mL}}\right)\left(\frac{1.06 \text{ qt}}{1 \text{ L}}\right) = 0.212 \text{ qt}$$

Example I: 123 dg = ____ lb.

$$? \text{ lb} = 123 \text{ dg}\left(\frac{1\text{g}}{10 \text{ dg}}\right)\left(\frac{1 \text{ lb}}{454 \text{ g}}\right) = 0.0271 \text{ lb}$$

Example J: 2.75 cm = ____ in.

$$? \text{ in} = 2.75 \text{ cm}\left(\frac{1 \text{ in}}{2.54 \text{ cm}}\right) = 1.08 \text{ in}$$

Example K: 6 ft 5 in = _____ m.

Step 1. Convert 6 feet into inches

$$? \text{ in} = 6 \text{ ft}\left(\frac{12 \text{ in}}{1 \text{ ft}}\right) = 72 \text{ in}$$

Step 2. Add the total number of inches

$$72 \text{ in} + 5 \text{ in} = 77 \text{ in}$$

Step 3. Convert 77 inches into meters

$$? \text{ m} = 77 \text{ in}\left(\frac{2.54 \text{ cm}}{1 \text{ cm}}\right)\left(\frac{1 \text{ m}}{100 \text{ cm}}\right) = 2.0 \text{ m}$$

Problem 3. Perform the following conversions:

a. 216 in = ____ cm

b. 309 qt = ____ L

c. 159 g = ____ lb

d. 5.85 cm = ____ ft

e. 285 g = ____ oz

f. 0.0586 m = ____ in

g. 6.00 yd = ____ m

h. 127 μL = ____ qt

i. 13.4 dg = ____ lb

j. 100. m = ____ ft

k. 0.00101 ton = ____ g

l. 0.35 L = ____ cups

m. 0.020 mile = ____ m

V. Fractional Conversions

Quantities are often expressed as the relationship between two types of measurements; for example, when purchasing gasoline, the price is expressed in dollars per gallon. Speed limits are posted in miles per hour (mi/hr) in the United States, and in kilometers per hour (km/hr) elsewhere. As before, the conversion factors that are used are those that lead to the cancellation of unwanted units.

Example L: Convert 939 km/hr to km/min.

$$\frac{?\ \text{km}}{\text{min}} = 939\frac{\text{km}}{\cancel{\text{hr}}}\left(\frac{1\ \cancel{\text{hr}}}{60\ \text{min}}\right) = 15.7\frac{\text{km}}{\text{min}}$$

Example M: Convert 0.112 L/min into cL/hr.

$$?\frac{\text{cL}}{\text{hr}} = 0.112\frac{\cancel{\text{L}}}{\cancel{\text{min}}}\left(\frac{100\ \text{cL}}{1\ \cancel{\text{L}}}\right)\left(\frac{60\ \cancel{\text{min}}}{1\ \text{hr}}\right) = 672\frac{\text{cL}}{\text{hr}}$$

Example N: Convert 0.106 cm/sec into in/hr.

$$?\frac{\text{in}}{\text{hr}} = 0.106\frac{\cancel{\text{cm}}}{\cancel{\text{sec}}}\left(\frac{1\ \text{in}}{2.54\ \cancel{\text{cm}}}\right)\left(\frac{60\ \cancel{\text{sec}}}{1\ \cancel{\text{min}}}\right)\left(\frac{60\ \cancel{\text{min}}}{1\ \text{hr}}\right) = 150.\frac{\text{in}}{\text{hr}}$$

Example O: 5.00 kg/L = ____ lb/mL.

$$?\frac{\text{lb}}{\text{mL}} = 5.00\frac{\cancel{\text{kg}}}{\cancel{\text{L}}}\left(\frac{1000\ \cancel{\text{g}}}{1\ \cancel{\text{kg}}}\right)\left(\frac{1\ \text{lb}}{454\ \cancel{\text{g}}}\right)\left(\frac{1\ \cancel{\text{L}}}{1000\ \text{mL}}\right) = 0.0110\frac{\text{lb}}{\text{mL}}$$

Problem 4. Perform the following conversions:

a. 271 g/min = ____ lb/sec

b. 310. lb/L = ____ g/mL

c. 731 in/min = ____ ft/sec

d. 147 cm/hr = _____ in/min

e. 106 μm/cL = ____ m/L

f. 233 L/lb = ____ qt/g

g. 0.00630 L/g = ____ mL/cg

h. 873 cm/gal = ____ m/L

i. 5.67 cents/g = ____ dollars/lb

VI. Density (d) and Specific Gravity (sp gr)

Density is a physical property that is the ratio of mass to volume.

$$\text{density} = \frac{\text{mass}}{\text{volume}} \quad \text{or} \quad d = \frac{m}{v}$$

Common units of density: liquids and solids $\rightarrow \frac{\text{g}}{\text{mL}}$ gases $\rightarrow \frac{\text{g}}{\text{L}}$

Specific gravity relates the density of any substance to the density of water. Both of these densities must be expressed in the same units, whether grams/mL, pounds/cubic ft, or any other mass to volume ratio.

$$\text{sp gr} = \frac{d_{\text{substance}}}{d_{\text{water@4°C}}} = \frac{d_{\text{substance}}}{1.00 \text{ g/mL}}$$

The density and specific gravity of any substance are numerically equal if the density is expressed in grams per milliliter. However, specific gravity is a *unitless* quantity. **For problem solving purposes, it is useful to convert specific gravity to density.**

If the density of a substance is known, the relationship between mass and volume may be expressed as a *conversion factor*. For example,

$$d_{\text{ice}} = 0.92\frac{\text{g}}{\text{mL}} \rightarrow \quad \textbf{Corresponding equality: 0.92 g ice = 1 mL ice}$$

To determine the density of a substance in the laboratory, the substance's mass and volume are measured. The volume of liquids can be measured with a graduated cylinder. The volume of certain solids can be obtained in one of the following ways:

a. Volume of solids by water displacement

   If the solid is more dense than water, it will sink when placed inside a graduated cylinder containing a known quantity of water. The volume of water displaced will be equal to the volume of the solid.

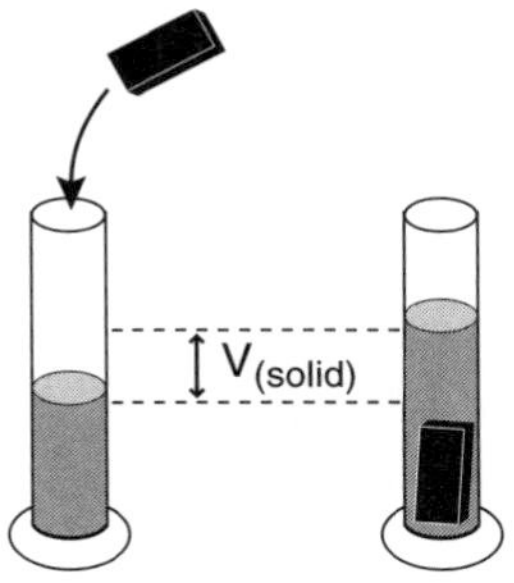

$$V_{\text{(combined)}} = V_{\text{(water)}} + V_{\text{(solid)}}$$

$$V_{\text{(solid)}} = V_{\text{(combined)}} - V_{\text{(water)}}$$

b. Volume of solids by measurements and mathematical equations

$$V_{\text{(cubic solid)}} = l \times w \times h \qquad \text{(for a cube: length = width = height)}$$

$$V_{\text{(rectangular solid)}} = l \times w \times h$$

NOTE: 1 mL = 1 cc = 1 cm³

Example P: 6.00 g of a liquid occupies a volume of 7.67 mL. Given this information, find the density, in g/mL, of the liquid.

$$?\frac{\text{g}}{\text{mL}} = \frac{6.00 \text{ g}}{7.67 \text{ mL}} = 0.782\frac{\text{g}}{\text{mL}}$$

Example Q: What is the volume, in mL, of 5.00 g of milk (d = 1.04 g/mL)?

Since the question is asking for volume and the answer needs to be in **mL**, we rewrite the **corresponding equality "1.04 g = 1 mL"** as

$$\frac{1\text{ mL}}{1.04\text{ g}}$$

Notice that the unit "mL" is in the numerator so the answer will be given in mL. Just like in the previous examples, when converting from one unit to another, the unit in the denominator must cancel with the preceding unit in the numerator.

$$?\text{ mL} = 5.00\,\cancel{\text{g}}\left(\frac{1\text{ mL}}{1.04\,\cancel{\text{g}}}\right) = 4.81\text{ mL}$$

Example R: What is the mass, in grams, of 17.7 mL of drinking alcohol (d = 0.79 g/mL)?

Since the question is asking for mass, in grams, we rewrite the equality "0.79 = 1 mL" as

$$\frac{0.79\text{ g}}{1\text{ mL}}$$

Notice that the units, grams, are placed in the numerator anticipating the answer in grams.

$$?\text{ g} = 17.7\,\cancel{\text{mL}}\left(\frac{0.79\text{ g}}{1\,\cancel{\text{mL}}}\right) = 14\text{ g}$$

Example S: What is the specific gravity of olive oil (d = 0.92 g/mL)?

$$\text{sp gr} = \frac{d_{\text{substance}}}{d_{\text{water@4°C}}} = \frac{0.92\text{ g/mL}}{1.00\text{ g/mL}} = 0.92$$

Example T: An irregularly shaped piece of metal with a mass of 114 g was placed into a graduated cylinder containing 50.00 mL of water; this raised the water level to 67.50 mL.

a. What is the density of the metal?

b. Will the metal sink or float in water?

a. $V_{(\text{metal})} = V_{(\text{metal + water})} - V_{(\text{water})}$

$V_{(\text{metal})} = 67.50\text{ mL} - 50.00\text{ mL} = 17.50\text{ mL}$

$$d = \frac{m}{v} = \frac{114\text{ g}}{17.50\text{ mL}} = 6.51\frac{\text{g}}{\text{mL}}$$

b. The metal will sink in water, because its density is greater than that of water (1.00 g/mL).

Example U: What is the density of a rectangular bar of lead that weighs 173 g and has the following dimensions: length = 2.00 cm, width = 3.00 cm, height = 2.54 cm?

$V_{(rec.\ solid)} = l \times w \times h$ (remember 1 cc = 1 mL)

$V = (2.00\ cm)\ (3.00\ cm)\ (2.54\ cm) = 15.2\ cm^3 = 15.2\ cc$

$$d = \frac{m}{v} = \frac{173\ g}{15.2\ cc} = 11.4\frac{g}{cc} = 11.4\frac{g}{mL}$$

Problem 5. Solve the following problems:

a. Calculate the density of a liquid which occupies 17.45 mL and which weighs 16.3 grams.

b. Concentrated sulfuric acid has a density of 1.84 g/mL. How many grams does 1.00 L of this acid weigh?

c. What is the volume, in mL, of a liquid (d = 2.07 g/mL) weighing 130. grams?

d. The density of glycerine is 1.26 g/mL. Calculate the mass in grams of 470. mL of glycerine.

e. Calculate the volume, in mL, of a sample of CCl_4 (d = 1.60 g/mL) having a mass of 80.0 g.

f. What is the density of a cube which measures 2.15 cm on its side and has a mass of 13.43 g?

g. What is the mass, in kg, of a rectangular solid (d = 1.00145 g/cm^3) with the following dimensions: l = 10. cm, w = 15 cm, h = 20. cm?

h. An unknown metal with a mass of 1.34 g was placed into a graduated cylinder containing 21.3 mL of water; this raised the level of the water to 26.7 mL. What is the density (in g/mL) of the unknown metal?

i. What is the specific gravity of an unknown sample that weighs 10.0 g and occupies a volume of 22.00 mL?

j. The average mass of blood serum in a typical adult is 5070. g. What volume of blood serum (d = 1.014 g/cc), in mL, would be present in a typical adult?

k. What is the specific gravity of a substance with a mass of 3.257 g and a density of 1.05 g/mL?

l. What is the mass of a glucose solution that fills a 500. mL intravenous bottle if the density of the glucose solution is 1.15 g/cc?

m. How many quarts of fat must be removed during liposuction if the specific gravity of body fat is 0.94 and 5.0 kg of adipose tissue were removed from the patient?

n. Most substances are more dense in the solid state than in the liquid state. Compare the density of ice with the density of liquid water. What do you think could happen to a lake, river, or an ocean in the winter time if these density values were reversed?

VII. Dosage and Clinical Calculations

Conversion factors or equalities are very useful for clinical calculations. Many medications list the number of milligrams of the active ingredient that are in each tablet or the number of milliliters of the active ingredient in each tablespoon of the medication. The "equality" or the conversion factor may come from a statement or phrase within the problem, for example, if an antihistamine medication states that there are 15 mL of the active ingredient doxylamine in a tablespoon of the medication, the equality would be: 1 tbsp = 15 mL.

Example V: Acetaminophen (Tylenol) comes in **325 mg** tablets and it's prescribed as two tablets every 6 hours. If a patient requires 2600 mg/day of acetaminophen, how many tablets does this patient need in a day?

Equality: 325 mg = 1 tablet

$$2600 \text{ mg} \times \frac{1 \text{ tablet}}{325 \text{ mg}} = 8 \text{ tablets}$$

Problem 6. Solve the following dosage problems:

a. The dosage required is 0.25 mg. The medicine is available in 0.50 mg tablets. How many tablets does the patient take?

b. A drug is available in 0.125 mg per tablet. 0.25 mg are required. How many tablets is that?

c. A drug is available in 0.05 mg per tablet. 0.15 mg must be administered. How many tablets should be given?

d. Tablets containing 0.025 mg of a drug are available. The patient needs 0.050 mg. How many tablets are needed?

e. The daily dosage required is 4 grams. 250 mg tablets are available. How many tablets must be consumed per day? Per week?

f. A solution contains 1.5 grams of a medication in 45 cc. How many cc's must be used to provide 0.1 g of this medication?

g. The daily dose of ampicillin for the treatment of an infection is 115 mg/kg of body weight. What would be the daily dose, in mg, for a 28.70 lb toddler?

h. Atropine is available as 0.50 g/mL. If a physician ordered 300 mg of atropine, how many milliliters would you need to administer?

i. The doctor ordered 1.5 g of tetracycline to be given every 6 hours. If each tablet contains 500 mg, how many tablets are needed for one day?

j. The recommended dosage for a medication is 4.00 mL/kg body weight. If you are giving 500 mL of this medication, what is the weight of your patient in kg? In pounds?

VIII. Temperature Measurements and Conversions

Comparison of Temperature Scales (not shown to scale)

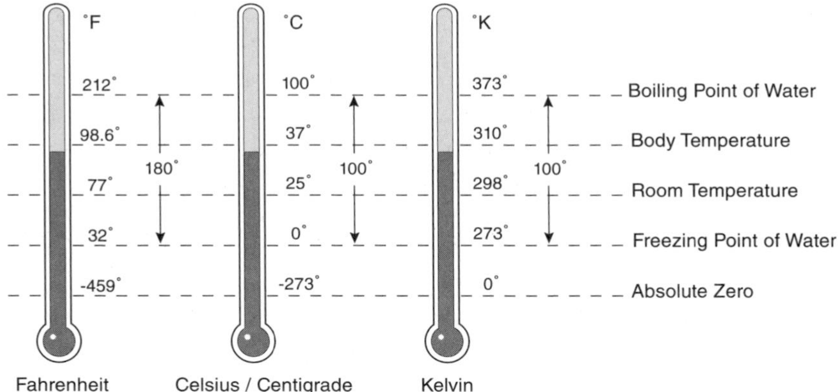

When we take the temperature of a substance, we are measuring how hot or how cold it is as compared to some standard. Interconversion among the above temperature scales can be accomplished by using the following formulas:

$$°F = (1.8 \times °C) + 32 \qquad K = °C + 273 \qquad °C = \frac{°F - 32}{1.8}$$

Example W: Normal body temperature is 98.6°F. Convert this to °C.

$$°F = (1.8 \times °C) + 32$$

$$98.6 = (1.8 \times °C) + 32$$

$$98.6 - 32 = (1.8 \times °C)$$

$$\frac{98.6 - 32}{1.8}\ °C = 37.0°$$

Example X: 100°C = ____ K.

$$K = °C + 273$$

$$K = 100 + 273 = 373K$$

Example Y: 0 K = ____ °F.

Step 1. First convert 0 K into °C

$$K = °C + 273$$

$$0\ K = °C + 273$$

$$°C = 0 - 273 = -273°C$$

Step 2. Convert −273°C into °F

$$°F = (1.8 \times °C) + 32$$

$$°F = (1.8 \times (-273)) + 32 = -459°F$$

Problem 7. Perform the following temperature conversions:

a. 62.0°C = ______°F   b. 65.3K = ______°C

c. −107.1°F = _____°C   d. 373K = ______°F

e. 200°C = ______K   f. 268°F = ______K

IX. Heat, Energy, and Nutrition

When we take the temperature of a substance we are measuring the intensity of heat. **Heat** is a form of **energy** and is associated with the motion of particles in a substance. When we heat water, the motion of water molecules increases as the water becomes hotter. We measure heat in calories or kilocalories.

1 kcal = 1000 cal = 1 **C**al (nutritional unit uses uppercase **C**)

We are familiar with the unit Calorie in food products. For example, a cup of yogurt may contain 200 Calories, or two cookies may contain 200 Calories. These Calories are actually kilocalories and should be expressed with a capital C, Calories or Cal. The heat content varies with the type of molecule found in food. These are: carbohydrate, fat (lipid), and protein. Conversion factors may be used to determine the total calorie count for a food product, depending on the relative composition of these three components.

We should learn to transfer equalities into **conversion factors** whenever these equalities are given as **statements within a problem**. For instance, the problem could state that "there are 4 kcal for every gram of carbohydrate, 4 kcal for every gram of protein, and 9 kcal for every gram of fat." To transfer these **statements** into **conversion factors** see the table below and example Z:

Conversion factors for caloric food values:

Food Type	**Carbohydrate**	**Fat (lipid)**	**Protein**
Caloric value	1 g = 4 kcal	1 g = 9 kcal	1 g = 4 kcal

Example Z: Two tablespoons of peanut butter constitutes a serving. If the serving of peanut butter provides 16 g of fat, 7 g of carbohydrates and 8 g of protein, how many kilocalories (Calories) are in a serving? Remember that every gram of carbohydrate provides 4 kcal, every gram of protein provides 4 kcal, and every gram of fat provides 9 kcal.

$$\text{carbohydrate} = 7\text{ g} \times \frac{4\text{ kcal}}{1\text{ g}} = 28\text{ kcal}$$

$$\text{fat} = 16\text{ g} \times \frac{9\text{ kcal}}{1\text{ g}} = 144\text{ kcal}$$

$$\text{protein} = 8\text{ g} \times \frac{4\text{ kcal}}{1\text{ g}} = 32\text{ kcal}$$

TOTAL kcal in 2 tablespoons: 204 kcal or 204 Calories

Problem 8. Solve the following nutrition problems.

a. If two slices of bread have 3 g of fat, 40 g of carbohydrates, and 8 g of protein, how many kcal will a peanut butter sandwich have if it contains 2 tablespoons of peanut butter? (See example Z)

b. A 150 lb person ate a cheeseburger with fries and a soda. Use Example Z to estimate the total amount of Calories in this meal.

	Protein (g)	**Fat (g)**	**Carbohydrate (g)**
Cheeseburger	31	29	34
Fries	3	11	26
Soda	0	0	51

c. If the number of Calories burned in an hour of walking is approximately 200 Cal, estimate how long will a person have to walk to burn a 450 Cal fancy Hot Fudge Sundae?

X. Energy and Specific Heat (OPTIONAL)

All substances can absorb heat. If you add heat to water you can increase its temperature and make it boil. Some substances are capable of absorbing more heat than others as they reach a certain temperature. **Water has a very high capability of absorbing heat.** This enables water to undergo minor changes in temperature compared to the environment. These specific energy requirements are described by a physical property called specific heat (SH). Specific heat is the amount of heat needed to raise the temperature of 1 g of a substance by 1°C. **Liquid water has a very high value of Specific Heat:**

$$SH_{water} = 1\frac{cal}{°C\ g} = 4.18\frac{Joule}{°C\ g}$$

The amount of heat a substance may absorb (or release) when heated (or cooled) is designated by the letter q. Heat is measured in calories or joules and can be calculated knowing the mass (m), the SH and the change in temperature of the substance (ΔT). Heat (q) is given by the formula:

$$q = m \times SH \times \Delta T$$

$$q = \text{mass} \times SH \times \text{temperature change}$$

Problem 9.

What is the amount of energy (in cal) absorbed if 50.0 g of water are heated from 20.0°C to 35.0 °C?

ANSWERS

1. a. 18 ft b. 4 yd c. 2 min d. 240 sec

2. a. 1.27 g b. 13.4 dL c. 2.030 mm d. 151.2 dL
   e. 0.471 g f. 2.68 m g. 0.367 cm h. 175 μL
   i. 631 mg j. 0.0163 ksec

3. a. 549 cm b. 292 L c. 0.350 lb d. 0.192 ft
   e. 10.0 oz f. 2.31 in g. 5.49 m h. 0.000135 qt
   i. 0.00295 lb j. 328 ft k. 917 g l. 1.5 cups
   m. 32 m

4. a. 0.00995 lb/sec b. 141 g/mL c. 1.02 ft/sec d. 0.965 in/min
   e. 0.0106 m/L f. 0.544 qt/g g. 0.0630 mL/cg h. 2.31 m/L
   i. 25.7 dollars/lb

5. a. 0.934 g/mL b. 1840 g c. 62.8 mL d. 592 g
   e. 50.0 mL f. 1.35 g/cc g. 3.0 kg h. 0.25 g/mL
   i. 0.455 j. 5000 mL k. 1.05 l. 575 g
   m. 5.6 qt
   n. The density of ice is 0.92 g/mL and liquid water is 1.0 g/mL. Most substances are more dense in the solid state than in the liquid, but ice floats on liquid water because it's less dense allowing marine life to continue in the winter time.

Iceberg

6. a. ½ tablet b. 2 tablets c. 3 tablets d. 2 tablets
   e. 16, 112 tablets f. 3 cc g. 1500 mg h. 0.60 mL
   i. 12 tablets j. 125 kg, 275 lbs

7. a. 144°F b. −208°C c. −77.28°C d. 212°F
   e. 473 K f. 404 K

8. a. 423 kcal b. 940 Cal c. 2 hrs 15 min

9. $q = 50.0\ g \times 1\ cal/\ °C\ g \times (35.0\ °C - 20.0\ °C) = 750\ cal$

Measurements

Assignment 1

Name

Student Number

Date Instructor

Appendix A and Module 1

1. Express the following numbers in scientific notation.

   a. 550,000 ____________ b. 0.000643 ______________

2. Express the following numbers in standard notation.

   a. 1.73×10^{-6} ____________ b. 4.81×10^{3} ______________

3. A metric measurement for mass is ______________________.

4. Write a conversion factor for meters to centimeters: __________

For questions 5–16, show your setups!

5. Perform the following conversions.

    a. 525 mL = ? L

    b. 1.97 dg = ? cg

    c. 437 mm = ? cm

    d. 5.67 cm = ? in

    e. 63.0 qt = ? mL

    f. 1.40 kg = ? oz

6. What is the speed of 43.2 meters/second in miles/hour?

7. A graduated cylinder contains 25.0 mL of water. If a solid weighing 52.4 grams is immersed in the water, the final volume reading is 33.7 mL. What is the density of the solid?

8. The density of aluminum is 2.70 g/mL. What is the volume in mL of 74.5 grams of aluminum?

9. The density of ethanol is 0.789 g/mL. What is the mass in kg of 4.50 quarts of ethanol?

10. a. 30.0°C = ? °F

    b. 50.0°F = ? °C

11. What is the height in centimeters of a person who is 6 feet 11 inches tall?

12. If a baby weighs 15 lbs, how much is that in grams? In kilograms?

13. Calculate the density of mercury if a 7.50 mL sample has a mass of 102 grams.

14. If the specific gravity of a urine sample is 1.09, what is the mass, in grams, of a 50.0 mL sample?

15. An order for a patient calls for 0.030 grams of medication. On hand are 10 mg tablets. What dose is needed for the patient?

16. Methane, CH_4, boils at –162°C. What is its boiling point in °F?

17. The number of Calories to be consumed daily by a person is estimated to be ten times the ideal body weight and typically 15% should be protein, 50% carbohydrates, and the remainder fat. Estimate the number of grams of protein, carbohydrates, and fat in your own ideal Caloric requirement.

	Ideal Wt	Cal/day	Prot	Carb	Fat	Prot	Carb	Fat
Example	120 lb	1200 Cal	180 Cal	600 Cal	420 Cal	45 g	150 g	47 g
You								

18. a. A cough suppressant—dextromethorphan—is ordered. If 120 mg of the cough suppressant is to be given each day for a week and it is supplied in liquid form as 15 mg per teaspoon (tsp) every 6 hours, how many teaspoons should be given per day?

    b. How many tsp should be given per dose?

19. Diphenhydramine is an antihistamine (used to relieve allergies) that may be supplied in liquid form. The dosage ordered is 0.5 mg per lb of body weight every 6 hours. Knowing that 1 tsp is 5 mL and there are 12.5 mg of the antihistamine in every 5 mL, how many teaspoons should be given to a 50 lb child in 12 hours?

20. An antibiotic dosage of 750 mg is ordered. If the antibiotic is supplied in liquid form, 250 mg in 5 mL, how many mL should be given?

2

Atoms, Elements, and Ions

Matter is anything that has mass and occupies space. Chemistry is the branch of science that studies matter and its changes. Examples of matter include copper in pennies, water to drink and bathe, and oxygen in air necessary to live.

I. Matter

A. Classification of Matter

The following diagram shows the classification of matter; from the simplest form (elements) to more complex combinations (compounds and mixtures).

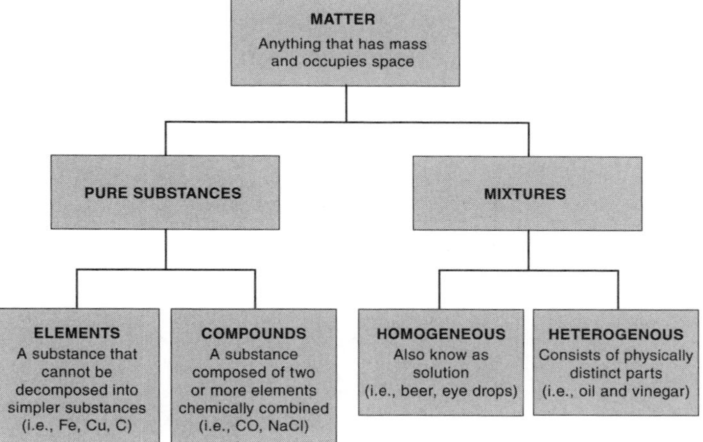

B. States of Matter

All matter is made up of tiny particles. Depending on the temperature, particles of matter can exist in any one of the following physical states: solid, liquid, or gas.

In the gaseous state, particles are moving very fast and are very far apart from each other. A gas completely fills its container and has no definite shape or volume. In the liquid state, particles move freely in all directions, yet these particles are close enough to one another so that liquids have definite volume but not definite shape.

In the solid state, particles have a strong force of attraction among themselves and are arranged much more orderly. This results in solids having both definite shape and volume.

The table below shows several properties for each state of matter.

State	Volume/Shape	Density	Compressibility
Gas, g	assumes shape and volume of container	Low	very compressible
Liquid, l	has definite volume but assumes shape of container	High	slightly compressible
Solid, s	has a definite shape and volume	High	virtually incompressible

The following diagram illustrates how temperature (and pressure) affect the interconversion among the three states, or phases, of matter:

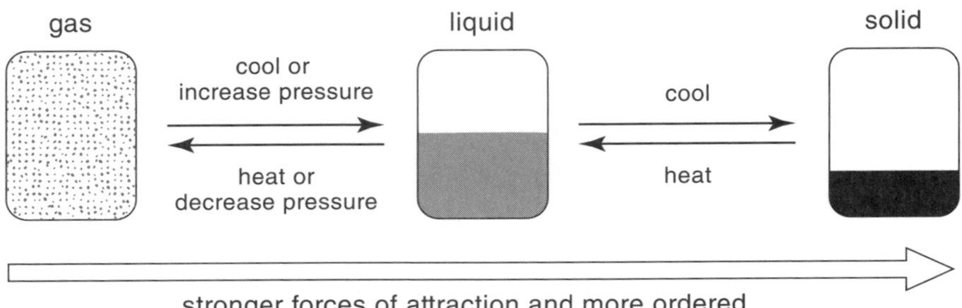

The terminology that is used during a phase transition is shown in the next diagram:

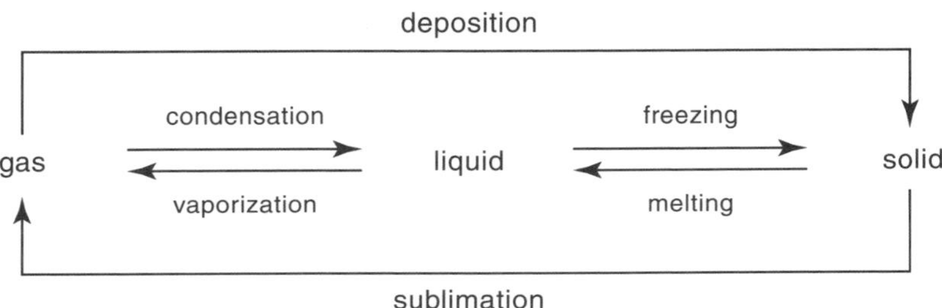

Problem 1. Answer the following questions.

a. $H_2O_{(l)}$ changing to $H_2O_{(s)}$ is called ________.

b. How can water be converted to steam?

c. Under normal laboratory conditions, dry ice, $CO_{2(s)}$, is converted to $CO_{2(g)}$. What is this phase transition called?

d. How can nitrogen gas be converted to liquid nitrogen?

C. Energy in Phase Transitions (OPTIONAL)

These transitions are accompanied by **changes in energy**. For example, the heat of vaporization refers to the amount of energy that a liquid substance **absorbs** when it turns into vapor; by the same token the heat of condensation is the amount of heat a gaseous substance **releases** when it turns into liquid. These quantities can be measured in calories per gram. One gram of liquid water needs **540 cal** to turn into water vapor at 100°C. This is called the heat of vaporization. **Water has a very high value of Heat of Vaporization.** The heat of condensation of water is –540 cal/g. (A negative sign means heat is released.)

Problem 2. Solve the following problem.
How many **calories** are needed to vaporize **100 g** of liquid water at its boiling point, 100°C? (The Heat of Vaporization of water is 540 cal/g.)

II. Elements

Elements are the basic substances from which all matter is formed. Each element has specific physical and chemical properties and has been assigned a chemical symbol. This chemical symbol is often the first letter or the first two letters of the element's English or Latin name. The first letter is always capitalized and the second letter is not. Newer elements have been assigned three letter symbol names representing their atomic number.

A. Common Elements

The elements are arranged in the periodic table of the elements according to their chemical properties. The following periodic chart shows most of the common elements found in nature, particularly in living things.

	IA	IIA	IIIB	IVB	VB	VIB	VIIB	VIII	VIII	VIII	IB	IIB	IIIA	IVA	VA	VIA	VIIA	VIIIA
1	H																H	He
2	Li	Be											B	C	N	O	F	Ne
3	Na	Mg											Al	Si	P	S	Cl	Ar
4	K	Ca	Sc	Ti	V	Cr	Mn	Fe	Co	Ni	Cu	Zn	Ga	Ge	As	Se	Br	Kr
5	Rb	Sr									Ag	Cd		Sn	Sb	Te	I	Xe
6	Cs	Ba	*La							Pt	Au	Hg		Pb				
7			†Ac															

Lanthanides *														
Actinides †			U											

B. Metals, Nonmetals, and Metalloids

Elements to the left of the bold staircase on the periodic chart are metals while those to the right are nonmetals. Elements shaded along the staircase are considered metalloids.

C. Monatomic and Diatomic Elements

The atom is the smallest particle of an element that maintains its chemical identity throughout all physical and chemical changes.

Most elements exist as single atoms; these are called monatomic elements. A few elements are found in nature as two atoms joined together: these are called diatomic elements. Diatomic elements are given in the figure to the right.

VA	VIA	VIIA
		H_2
N_2	O_2	F_2
		Cl_2
		Br_2
		I_2
		At_2

D. Physical State of the Elements

All elements are solids at room temperature except for:

a. those that are liquids (Hg and Br_2)

b. those that are gases

(gases are shown in the figure on the right)

VA	VIA	VIIA	VIIIA
		H_2	He
N_2	O_2	F_2	Ne
		Cl_2	Ar
			Kr
			Xe
			Rn

E. Luster, Malleability, and Ductility of Elements

Most metals have luster, while nonmetals are dull. *Most* metals are **malleable** (can be hammered into a specific shape), ductile (can be drawn into wires), and are **hard**. Nonmetals are neither malleable, ductile, nor hard.

Problem 3. Complete the following table.

Symbol	Name	Monatomic or Diatomic	Metal or Nonmetal
Hg			
	iron		
	gold		
K			
	bromine		
Cu			
	nitrogen		

III. The Atom

The atom is the smallest particle of an element that retains its physical and chemical properties. Atoms are the building blocks of everything we see around us.

A. Subatomic Particles

Atoms are composed of even smaller particles called subatomic particles. Although many subatomic particles have been identified within the past century, only three are necessary to explain the nature of chemical reactions. These subatomic particles are: electrons, protons, and neutrons.

Subatomic Particle	Symbol	Electrical Charge	Approximate Mass
Proton	p^+	+1	1 amu
Neutron	n	0	1 amu
Electron	e^-	–1	0 amu*

amu = atomic mass unit   1 amu = 1.66×10^{-24} g   *0.0005 amu

Arrangement of subatomic particles in the atom:

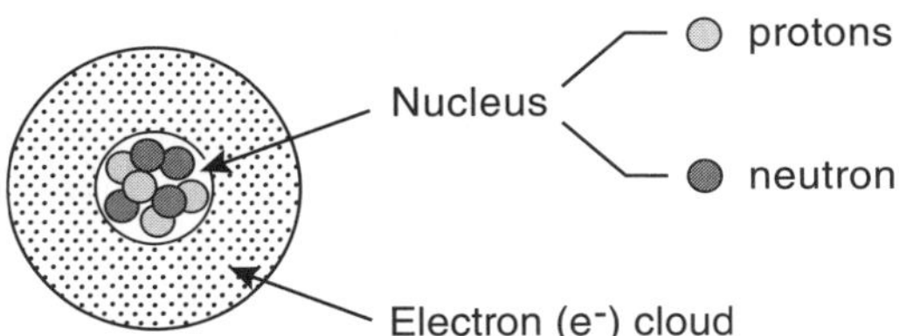

The protons and neutrons are tightly packed in the nucleus. The rest of the atom consists of mostly empty space where the electrons are found.

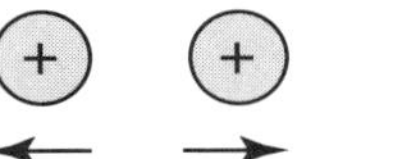
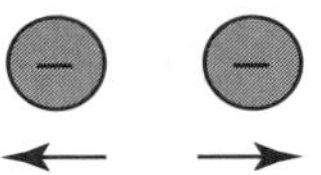
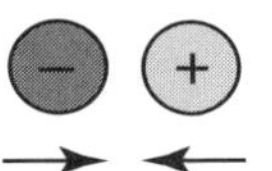

B. Atomic Number and Mass Number

The **number of protons** in the nucleus of an element determines the identity of the element and is called the **atomic number.** For example, if an atom contains 6 protons in the nucleus it is *always* the element carbon (C); if there are 7 protons in the nucleus, then it is *always* the element nitrogen (N). The periodic chart is arranged in order of increasing atomic number (note that nitrogen is to the right of carbon in the chart).

# of protons in atom = atomic number

A second very important value associated with an element is the **mass number.** This mass number is the **sum of protons and neutrons** in an atom. The number of electrons is ignored in mass calculation since, while the approximate mass of both protons and neutrons is 1 amu, that of electrons is almost 0.

mass number = # of protons + # of neutrons

Some periodic tables may place the atomic number above the symbol of the element and the average atomic mass below, while others may reverse them. The periodic table DOES NOT give the mass number of an element.

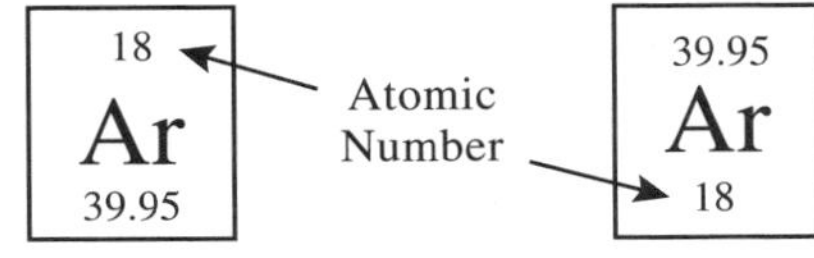

As noted earlier, the third subatomic particle that participates in ordinary chemical reactions, **the electron**, has a charge of −1. Neutral atoms contain the same number of electrons and protons (i.e., positive and negative charges balance each other).

For neutral atoms: # of protons = # of electrons (i.e., atoms are electrically neutral).

C. Isotopes

In nature, nitrogen (N) is a mixture of two types of atoms. These atoms have the **same number of protons**, 7, (otherwise they would not be nitrogen), but with a **different number of neutrons**. Nitrogen-14 has 7 neutrons while nitrogen-15 has 8 neutrons.

These different forms of an element, with the same number of protons but varying number of neutrons, are called isotopes.

To distinguish between different isotopes of the same element, an *isotope symbol* is used. *The periodic table does not give isotope symbols.*

The following diagram represents the arrangement of subatomic particles in an atom of Argon-40 (40 stands for the mass number):

Isotope Symbol

$^{40}_{18}\text{Ar}$

atomic number = 18
mass number = 40
of p^+ = 18
of e^- = 18
# of n = 40 – 18 = 22

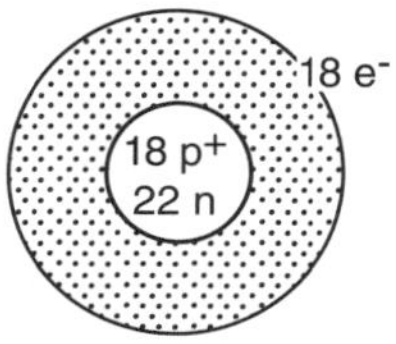

18 e^-
18 p^+
22 n

Example A: Give the mass number, number of protons, number of electrons, and number of neutrons for each of the following:

a. $^{6}_{3}\text{Li}$ b. $^{13}_{6}\text{C}$ c. $^{63}_{29}\text{Cu}$

	Mass Number	# of p^+	# of e^-	# of n
a. $^{6}_{3}\text{Li}$	6	3	3	3
b. $^{13}_{6}\text{C}$	13	6	6	7
c. $^{63}_{29}\text{Cu}$	63	29	29	34

Problem 4. Complete the following table.

Atomic Number	Mass Number	# of Protons	# of Electrons	# of Neutrons	Name	Symbol
16	32					
	37				chlorine	
	25	12				
			8	10		
				30		Fe
	238				uranium	
7				8		
	65			35		
		1		2		

D. Calculation of Average Atomic Mass (OPTIONAL)

The atomic mass (or atomic weight) of an element is the average mass of all naturally occurring isotopes of that element. To calculate the average atomic mass, the percent abundance of each isotope must be known. For example, there are two naturally occurring isotopes for Cl → chlorine-35 (with a natural abundance of 75.5%) and chlorine-37 (with a natural abundance of 24.5%).

Isotope	Percent		Mass Number		Contribution to Average Mass
$^{35}_{17}Cl$	75.5% (0.755)	×	35	=	26.4
$^{35}_{17}Cl$	24.5% (0.245)	×	37	=	+9.1
			Atomic Mass given in Periodic Table →		35.5

The previous calculation illustrates how the average atomic mass of an element is affected by the percentage of each isotope.

E. Valence Electrons

Electrons are found outside the nucleus of an atom. These electrons are arranged in an orderly manner in regions called shells. A limited number of electrons are able to fit in each shell or energy level surrounding the nucleus. The electrons occupying the outermost, or valence shell, are referred to as the valence electrons. Chemical reactions involve these valence electrons. Sharing or transferring of valence electrons will bring about the formation of compounds. A study of the periodic table of the elements allows us to determine the number of valence electrons present in any element and to understand the bonding in compounds.

IV. The Periodic Table

By the late 1800s, scientists had discovered many elements and they realized the need to organize them. In 1872, Dimitry Mendeleev organized the 60 elements known at that time in order of ascending atomic mass and arranged them into groups of similar properties. Today's version of the periodic table uses Mendeleev's model but it arranges the elements in order of increasing atomic number.

Depending on the periodic table, the atomic mass is either written above or below the element's symbol:

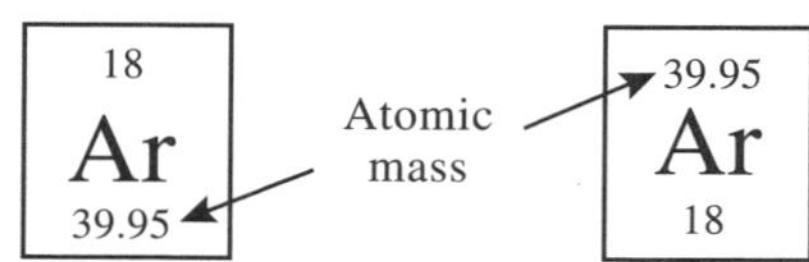

Metals are usually shiny solids which conduct electricity. In a periodic table, metals are located to the left of the bold staircase. Nonmetals, on the other hand, are dull and do not conduct electricity. Nonmetals are located to the right of the bold staircase in a periodic table.

In the periodic table, horizontal rows are referred to as *periods*. All of the elements in a given period have their outermost, or valence, electrons in the same energy level. The period number is equal to the valence shell, or outermost shell. The valence shell for an element in the second period, Li through Ne, is two; the valence shell for an element in the third period, Na through Ar, is three.

Elements within a vertical column in the periodic table are considered to be in the same *group or family*. The reason for this classification is that these elements have the same number of valence, or outermost electrons. They therefore behave similarly during chemical reactions. In a periodic chart group A elements are called representative elements. The number of valence electrons for the representative elements is the same as the group number. Group IA elements have one valence electron, group IIA elements have 2 valence electrons, elements in group VIIA have 7 valence electrons.

	IA	IIA	IIIB	IVB	VB	VIB	VIIB	VIII	VIII	VIII	IB	IIB	IIIA	IVA	VA	VIA	VIIA	VIIIA
1	H																H	He
2	Li	Be											B	C	N	O	F	Ne
3	Na	Mg											Al	Si	P	S	Cl	Ar
4	K	Ca	Sc	Ti	V	Cr	Mn	Fe	Co	Ni	Cu	Zn	Ga	Ge	As	Se	Br	Kr
5	Rb	Sr									Ag	Cd		Sn	Sb	Te	I	Xe
6	Cs	Ba	*La							Pt	Au	Hg		Pb				
7			†Ac															

Lanthanides *														
Actinides †			U											

Periods – horizontal rows

Family or Group – vertical columns

Metals – elements to the left of bold staircase

Nonmetals – elements to the right of the bold staircase

Metalloids – shaded elements along the bold staircase

Representative Elements – elements in columns IA – VIIIA

Transition Elements – elements in columns IIIB – IIB

Inner Transition Elements – Actinides and Lanthanides

Alkali Metals – Group IA (Except H)

Alkaline Earth Metals – Group IIA

Halogens – Group VIIA (except H)

Noble Gases – Group VIIIA

Element	Group Number	# of Valence Electrons
Na	IA	1
Ba	IIA	2
Ge	IVA	4
Xe	VIIIA	8

Example B: How many valence electrons do the following elements have?

a. Li b. O c. Al

Solution:

a. 1 (Li is in column IA) b. 6 (O is in column VIA) c. 3 (Al is in column IIIA)

Problem 5. How many valence electrons do the following elements have?

a. B	b. Rb	c. S	d. C
e. Ca	f. F	g. P	h. Ar

Example C: Choose one or more from the following list to describe each element:

1. Metal	2. Nonmetal
3. Representative Element	4. Transition Element
5. Alkali Metal	6. Alkaline Earth Metal
7. Halogen	8. Noble Gas

a. Cl b. Kr c. Cu d. Li e. P

Solution:

a. 2, 3, 7 b. 2, 3, 8 c. 1, 4 d. 1, 3, 5 e. 2, 3

Problem 6. Choose one or more from the following list to describe each element.

1. Metal	2. Nonmetal
3. Representative Element	4. Transition Element
5. Alkali Metal	6. Alkaline Earth Metal
7. Halogen	8. Noble Gas

a. Mg b. I c. As d. Sn e. Cd

V. Electronic Arrangement

A. Shorthand Notation

Electrons are arranged in an orderly fashion in specific regions called energy levels or shells. The following gives the electron capacity for the first four shells.

Electron Shell n	Maximum Number of Electrons $2n^2$
1	2
2	8
3	18
4	32

The first 2 electrons go into shell 1, the next 8 electrons go into shell 2. Though the third shell can hold 18 electrons, once the element has 8 electrons in the third shell, the next two electrons go into the fourth shell. This accounts for the electron arrangement for the first 20 elements (2 + 8 + 8 + 2).

NOTE: the electron arrangements for elements beyond atomic number 20 will not be considered here.

The electron arrangement of an atom gives the number of electrons in each shell. To draw a simple diagram of the electron arrangement and nucleus of an atom:

a. The number of protons and neutrons inside the nucleus are shown enclosed by a circle.

b. Curved lines are drawn to represent each occupied shell, and the number of electrons in that shell are indicated.

Electron Arrangements of Elements

Isotope	Nucleus and Electronic Arrangement	Shorthand Electronic Arrangement
$^{1}_{1}H$	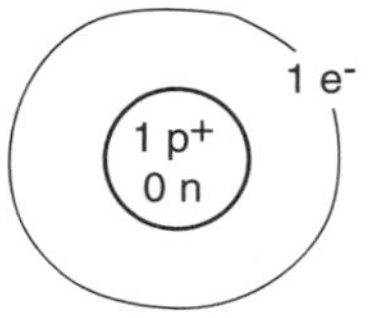 1 p+ 0 n; 1 e⁻	1
$^{7}_{3}Li$	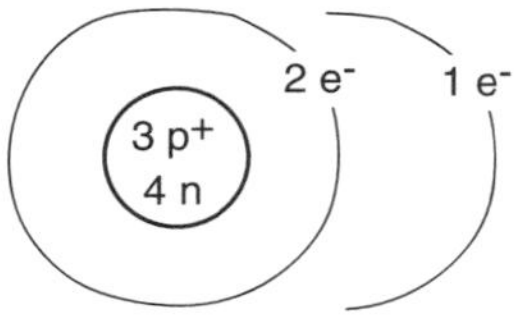 3 p+ 4 n; 2 e⁻ 1 e⁻	2 - 1
$^{23}_{11}Na$	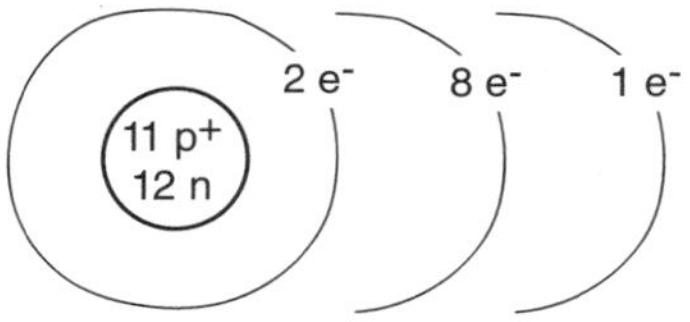 11 p+ 12 n; 2 e⁻ 8 e⁻ 1 e⁻	2 - 8 - 1
$^{40}_{20}Ca$	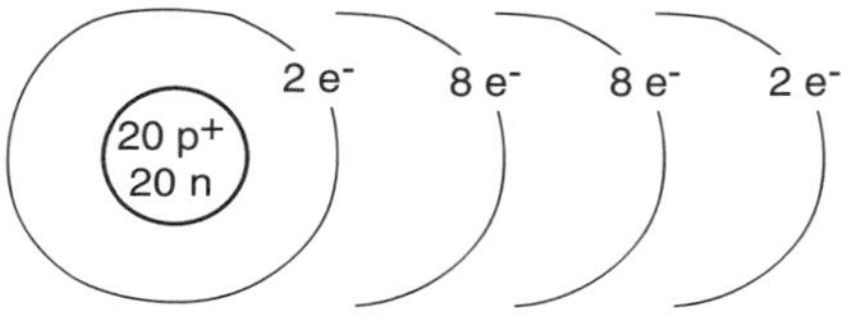 20 p+ 20 n; 2 e⁻ 8 e⁻ 8 e⁻ 2 e⁻	2 - 8 - 8 - 2

Problem 7. Write the shorthand electron arrangement for each of the following:

a. Ar b. K c. Si d. Cl e. B

B. Electronic Arrangement-Orbital Notation (OPTIONAL)

We have already seen the arrangement of electrons in the first 3 shells, now we will take a closer look at the distribution and spatial arrangements of electrons in these first 3 shells. Each shell (energy level) consists of one or more subshells (subenergy levels). The subshells are designated by the letters *s, p, d* and *f*. The number of subshells in a shell are equal to the shell number. The subshells may be further subdivided into orbitals. An *s* subshell has only one orbital and *p* subshells are comprised of a set of 3 orbitals. **Orbitals are defined as the region in space where there is the highest probability of finding the electron**. Each type of orbital has a unique shape. An s orbital is spherical in shape and p orbitals have a dumb bell shape aligned along the x, y and z axes. **Each orbital can hold 2 electrons.**

In the lowest energy level, the first shell, a 1s orbital of spherical shape exists. (The 1 is the shell number and the s designates the type of subshell.) The 1s subshell has only one orbital and can accommodate 2 electrons. In the second shell, two types of subshells exist; these are the 2s and 2p. There are 3 types of p orbitals: p_x, p_y and p_z. (See following diagram) We can accommodate 6 electrons in the 2p orbitals : two in each p_x, p_y and p_z $(2 \times 3 = 6)$.

The third shell has 3s, 3p and 3d subshells. (We will not be discussing the *d* subshells.) The first two electrons are in a 3s orbital and the 3p orbitals can accommodate 6 electrons in the 3p: two in each p_x, p_y and p_z. Remember, that after shell 3 contains a total of 8 electrons, the next two electrons will be into the fourth shell.

The following table gives the electron capacity for the first three energy levels

Electron Shell n	Maximum Number of Electrons: $2n^2$	Orbitals (NEW)
1	2	**1s**
2	8	**2s 2p**
3	18	**3s 3p 3d**

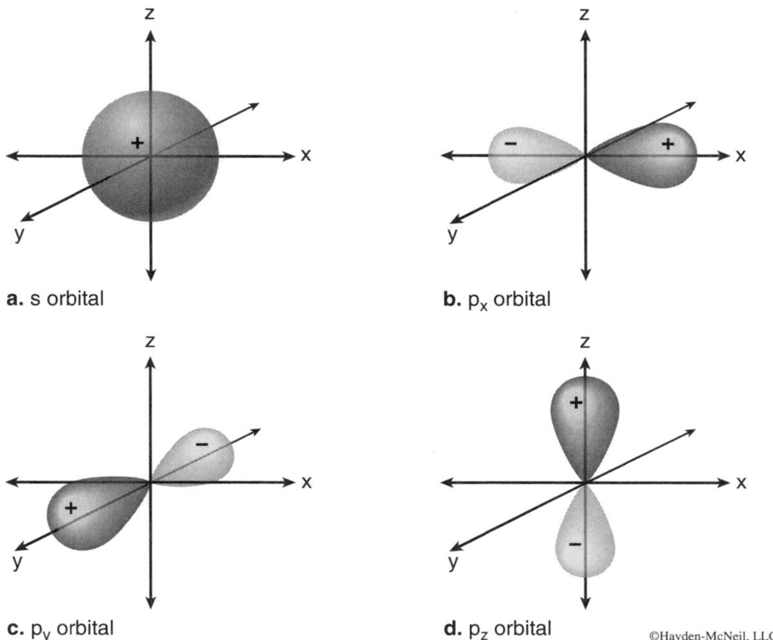

Diagram of S and P orbitals

Recall that the electronic configuration of Hydrogen was given as "1" meaning there is 1 electron in the first shell. This electron will be located in an "s" orbital in the first energy level. This electronic configuration will now be designated $\mathbf{1s^1}$ (one electron).

The electronic arrangement for Helium was given as "2" meaning n = 1 and having 2 electrons. These two electrons are located in an "s" orbital so the electronic configuration is now designated as: $\mathbf{1s^2}$ meaning shell = n = 1 having 2 electrons in an "s" orbital.

By the same token, Lithium electronic configuration instead of "2 - 1" will be designated: $\mathbf{1s^2\ 2s^1}$.

Electron Arrangements of Some Elements

Element	Shorthand Electronic Configuration	Spectroscopic Notation Electronic Configuration
H	1	$1s^1$
He	2	$1s^2$
Li	2 - 1	$1s^2\ 2s^1$
Be	2 - 2	$1s^2\ 2s^2$
B	2 - 3	$1s^2\ 2s^2\ 2p^1$
C	2 - 4	$1s^2\ 2s^2\ 2p^2$
N	2 - 5	$1s^2\ 2s^2\ 2p^3$
O	2 - 6	$1s^2\ 2s^2\ 2p^4$
F	2 - 7	$1s^2\ 2s^2\ 2p^5$
Ne	2 - 8	$1s^2\ 2s^2\ 2p^6$
Na	2 - 8 -1	$1s^2\ 2s^2\ 2p^6\ 3s^1$
Al	2 - 8 - 3	$1s^2\ 2s^2\ 2p^6\ 3s^2\ 3p^1$
P	2 - 8 - 5	$1s^2\ 2s^2\ 2p^6\ 3s^2\ 3p^3$
Cl	2 - 8 - 7	$1s^2\ 2s^2\ 2p^6\ 3s^2\ 3p^5$
Ar	2 - 8 - 8	$1s^2\ 2s^2\ 2p^6\ 3s^2\ 3p^6$

As we already know, the chemical properties of the elements depend on the electronic configuration of the outermost or VALENCE shell. Electrons in the valence shell are called "valence electrons." For representative elements, the number of valence electrons equals the Group number (Group A).

Valence Configurations of Elements in Periods 1, 2 and 3

IA	IIA	IIIA	IVA	VA	VIA	VIIA	VIIIA
H $1s^1$							He $1s^2$
Li $2s^1$	Be $2s^2$	B $2s^2\ 2p^1$	C $2s^2\ 2p^2$	N $2s^2\ 2p^3$	O $2s^2\ 2p^4$	F $2s^2\ 2p^5$	Ne $2s^2\ 2p^6$
Na $3s^1$	Mg $3s^2$	Al $3s^2\ 3p^1$	Si $3s^2\ 3p^2$	P $3s^2\ 3p^3$	S $3s^2\ 3p^4$	Cl $3s^2\ 3p^5$	Ar $3s^2\ 3p^6$

Problem 8.

Identify the total number of electrons, the valence electrons, and the name and symbol of the element with each electronic configuration:

a. $1s^2\ 2s^2\ 2p^3$　　b. $1s^2\ 2s^2\ 2p^6\ 3s^2\ 3p^1$

Problem 9.

Identify the number of protons, neutrons and electrons for an isotope having a mass number of 24 and an electronic configuration of $1s^2\ 2s^2\ 2p^6\ 3s^1$:

a. 13 protons, 11 neutrons, 11 electrons

b. 11 protons, 13 neutrons, 12 electrons

c. 11 protons, 13 neutrons, 11 electrons

d. 11 protons, 12 neutrons, 11 electrons

VI. Atomic Radius (OPTIONAL)

The comparative sizes (atomic radii) of the elements can be estimated from their relative positions in the periodic table. Going from top to bottom within a group (vertical column) the size increases as the number of shells increases. For example, sodium is larger than lithium, since sodium has electrons in three shells, while lithium has only two shells containing electrons. From left to right within a period (horizontal row), the atomic radius **decreases**. The number of protons increases as we go from left to right across a period, resulting in a stronger attraction for each electron in the atom with no increase in the number of shells, thereby "shrinking" the atomic radius.

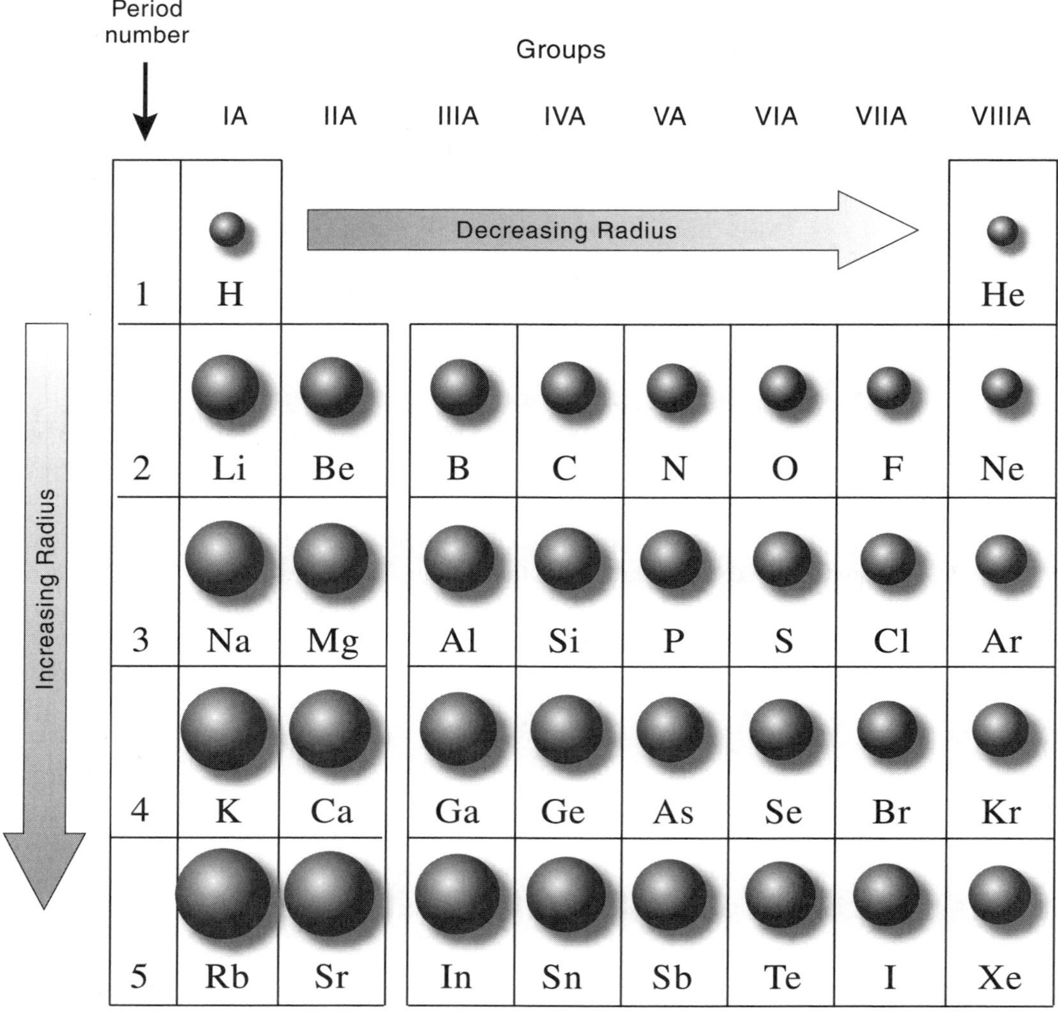

VII. The Octet Rule

Noble gases (VIIIA elements) do not readily combine with other elements to form compounds (pure substances made of two or more elements). This lack of reactivity is because their electronic structures are very stable. All noble gases (except helium which has 2 valence electrons) have **8 valence electrons or an octet of electrons**. The octet rule states that the atoms of the elements in a compound may lose, gain, or share valence electrons in order to produce a stable noble gas electronic configuration (of 8 electrons). This is to say that elements may combine to form compounds and they will transfer valence electrons or share valence electrons to complete an octet, 8 valence electrons.

VIII. Ions

Ions are produced when elements lose or gain electrons. When elements, usually metals, lose electrons, they form positively charged ions (cations). Negatively charged ions (anions) are formed when elements, usually nonmetals, gain electrons. In the body, there are a number of ions that are physiologically important. Na^+, K^+, and Cl^- help regulate body fluids; Fe^{2+} is part of hemoglobin; Mg^{2+} is essential for certain enzymes, muscles, and nerve control; Ca^{2+} is the major cation in bones. Some of these physiologically important ions are listed below:

Na^+ K^+ Ca^{2+} Mg^{2+} Fe^{2+}

To determine the charge of ions, a periodic table will be used. Group numbers (IA–VIIIA) can be used to determine the ionic charges for those elements. Group IA metals lose 1 electron to form +1 ions. Group IIA metals lose 2 electrons to become +2 ions.

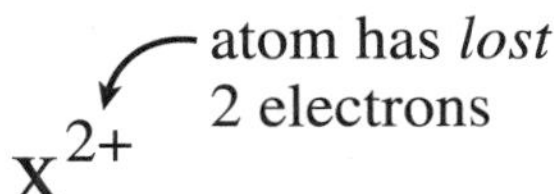

If aluminum loses 3 electrons, it becomes Al^{3+}. Notice from the chart, that the electrons lost are the valence electrons. Futhermore, for representative elements, the electron configuration of the ion is the same as the electron configuraton for the noble gas closest to it (Group VIIIA).

Electron Arrangements of Positive Ions

Element	Group No.	# of Protons and Electronic Arrangement of Element	Ion Formed	# of Protons and Electronic Arrangement of Ion
Li	IA	3 p^+; 2 e^-, 1 e^-	Li^+	3 p^+; 2 e^-
Ca	IIA	20 p^+; 2 e^-, 8 e^-, 8 e^-, 2 e^-	Ca^{2+}	20 p^+; 2 e^-, 8 e^-, 8 e^-
Al	IIIA	13 p^+; 2 e^-, 8 e^-, 3 e^-	Al^{3+}	13 p^+; 2 e^-, 8 e^-

Group VIIA elements gain 1 electron to become –1 ions, while Group VIA elements gain 2 electrons and form –2 ions.

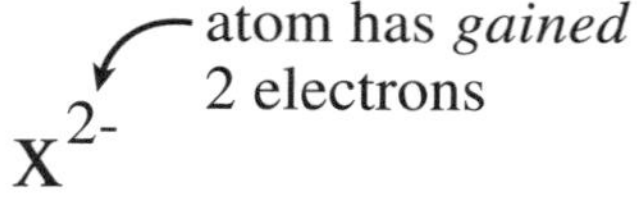

Electron Arrangements of Negative Ions

Element	Group No.	# of Protons and Electronic Arrangement of Element	Ion Formed	# of Protons and Electronic Arrangement of Ion
F	VIIA	$9\ p^+$; $2\ e^-$, $7\ e^-$	F^-	$9\ p^+$; $2\ e^-$, $8\ e^-$
S	VIA	$16\ p^+$; $2\ e^-$, $8\ e^-$, $6\ e^-$	S^{2-}	$16\ p^+$; $2\ e^-$, $8\ e^-$, $8\ e^-$
N	VA	$7\ p^+$; $2\ e^-$, $5\ e^-$	N^{3-}	$7\ p^+$; $2\ e^-$, $8\ e^-$

Representative Elements: Some Common Ions
Oxidation Numbers

IA	IIA	IIIA	IVA	VA	VIA	VIIA	VIIIA
H^+ Hydrogen							
Li^+ Lithium	Be^{2+} Beryllium			N^{3-} Nitride	O^{2-} Oxide	F^- Fluoride	
Na^+ Sodium	Mg^{2+} Magnesium	Al^{3+} Aluminum		P^{3-} Phosphide	S^{2-} Sulfide	Cl^- Chloride	
K^+ Potassium	Ca^{2+} Calcium					Br^- Bromide	
Rb^+ Rubidium	Sr^{2+} Strontium					I^- Iodide	
Cs^+ Cesium	Ba^{2+} Barium						

Some metals form ionic compounds using *fixed* charges or *fixed* oxidation numbers. The following metals have the *fixed* oxidation number indicated: Group IA , +1; Group IIA, +2; Al^{+3}, Zn^{+2}, Cd^{+2}, and Ag^{+1}.

All other metals have *variable* oxidation numbers when they form compounds. Some examples of metals with variable oxidation numbers are given in the table below.

Metal Ions with Variable Oxidation Numbers

Symbol	Name
Fe^{2+}	Iron (II)
Fe^{3+}	Iron (III)
Sn^{2+}	Tin (II)
Sn^{4+}	Tin (IV)
Cu^{+}	Copper (I)
Cu^{2+}	Copper (II)
Pb^{2+}	Lead (II)
Pb^{4+}	Lead (IV)

Problem 10. Complete the following table:

Element	# of p^+	# of e^-	Ion Formed	# of p^+	# of e^-	Ion Name
H						
Cl						
P						
O						
Be						

ANSWERS

1. a. freezing b. by heating c. sublimation d. by cooling

2. 54,000 cal or 54 kcal

3.

Symbol	Name	Monatomic or Diatomic	Metal or Nonmetal
Hg	mercury	monatomic	Metal
Fe	iron	monatomic	Metal
Au	gold	monatomic	Metal
K	potassium	monatomic	Metal
Br	bromine	diatomic	Nonmetal
Cu	copper	monatomic	Metal
N	nitrogen	diatomic	Nonmetal

4.

Atomic Number	Mass Number	# of Protons	# of Electrons	# of Neutrons	Name	Symbol
16	32	16	16	16	sulfur	S
17	37	17	17	20	chlorine	Cl
12	25	12	12	13	magnesium	Mg
8	18	8	8	10	oxygen	O
26	56	26	26	30	iron	Fe
92	238	92	92	146	uranium	U
7	15	7	7	8	nitrogen	N
30	65	30	30	35	zinc	Zn
1	3	1	1	2	hydrogen	H

5. a. 3 b. 1 c. 6 d. 4
   e. 2 f. 7 g. 5 h. 8

6. a. 1, 3, 6 b. 2, 3, 7 c. 2, 3 d. 1, 3 e. 1, 4

7. a. 2 - 8 - 8 b. 2 - 8 - 8 - 1 c. 2 - 8 - 4 d. 2 - 8 - 7 e. 2 - 3

8. a. 7, 5, Nitrogen, N b. 13, 3, Aluminum, Al

9. Correct choice: c
   Adding all electrons in $1s^2\ 2s^2\ 2p^6\ 3s^1$ gives:
   $2 + 2 + 6 + 1 = 11$ = # electrons = # protons;
   isotope ^{24}Na therefore has $24 - 11 = 13$ neutrons

10.

Element	# of p^+	# of e^-	Ion Formed	# of p^+	# of e^-	Ion Name
H	1	1	H^+	1	0	hydrogen ion
Cl	17	17	Cl^-	17	18	chloride ion
P	15	15	P^{3-}	15	18	phosphide ion
O	8	8	O^{2-}	8	10	oxide ion
Be	4	4	Be^{2+}	4	2	beryllium ion

Atoms, Elements, and Ions

Assignment 2

____
Name

____
Student Number

____
Date *Instructor*

1. A homogeneous mixture is called a/an ________________.

2. A pure substance which is composed of two or more elements is called a/an ____________.

3. A mixture of oil and water is ___________________ (heterogenous or homogeneous).

4. If a substance takes the shape of its container, but has a definite volume, it is a __________ (solid, liquid, or gas).

5. A solid has ____________________ (a definite/no definite) volume and ___________________ (a definite/no definite) shape.

6. The process by which a substance is converted from the solid phase to the gas phase is called _____________________.

7. The process in which gaseous chlorine is converted to liquid chlorine is called ____________________.

8. Write names for each of the following elements.

a. K ____________ b. Ag ____________ c. Sn ____________

d. Hg ____________ e. Mn ____________ f. Se ____________

9. Write symbols for each of the following elements.

a. gold_____ b. iron_____ c. sodium_____ d. xenon_____ e. fluorine _____

10. Classify each of the following elements as a metal, nonmetal, or metalloid.

a. Si ____________ b. Ga ____________ c. Se ____________

11. Which of the following elements are diatomic in their natural form? Underline the correct choice or choices.

helium, nitrogen, boron, carbon, hydrogen, lithium, iron, arsenic, iodine, tin, beryllium

12. Complete the following table.

Isotope	Protons	Neutrons	Electrons
C-14			
	24	29	
		12	12
Cl-37			
	15	16	
K-41			
I-131			
^{60}Co			

13. Consider the following elements:

    Cs, Ba, Ce, V, Zn, Ge, Br, Kr, U, Be, Li, F, S, Sn, Fe, Al

    a. Which are representative elements? ________________

    b. Which are inner-transition elements? ________________

    c. Which are in Group IIIA? ________________

    d. Which are in the fourth period? ________________

    e. Which are transition elements? ________________

    f. Which are halogens? ________________

    g. Which are noble gases? ________________

    h. Which are alkali metals? ________________

    i. Which are alkaline earth elements? ________________

14. For each of the following elements, give the number of valence electrons.

    a. S _____ b. Al _____ c. Mg _____ d. Si _____ e. Cl _____

15. Complete the following table.

Symbol for Element	Electronic Configuration
N	
Si	
	2 - 1
	2 - 8 - 8 - 2
Mg	
K	
	2 - 8 - 5
O	
Ne	
	2 - 8 - 7

16. Give the ion normally formed by each of the following elements. Indicate the number of electrons gained or the number of electrons lost when the ion is formed.

a. Na

b. Al

c. P

d. S

e. Ba

f. Br

3

From Elements to Compounds

Most of the things around us are made of compounds. A compound is a pure substance consisting of two or more elements combined in a fixed ratio. Water, carbon dioxide, and sodium chloride are examples of compounds. This module examines how elements are combined to form compounds and the different types of compounds produced. Properties of compounds and methods for naming them will also be studied.

I. Lewis Dot or Electron-Dot Structure

Gilbert Lewis, an American professor and researcher, developed a simplified representation, or symbol, of an element and its valence shell. This symbol is very useful in depicting the structure of elements and compounds.

A. Lewis Dot or Electron-Dot Structure for Elements

For elements, the symbol for the element represents the nucleus and all but the outermost shell. The electrons in the outermost or valence shell are represented by dots arranged on the four sides of an imaginary square (with a maximum of 2 dots per side). Each side receives one electron until the four imaginary sides have one electron each; additional valence electrons are placed as needed, with a maximum of 8 valence electrons (2 at each side).

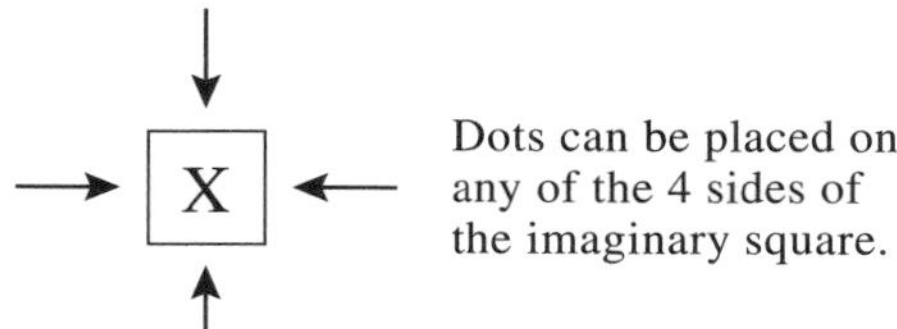

A generalized example of the Lewis Dot or Electron-Dot structure for the representative elements ("A" elements in the periodic table) for the atoms in each group is shown below.

IA	IIA
$\dot{\text{E}}$	$\dot{\text{E}}\cdot$

IIIA	IVA	VA	VIA	VIIA	VIIIA
$\dot{\underset{\cdot}{\text{E}}}\cdot$	$\cdot\dot{\underset{\cdot}{\text{E}}}\cdot$	$\cdot\ddot{\underset{\cdot}{\text{E}}}\cdot$	$\cdot\ddot{\underset{\cdot}{\text{E}}}:$	$\cdot\ddot{\underset{\cdot\cdot}{\text{E}}}:$	$:\ddot{\underset{\cdot\cdot}{\text{E}}}:$ except $\dot{\text{He}}\cdot$

Example A: Write the Electron-Dot structure of the following elements:

a. C b. Al c. F

Solution

a. Since carbon, C, is in Group IVA, it has 4 valence electrons; the Electron-Dot structure is:

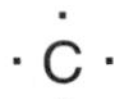

b. Since aluminum, Al, is in Group IIIA, it has 3 valence electrons; the Electron-Dot structure is:

c. Since fluorine, F, is in Group VIIA, it has 7 valence electrons; the Electron-Dot structure is:

$$\cdot\ddot{\underset{\cdot\cdot}{\mathrm{F}}}:$$

Problem 1. Complete the following table:

Element	# of Valence Electrons	Electron-Dot Structure
Mg		
Na		
H		
He		
Ar		
P		
Ga		
S		

B. Electron-Dot Structure for Ions

To draw the Electron-Dot structure for an ion, the Electron-Dot structure for the element is first drawn, then electrons are added or removed to form the ion. *Positive ions are formed when electrons are lost by a metal, while negative ions result when nonmetals gain electrons.*

Example B: Write the Electron-Dot structure for the ions produced from the elements listed below:

a. Na b. Mg c. Cl

Solution

a. For the metal sodium, Na, the 1 valence electron is lost; the resulting ion has a +1 charge

$$\text{Na}\cdot \longrightarrow \text{Na}^+ + 1e^-$$

b. For the metal magnesium, Mg, the 2 valence electrons are lost and a +2 ion is formed

$$\dot{\text{Mg}}\cdot \longrightarrow \text{Mg}^{2+} + 2e^-$$

c. Cl, a nonmetal, has 7 valence electrons and will gain 1 more; completing its octet as a –1 ion

$$\cdot\ddot{\underset{..}{\text{Cl}}}: + 1e^- \longrightarrow :\ddot{\underset{..}{\text{Cl}}}:^-$$

Problem 2. Draw the Electron-Dot structure for the ions produced from the following elements: (remember to first classify them as metals or nonmetals)

a. K b. O c. F d. Al

e. P f. S g. Ca h. Br

Problem 3. Why do elements in a given group or family have similar chemical properties?

II. Compounds and Their Bonds

Compounds are substances produced when two or more elements combine chemically. Compounds may have two different types of bonds holding the atoms together. These two types of bonds are ionic and covalent.

A. Ionic Bond

An ionic bond is formed by the attraction of oppositely charged ions. These ions are the result of the transfer of one or more electrons from a metal to a nonmetal. Usually, if one of the elements in a compound is a metal, then the compound is ionic. Ionic compounds are made up of ions whose repeating basic unit is called a formula unit.

B. Covalent Bond

A covalent bond is formed when electrons are shared between the elements in a compound. If *all* the elements in a compound are *nonmetals*, then the compound is considered *covalent*. The basic repeating unit in a covalent compound is a molecule.

Problem 4. Classify each of the following as an element, an ionic compound, or a covalent compound:

a. He b. NaCl c. CO d. AgBr e. CH_4

III. Ionic Compounds

When an ionic compound is formed, the total number of electrons lost by the metal must be equal to the number of electrons gained by the nonmetal. The total charge on the compound must be zero.

A. Writing Formulas in Ionic Compounds

The ionic charge of an ion is also called its oxidation number. The following examples represent the formation of several ionic compounds from their respective elements. Each ion has a "noble gas electronic configuration" and the total charge on the compound is equal to zero (the sum of the positive charges = the sum of the negative charges).

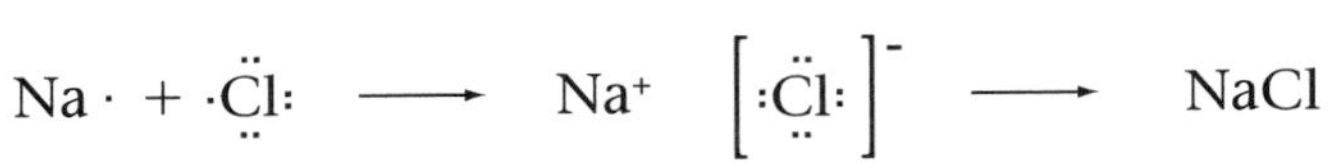

$$\underset{\text{metal}}{Na\cdot} + \underset{\text{nonmetal}}{\cdot\ddot{\underset{\cdot\cdot}{Cl}}:} \longrightarrow \underset{\text{ions}}{Na^+\ [:\ddot{\underset{\cdot\cdot}{Cl}}:]^-} \longrightarrow \underset{\text{ionic compound}}{NaCl}$$

$$\underset{\text{metal}}{\dot{M}g\cdot} + \underset{\text{nonmetal}}{\cdot\ddot{\underset{\cdot}{O}}:} \longrightarrow \underset{\text{ions}}{Mg^{2+}\ [:\ddot{\underset{\cdot\cdot}{O}}:]^{2-}} \longrightarrow \underset{\text{ionic compound}}{MgO}$$

When the charge on the positive ion is not equal to the charge on the negative ion, subscripts must be used to balance the charges. (Subscripts of one are omitted.) The formula represents the simplest ratio of elements comprising the compound.

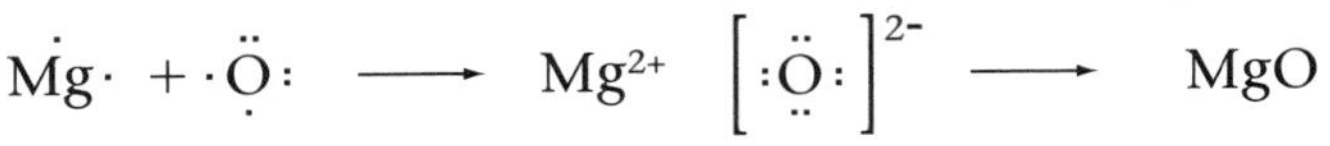

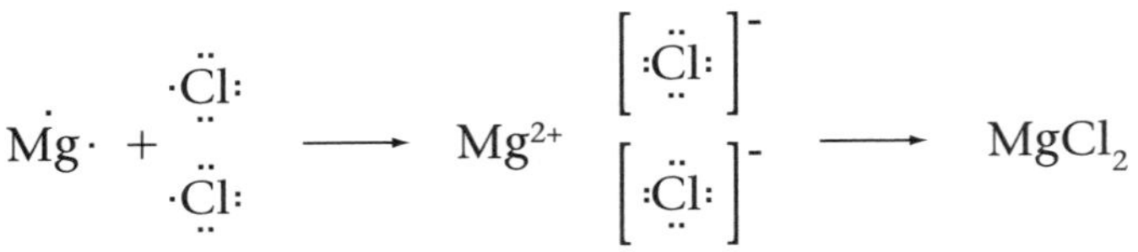

$$\underset{\text{metal}}{\dot{M}g\cdot} + \underset{\text{nonmetal}}{\begin{matrix}\cdot\ddot{\underset{\cdot\cdot}{Cl}}: \\ \cdot\ddot{\underset{\cdot\cdot}{Cl}}:\end{matrix}} \longrightarrow \underset{\text{ions}}{Mg^{2+}\ \begin{matrix}[:\ddot{\underset{\cdot\cdot}{Cl}}:]^- \\ [:\ddot{\underset{\cdot\cdot}{Cl}}:]^-\end{matrix}} \longrightarrow \underset{\text{ionic compound}}{MgCl_2}$$

$$\underset{\text{metal}}{\begin{matrix}\dot{K} \\ \dot{K}\end{matrix}} + \underset{\text{nonmetal}}{\cdot\ddot{\underset{\cdot}{S}}:} \longrightarrow \underset{\text{ions}}{\begin{matrix}K^+ \\ K^+\end{matrix}\ [:\ddot{\underset{\cdot\cdot}{S}}:]^{2-}} \longrightarrow \underset{\text{ionic compound}}{K_2S}$$

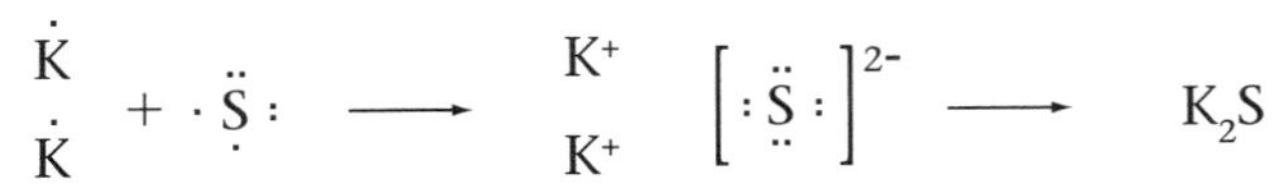

The formula for an ionic compound produced by the chemical combination of two elements can be determined by following the steps below:

a. refer to the periodic table to predict the ionic charges;

b. cross the ionic charges to give the ratio of the elements in the compound;

c. review the result to ensure that these subscripts are the simplest whole number ratios in the formula.

The following examples use the method described above.

$Mg^{2+} \times Cl^{1-}$	The formula would be $MgCl_2$ (Only the number and not the "positive" or "negative" signs appear in the formula.)
$Sn^{+4} \times O^{2-}$	Crossing charges would give Sn_2O_4; however, the formula is SnO_2. *In cases such as this, use the simplest whole number ratio.*

Example C: Write the formulas for the ionic compounds formed between the following elements:

a. Ca & O b. Be & Br c. Al & S

a. Ca is in group IIA and will form a +2 ion → Ca^{2+}

O is in group VIA and will form a -2 ion → O^{2-}

Since the charge on the cation is equal to the charge on the anion, the formula is:

CaO

b. Be is in group IIA and will form a +2 ion → Be^{2+}

Br is in group VIIA and will form a -1 ion → Br^{-}

Since the charge on the cation is not equal to the charge on the anion, subscripts need to be used. Crossing the ionic charges gives the following formula: $BeBr_2$.

c. Al is in group IIIA and will form a +3 ion → Al^{3+}

S is in group VIA and will form a -2 ion → S^{2-}

Since the charge on the cation is not equal to the charge on the anion, subscripts need to be used. Crossing the ionic charges gives the following formula: Al_2S_3.

Problem 5. Complete the following table:

Metal	Metal Ion	Nonmetal	Nonmetal Ion	Formula of Ionic Compound
K		P		
Mg		N		
Al		Cl		
Ca		S		

B. Nomenclature of Binary Ionic Compounds

To name an ionic compound, the positive metal ion is named first, followed by the nonmetal ion whose name is changed to have an "ide" ending. The following table gives the formula and name of some ionic compounds.

Some metals form ionic compounds using *fixed* charges or *fixed* oxidation numbers. The following metals have the *fixed* oxidation number indicated: Group IA , +1; Group IIA, +2; Al^{+3}, Zn^{+2}, Cd^{+2}, and Ag^{+1}.

Formula	Metal Ion	Nonmetal Ion	Name
NaCl	Na^+	Cl^-	sodium chloride
Ag_2O	Ag^+	O^{2-}	silver oxide
CaS	Ca^{2+}	S^{2-}	calcium sulfide
AlI_3	Al^{3+}	I^-	aluminum iodide
Zn_3P_2	Zn^{2+}	P^{3-}	zinc phosphide

Note: When the metal present in an ionic compound has variable oxidation numbers, like iron, the oxidation number is written as a Roman numeral in parenthesis after the name of the metal (i.e., $FeCl_3$ is iron(III) chloride; $FeCl_2$ is iron(II) chloride). (Refer to Module 2.)

Problem 6. Complete the following table:

Formula	Metal Ion	Nonmetal Ion	Name
$BeCl_2$			
			barium nitride
Cs_2S			
			strontium bromide
			lithium phosphide

IV. Covalent Compounds

A covalent compound is formed when atoms from two (or more) nonmetals chemically combine. These atoms are held together when they share one or more electron pairs. Electron-Dot structures may be used to understand the bonding in covalent compounds.

A. Drawing Electron Dot Structures of Covalent Compounds

Chlorine, which is a nonmetal, acquires a stable noble gas configuration by sharing 1 of its 7 valence electrons with a second chlorine atom. This sharing of an electron pair results in a covalent bond being formed between the two chlorine atoms. Each Cl contributed one electron to the bond and both chlorine atoms attain an octet of electrons, a more stable configuration. The shared electrons contribute to the octet for both atoms.

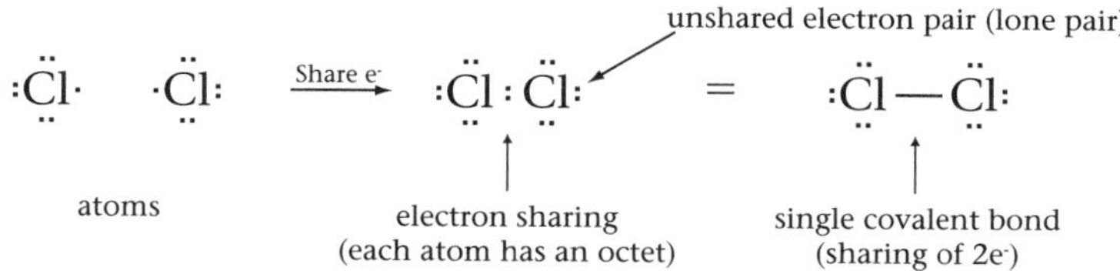

Exception: Hydrogen never achieves an octet of electrons. In H_2, each hydrogen acquires the stable noble gas configuration of He by sharing its electron with a second hydrogen atom. Each hydrogen contributes one electron to the bond. The electrons in hydrogen occupy the first energy level where a *maximum* of two electrons may be accommodated.

To differentiate between the electrons of each hydrogen atom in H_2, x's and dots are used:

H· xH —Share e⁻→ H $\overset{\cdot}{\underset{x}{}}$ H

atoms covalent bond

Atoms that are bonded together through covalent bonds produce a *molecule* of that compound.

To draw the Lewis Dot or Electron-Dot structure of covalent compounds, the following steps may be used:

a. usually the first element in a formula is the central atom (except for hydrogen, which can never be the central atom since H can only form one bond);

b. the other atoms are arranged around the central atom;

c. the Electron-Dot structure for each atom is drawn;

d. the covalent bonds are indicated by placing the shared electron pairs between the two atoms.

Example D: Draw the Electron-Dot structure for CH_4.

Step 1: C is the central element (it has the smaller subscript). Distribute Carbon's four valence electrons to all four sides.

Step 2: Place the four Hydrogens with their one valence electron around C.

Step 3: Form covalent bonds by sharing a pair of electrons between atoms.

Step 4: Form one covalent bond for each shared electron pair.

```
      H
      |
  H — C — H
      |
      H
```

Note, C (in CH_4) has 4 single bonds.

Try drawing the Electron-Dot structure for SiH_4.

Example E: Draw the Electron-Dot structure for NH_3.

Guidelines	Example
a. The central element is the element that is written first in the formula.	NH_3 ↖ Central Element
b. Place the other atoms in the formula around the central element.	H N H H
c. Draw the Electron-Dot structure for each atom.	H• •N̈• •H • • H
d. Share dots to form an octet. Each atom contributes one electron and a shared pair results.	H : N̈ : H ·· H Note how N has an octet.
e. Form a *covalent* bond for each pair of electrons being shared.	H — N̈ — H | H Note that there are three single covalent bonds and that N has one lone electron pair.

Single, double, and triple covalent bonds can be formed, depending on the number of electron pairs being shared:

Single bond → the sharing of 2 electrons (1 pair of electrons) X – Y

Double bond → the sharing of 4 electrons (2 pairs of electrons) X = Y

Triple bond → the sharing of 6 electrons (3 pairs of electrons) X ≡ Y

The following are examples of the Electron-Dot structure for several covalent molecules:

Molecule	Electron-Dot Structure for Each Atom	Electron Sharing	Covalent Bonds
SiH_4	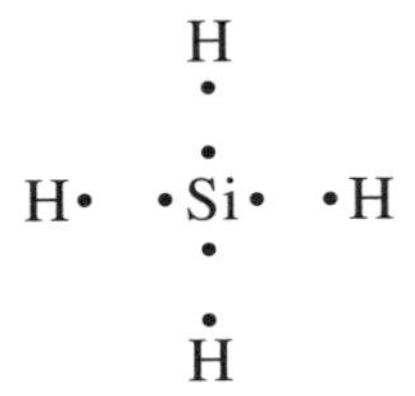 H• •Si• •H (four H atoms, each with one dot, around Si with four dots)	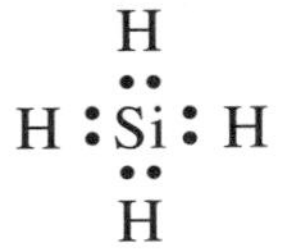 H:Si:H with H above and below (Si shares a pair with each H) Silicon acquired an octet of electrons by sharing its valence electrons with those of hydrogen.	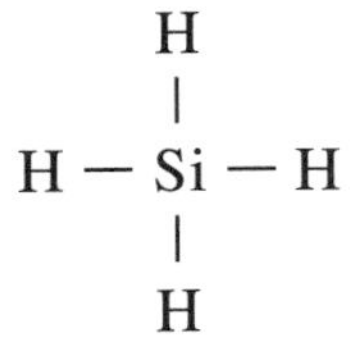 H–Si–H with H above and below (four single bonds)
H_2O	 H• •Ö• •H (O with six dots)	 H:Ö:H (O with two lone pairs) Oxygen acquired an octet of electrons by sharing its valence electrons with those of hydrogen.	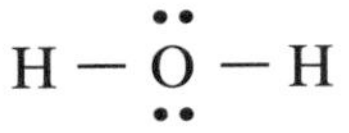 H – Ö – H (O with two lone pairs) Two covalent bonds and two lone pairs result.
PCl_3	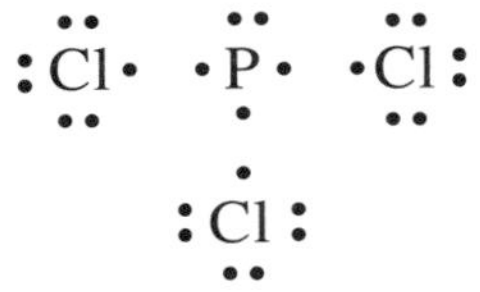 :Cl• •P• •Cl: and :Cl: below P (each Cl with seven dots, P with five)	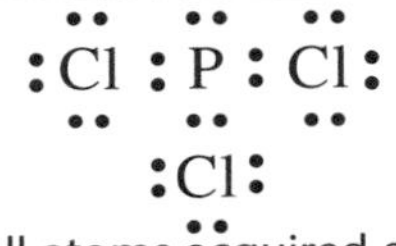 :Cl:P:Cl: with :Cl: below P All atoms acquired an octet of electrons by sharing their valence electrons.	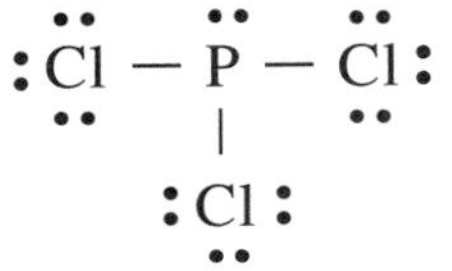 :Cl – P – Cl: with :Cl: below P (P with one lone pair) Three covalent bonds and one lone pair results.
O_2	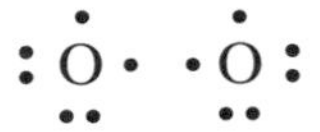 :O• •O: (each O with six dots)	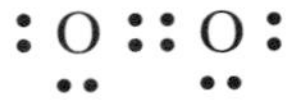 :O::O: Each oxygen contributes two electrons to the bond and a *double bond* results.	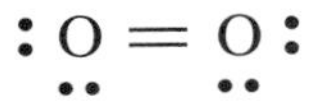 :O = O:
CO_2	 :O• •C• •O: (each O with six dots, C with four)	 :O::C::O: Two pairs of electrons are shared between carbon and each oxygen, resulting in two double bonds. Each element has an octet of electrons.	 :O = C = O:

Problem 7. Draw Electron-Dot structures for each of the following molecules:

a. NI_3 b. F_2 c. N_2

d. $SiCl_4$ e. OCl_2 f. HCl

Problem 8. For the following compounds, determine the number of covalent bonds and the number of lone pairs present around the central atom: (Hint: draw Electron-Dot structures):

a. H_2S b. NCl_3 c. CCl_4 d. CS_2 e. $AsBr_3$

B. Nomenclature

In naming covalent compounds, the ending for the name of the first element is not modified. However, if more than one atom of the first element is present, a prefix is used to denote the number of atoms of that element present.

The ending of the second element is changed to *ide*. A prefix is used to denote the number of atoms of the second element present in the formula, even if this number is one.

For prefixes that end in *a* or *o*, that vowel is dropped if the name of the second element starts with a vowel.

Prefix	*Number*
mono	1
di	2
tri	3
tetra	4
penta	5
hexa	6
hepta	7
octa	8
nona	9
deca	10

Example F: Write the name of the following compounds:

a. CO b. Cl_2S_7 c. IF_3

Solution

a. carbon monoxide

The first element is carbon. Its name is not modified and the prefix *mono* is not needed → **carbon**.

The second element is oxygen. It is modified so that it ends in ide → **oxide**.

The prefix *mono* is used since there is one O. Instead of the name being monooxide, the last vowel on the prefix is dropped → **monoxide**. Therefore, the name for CO is carbon monoxide.

b. dichlorine heptasulfide

The first element is chlorine. Its name is not modified. The prefix *di* is used since there are two chlorine atoms → **dichlorine**.

The second element is sulfur. It is modified so that it ends in ide → **sulfide**. The prefix *hepta* is used since there are seven S → **heptasulfide**. The name is dichlorine heptasulfide.

c. iodine trifluoride

The first element is iodine. Its name is not modified and the prefix *mono* is not needed → **iodine**.

The second element is fluorine. It is modified so that it ends in ide → fluoride. The prefix *tri* is used since there are three F → **trifluoride**. The name for this compound is iodine trifluoride.

Example G: Write formulas for the following compounds:

a. dichlorine pentoxide
b. sulfur hexafluoride
c. phosphorous pentabromide
d. diphosphorous pentoxide

Solution

a. Cl_2O_5 b. SF_6 c. PBr_5 d. P_2O_5

Problem 9. Complete the following table:

Formula	Name
SCl_2	
	dinitrogen pentoxide
CO_2	
	iodine pentafluoride
CCl_4	
	dichlorine monoxide
OF_2	

V. Polyatomic Ions

Polyatomic ions are ionic species containing two or more atoms bonded together. The following are the names and formulas of some common polyatomic ions.

Formula	Ion Name
NH_4^+	ammonium
OH^-	hydroxide
CN^-	cyanide
NO_3^-	nitrate
HCO_3^-	bicarbonate
$C_2H_3O_2^-$	acetate
CO_3^{2-}	carbonate
SO_4^{2-}	sulfate
PO_4^{3-}	phosphate

In naming compounds containing polyatomic ions, the rules are the same as those for naming binary compounds, except that the name of the polyatomic ion is not modified.

When writing formulas for compounds containing polyatomic ions, the positive charges must balance the negative charges. Subscripts may be needed if the charge on the positive ion is not equal to the charge on the negative ion and the polyatomic ion is enclosed in parentheses; the subscript is placed outside the parentheses.

The following table gives examples of some ionic compounds containing polyatomic ions.

Formula	Cation	Anion	Name
Na_3PO_4	Na^+	PO_4^{3-}	sodium phosphate
$LiOH$	Li^+	OH^-	lithium hydroxide
$Ca(HCO_3)_2$	Ca^{2+}	HCO_3^-	calcium bicarbonate
$Al_2(SO_4)_3$	Al^{3+}	SO_4^{2-}	aluminum sulfate
NH_4NO_3	NH_4^+	NO_3^-	ammonium nitrate
$(NH_4)_2O$	NH_4^+	O^{2-}	ammonium oxide

Problem 10. Complete the following table:

Formula	Cation	Anion	Name
$KHCO_3$			
			aluminum carbonate
$MgSO_4$			
			calcium phosphate
NH_4OH			
			beryllium cyanide

Problem 11. Complete the following table:

Formula	Name	Ionic or Covalent
PCl_5		
	cesium nitride	
BaI_2		
	aluminum hydroxide	
N_2O_5		
	sulfur hexafluoride	
$(NH_4)_2CO_3$		
	dihydrogen monoxide (water)	

VI. Molecular Shapes (OPTIONAL)

The atoms in a molecule have definite three-dimensional shapes. These shapes are used to predict the properties of molecules. If only two atoms are present in a molecule, then the molecule is linear. All diatomic molecules are linear. When 3 or more atoms are present in a molecule, Electron-Dot structures aid in determining the shape of that molecule. Since electrons carry negative charges, repulsive forces play an important role in the geometry of molecules.

After drawing the Electron-Dot structure of a covalent compound, the number of atoms and lone electron pairs surrounding the central atom are counted. The table given below may be used to determine the shape of a molecule.

MOLECULAR SHAPES

Groups* About Central Atom	Number of Lone Pairs: Zero	Number of Lone Pairs: One	Number of Lone Pairs: Two
2	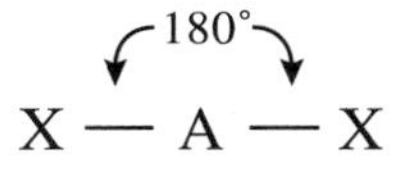 180° X — A — X Linear	X — A : Linear	: A :
3	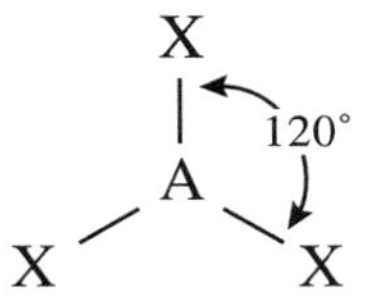 120° Planar Triangle or Triangular Planar	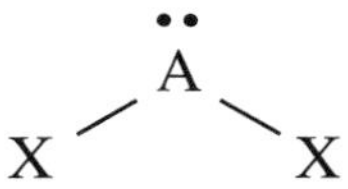 V-shaped, Bent, or Angular	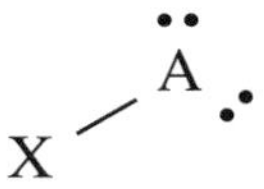 Linear
4	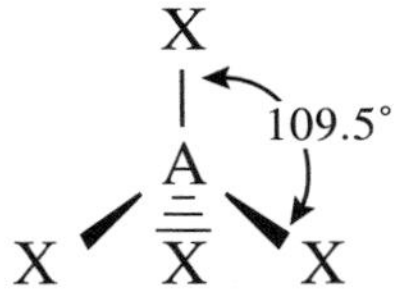 109.5° Tetrahedral (tetrahedron)	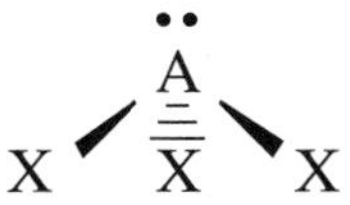 Trigonal Pyramid	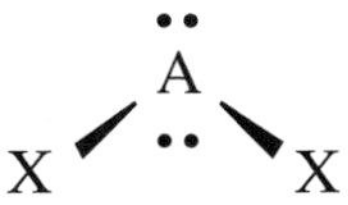 V-shaped, Bent, or Angular

To determine the shape of a molecule:

1. The Electron-Dot structure is drawn;
2. The table above is used, after counting the number of atoms and lone pair(s) around the central element.

Example H: What is the shape for NH_3?

```
     ••
  H ⁄ N ⁀ H
      |
      H
```

Shape: Trigonal Pyramid—because there are four "groups" (one lone pair and 3 H's) around the central element, N.

Example I: What is the shape for H_2O?

```
     ••
  H ⁄ O ⁀ H
     ••
```

Shape: V-shaped—because there are 2 lone pairs and 2 hydrogen atoms (a total of 4) around the central element, O.

Problem 12. Determine the shape of the following compounds:

a. H_2S b. NCl_3 c. CCl_4 d. CS_2 e. $AsBr_3$

VII. Electronegativity and Polarity (OPTIONAL)

In a covalent bond, electrons are not always shared equally. The ability of an atom to attract shared electrons is called electronegativity (EN). The greater the electronegativity, the greater the attraction for the bonding electrons. The most electronegative element is fluorine and the least electronegative is francium. The periodic chart is used to predict the relative electronegativities for elements. Electronegativities generally increase from left to right in a period and decrease going down a group. (Note: Group VIII elements—the noble gases—are not included in this trend since they do not form bonds readily.)

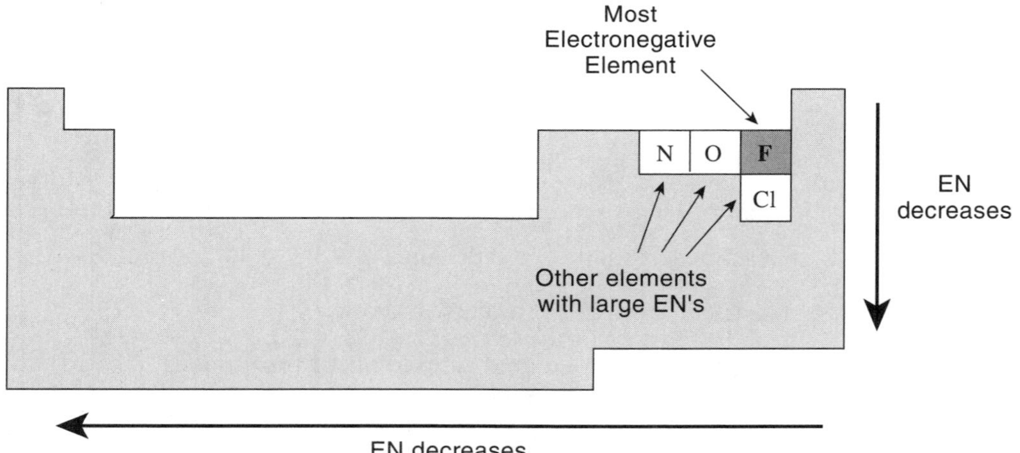

A. Polarity of Bonds

Covalent bonds may be polar or nonpolar.

A *nonpolar* covalent bond consists of a pair of electrons shared equally by both elements (when the difference in the electronegativity of the two elements is the same or very small).

A *polar* covalent bond consists of a pair of electrons shared unequally between the two elements (when there is a difference in electronegativity of the two elements). Generally, covalent bonds between two different elements are polar.

The larger the difference in EN between the two elements involved in a covalent bond, the more polar the bond. The more electronegative atom has the electrons closer to itself and therefore develops a partial negative charge ($\delta-$) while the less electronegative atom develops a partial positive charge ($\delta+$).

Nonpolar Covalent Bond	Polar Covalent Bond
Y : Z Atoms in a nonpolar covalent bond are sharing the electron pair "equally."	$\overset{\delta+}{X} : \overset{\delta-}{Y}$ The more electronegative element pulls the electron pair closer to itself and develops a partial negative charge ($\delta-$) while the less electronegative element develops a partial positive charge ($\delta+$).

An ionic bond is formed when the difference in electronegativity between the two elements is very large (i.e., a metal and nonmetal). The more electronegative element takes the electrons away from the less electronegative element, and ions are formed. The more electronegative element gains the electrons (becomes an anion) while the less electronegative element loses its electrons (becomes a cation).

Ionic Bond	Covalent Bond
$X\cdot \ \cdot Y \longrightarrow X^{+} :Y^{-}$ An ionic bond is electrostatic in nature (attraction of positive and negative charges). The ions are formed by the transfer of one or more electrons from one atom to another. Ionic bonds are formed between metals and nonmetals because the difference in their EN is very large.	$Y\cdot \ \cdot Z \longrightarrow Y : Z$ or $Y — Z$ Covalent Bond Atoms in a covalent bond are held together by the sharing of one or more electron pairs. Covalent bonds are formed by two nonmetals because the difference in their EN is not too large.

Problem 13. Identify the bonding between the following pairs of elements as nonpolar covalent, polar covalent, or ionic:

a. H and H b. N and H c. F and F d. C and O

e. Na and O f. H and O

Problem 14. Place the symbols δ− and δ+ above the appropriate atoms.

a. H – F b. N – H c. H – Cl d. O – H

B. Polarity of Molecules

Even though a bond may be polar, the molecule as a whole may be nonpolar if it is symmetrical. To determine the polarity of molecules, the Electron-Dot structure of the molecule must first be drawn and its shape determined. If all atoms bonded to the central element are identical and there are no lone pairs present around the central element, the molecule is nonpolar. Molecules that have no lone pairs around the central atom and are linear, triangular, or tetrahedral are nonpolar molecules. CO_2 and CH_4 are two examples of nonpolar molecules.

If polar bonds are present in a molecule that is asymmetrical and lone pairs are present around the central atom, then the molecule is polar. Water is polar since it is V-shaped and has two lone pairs of electrons.

The following are examples of several polar and nonpolar molecules.

:Cl: (×4) around C — CCl_4	O with H, H (V-shaped)	:O=O:	:O=C=O:
Molecule is nonpolar because central element, C, has no lone pair of electrons (symmetrical).	Molecule is polar because central element, O, has lone electron pairs and it is V-shaped (not symmetrical).	Molecule is nonpolar. Any molecule containing nonpolar bonds is nonpolar.	Molecule is nonpolar because central element, C, has no lone pair of electrons and it is linear (symmetrical).

ANSWERS

1.

Element	# of Valence Electrons	Electron-Dot Structure
Mg	2	$\overset{\cdot}{\text{Mg}}\cdot$
Na	1	$\overset{\cdot}{\text{Na}}$
H	1	$\overset{\cdot}{\text{H}}$
He	2	$\overset{\cdot}{\text{He}}\cdot$
Ar	8	$:\overset{\cdot\cdot}{\underset{\cdot\cdot}{\text{Ar}}}:$
P	5	$\cdot\overset{\cdot\cdot}{\underset{\cdot}{\text{P}}}\cdot$
Ga	3	$\overset{\cdot}{\underset{\cdot}{\text{Ga}}}\cdot$
S	6	$\cdot\overset{\cdot\cdot}{\underset{\cdot}{\text{S}}}:$

2. a. K^{1+} b. $:\overset{\cdot\cdot}{\underset{\cdot\cdot}{\text{O}}}:^{2-}$ c. $:\overset{\cdot\cdot}{\underset{\cdot\cdot}{\text{F}}}:^{1-}$ d. Al^{3+}

   e. $:\overset{\cdot\cdot}{\underset{\cdot\cdot}{\text{P}}}:^{3-}$ f. $:\overset{\cdot\cdot}{\underset{\cdot\cdot}{\text{S}}}:^{2-}$ g. Ca^{2+} h. $:\overset{\cdot\cdot}{\underset{\cdot\cdot}{\text{Br}}}:^{1-}$

3. Elements in a given group have similar valence electronic configuration.

4. a. element b. ionic c. covalent d. ionic e. covalent

5.

Metal	Metal Ion	Nonmetal	Nonmetal Ion	Formula of Ionic Compound
K	K^+	P	P^{3-}	K_3P
Mg	Mg^{2+}	N	N^{3-}	Mg_3N_2
Al	Al^{3+}	Cl	Cl^-	$AlCl_3$
Ca	Ca^{2+}	S	S^{2-}	CaS

6.

Formula	Metal Ion	Nonmetal Ion	Name
$BeCl_2$	Be^{2+}	Cl^-	beryllium chloride
Ba_3N_2	Ba^{2+}	N^{3-}	barium nitride
Cs_2S	Cs^+	S^{2-}	cesium sulfide
$SrBr_2$	Sr^{2+}	Br^-	strontium bromide
Li_3P	Li^+	P^{3-}	lithium phosphide

7. a. :Ï̤ — N̈ — Ï̤: with :I̤: bonded below N

b. :F̤̈ — F̤̈:

c. :N:::N:

d. :C̤̈l — Si — C̤̈l: with :C̈l: above Si and :C̤l: below Si

e. :C̤̈l — Ö̤ — C̤̈l:

f. H — C̤̈l:

8. a. 2 single covalent bonds, 2 lone pairs

b. 3 single bonds, 1 lone pair

c. 4 single covalent bonds

d. 2 double bonds, no lone pairs

e. 3 single bonds, 1 lone pair

9.

Formula	Name
SCl_2	sulfur dichloride
N_2O_5	dinitrogen pentoxide
CO_2	carbon dioxide
IF_5	iodine pentafluoride
CCl_4	carbon tetrachloride
Cl_2O	dichlorine monoxide
OF_2	oxygen difluoride

10.

Formula	Cation	Anion	Name
$KHCO_3$	K^+	HCO_3^-	potassium bicarbonate
$Al_2(CO_3)_3$	Al^{3+}	CO_3^{2-}	aluminum carbonate
$MgSO_4$	Mg^{2+}	SO_4^{2-}	magnesium sulfate
$Ca_3(PO_4)_2$	Ca^{2+}	PO_4^{3-}	calcium phosphate
NH_4OH	NH_4^+	OH^-	ammonium hydroxide
$Be(CN)_2$	Be^{2+}	CN^-	beryllium cyanide

11.

Formula	Name	Ionic or Covalent
PCl_5	phosphorus pentachloride	covalent
Cs_3N	cesium nitride	ionic
BaI_2	barium iodide	ionic
$Al(OH)_3$	aluminum hydroxide	ionic
N_2O_5	dinitrogen pentoxide	covalent
SF_6	sulfur hexafluoride	covalent
$(NH_4)_2CO_3$	ammonium carbonate	ionic
H_2O	water	covalent

12. a. V-shaped b. trigonal pyramid c. tetrahedral d. linear e. trigonal pyramid

13. a. nonpolar b. polar c. nonpolar
d. polar e. ionic f. polar

14. $\overset{\delta+}{H} - \overset{\delta-}{F}$ $\overset{\delta-}{N} - \overset{\delta+}{H}$ $\overset{\delta+}{H} - \overset{\delta-}{Cl}$ $\overset{\delta-}{O} - \overset{\delta+}{H}$

From Elements to Compounds

Assignment 3

Name

Student Number

Date Instructor

1. A –3 ion of phosphorus contains ____ electrons.

2. Magnesium has ____valence electrons.

3. To achieve an octet, sulfur (gains/loses)__________ electrons.

4. When a metal and a nonmetal are combined, a(n) ___________ bond usually forms.

5. What is the charge on a fluoride ion? ________

6. What is the charge on a calcium ion? ________

7. Draw Lewis Dot structures for the following elements and ions.

   a. S b. Mg c. P d. O^{2-} e. Al^{3+} f. Cl^{-}

8. Classify each of the following compounds as covalent or ionic.

   a. K_2O ________ b. CCl_4 ________ c. $BaCl_2$ ________ d. SO_2 ________

9. Write formulas for the compounds formed between the following elements.

   a. Li & O __________ b. Al & Cl __________

   c. Ca & N __________ d. Mg & S __________

10. Draw Lewis Dot structures (electron dot formulas) for the following compounds.

    a. PCl_3 b. SiH_4

    c. N_2 d. OF_2

    e. SO_3

11. Write names for the following compounds.

a. $(NH_4)_2SO_4$ ______________ b. $Al(HCO_3)_3$ ____________________

c. $MgCl_2$ __________________ d. CO_2 _________________________

e. Na_3PO_4 ________________ f. K_3N ________________________

g. Cl_2O_5 __________________ h. $Ca(NO_3)_2$ ____________________

12. Write formulas for the following compounds.

a. beryllium cyanide __________ b. nitrogen trifluoride __________

c. barium phosphide __________ d. calcium bicarbonate __________

e. lithium sulfide __________ f. ammonium carbonate __________

g. strontium hydroxide __________ h. sulfur hexafluoride __________

13. For each of the following pairs of elements, underline the one which is the most electronegative.

a. K & Cl b. Ca & Mg c. S & Cl

d. O & F e. Sb & Br f. H & F

14. Underline the bond which is the most polar.

H–S H–Se H–O H–Te

15. Complete the following table by writing formulas and names of the ionic compounds formed by the combination of ions given below:

	Cl^{1-}	PO_4^{3-}	NO_3^{1-}	CO_3^{2-}
K^{1+}				
Be^{2+}				
Co^{3+}				
Ca^{2+}				
Fe^{2+}				

4

Chemical Reactions

Chemical reactions, or chemical changes, are those that result in a change in the chemical composition of matter. The original substances are called the reactants and the resulting substances are called the products. Chemical equations are used to describe these changes. In this module we will be dealing with the basics of chemical arithmetic. Chemical reactions and mass relationships in chemical reactions will be discussed in this module.

I. Atomic Mass (AM) and Formula Mass (FM)

The atomic mass is the mass (quantity of matter) of an atom of an element, given in atomic mass units (amu). The periodic table gives the atomic mass for each element. For example, one atom of hydrogen, the lightest element, has been assigned a mass of 1 amu. This value may be found either above or below the element's symbol, depending on the periodic table used.

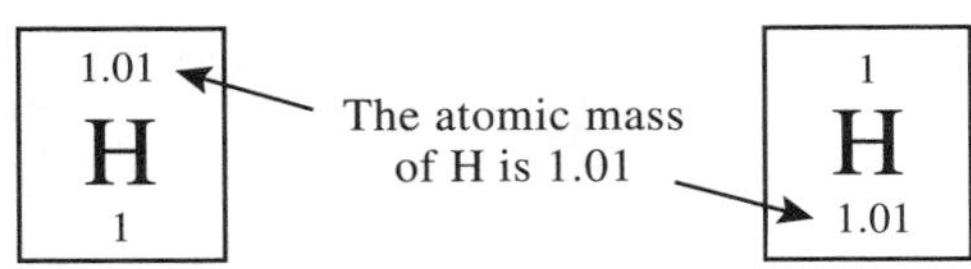

The formula mass of a compound is simply the sum of the atomic masses of all atoms in that compound.

Example A: What is the formula mass of H_2?

$$2\ H = 2 \times 1.0 = 2.0\ \text{amu}$$

The formula mass of H_2 is 2.0 amu = 1 molecule of H_2

Example B: What is the formula mass of H_2O?

2 H	=	2 × 1.0	=	2.0
1 O	=	1 × 16.0	=	16.0
Formula Mass			=	18.0 amu = 1 molecule of H_2O

Example C: What is the formula mass of $(NH_4)_2O$?

2 N	=	2 × 14.0	=	28.0
8 H	=	8 × 1.0	=	8.0
1 O	=	1 × 16.0	=	16.0
Formula Mass			=	52.0 amu

Problem 1. Calculate the formula mass for each of the following:

a. NaF b. ZnI_2

c. CH_4 d. C_2H_5ONa

e. CH_3SO_2Cl f. $Ca(IO_3)_2$

II. The Mole and Molar Mass

An atomic mass unit is an incredibly small value, so small that scientists cannot possibly work with single atoms. Chemists decided that working with grams was a more sensible approach, so they measured the number of atoms of an element with a mass in grams that matched the atomic mass in amu's. For example, since aluminum has an atomic mass of 27 amu, they used 27 grams of aluminum and "counted" how many atoms it contained. They found that it contained 602,000,000,000,000,000,000,000 aluminum atoms. When they checked other elements, they found that using the mass of any element in grams always gave them the same number of atoms, 602,000,000,000,000,000,000,000. They gave this number the name **mole**.

Samples of one mole

Just like a dozen represents 12 items and a pair refers to 2 objects, the "collective" term, one used by chemists, is the mole. The mole has been defined to represent 602,000,000,000,000,000,000,000 of anything.

$$602{,}000{,}000{,}000{,}000{,}000{,}000{,}000 = \mathbf{6.02 \times 10^{23}}$$

This number, 6.02×10^{23}, is called Avogadro's number, in honor of a famous Italian scientist.

Another example: 25 pennies have a mass of approximately 63.5 grams. If the pennies are pure copper, then they contain one mole of copper. So in 25 pennies there are close to 6.02×10^{23} atoms of copper.

602,000,000,000,000,000,000,000 atoms of copper = 1 mole of copper

We can use Avogadro's number to refer to any element, compound, or even other objects. So if we refer to carbon, then

602,000,000,000,000,000,000,000 atoms of carbon = 1 mole of carbon = 12.0 g carbon

A mole of an element is simply its atomic mass or **molar mass** expressed in **grams.**

By the same token, one mole of a compound is simply given by its formula mass or **molar mass** expressed in **grams**.

1 mole He = 4.0 **g** He

1 mole NaF = 42.0 **g** NaF

Atomic mass	Na	23 g/mole
Atomic mass	F	<u>19 g/mole</u>
Molar mass NaF		42 g/mole

We can now measure the mass of elements and compounds in grams and refer to moles of them. Molar mass will be used as a conversion factor from grams to moles and from moles to grams.

A. Mole of an Element—Units for Atomic Mass → grams/mole

Example D: What is the molar mass or atomic mass of He?

4.0 g/mole (This means that one mole of He atoms weigh 4.0 g)

Example E: What is the mass of 1 mole of C?

12.0 g

Example F: How many grams are there in 2.00 mole of He?

1 mole He = 4.0 g He

$$?\text{ g He} = 2.00\text{ mole He}\left(\frac{4.0\text{ g He}}{1\text{ mole He}}\right) = 8.00\text{ g He}$$

Example G: How many moles of carbon are there in 26.0 g of carbon?

1 mole C = 12.0 g C

$$?\text{ mole C} = 26.0\text{ g C}\left(\frac{1\text{ mole C}}{12.0\text{ g C}}\right) = 2.17\text{ mole C}$$

Problem 2. Calculate the number of:

a. moles of lithium in 6.94 grams of lithium

b. moles of Na in 27.0 g Na

c. grams of aluminum in 3.00 moles of aluminum

d. grams of Fe in 2.00 moles of Fe

B. Mole of a Compound

1 mole H_2 = 2.0 g H_2 1 mole H_2O = 18.0 g H_2O

Example H: How many grams are there in 4.00 moles of H_2?

1 mole H_2 = 2.0 g H_2

$$? \text{ g } H_2 = 4.00 \text{ mole } H_2\left(\frac{2.0 \text{ g } H_2}{1 \text{ mole } H_2}\right) = 8.00 \text{ g } H_2$$

Example I: How many moles of H_2O are there in 20.0 g of H_2O?

1 mole H_2O = 18.0 g H_2O

$$? \text{ mole } H_2O = 20.0 \text{ g } H_2O\left(\frac{1 \text{ mole } H_2O}{18.0 \text{ g } H_2O}\right) = 1.11 \text{ mole } H_2O$$

Problem 3. Calculate the number of:

a. moles of NaF (MM = 42.0) in 82.0 grams

b. moles of ZnI_2 (MM = 319.2) in 500. g of ZnI_2

c. moles of CH_4 (MM = 16.0) in 28.0 g of CH_4

d. grams of CH_4 (MM = 16.0) in 3.00 moles of CH_4

e. grams of C_2H_5ONa (MM = 68.1) in 2.00 moles of C_2H_5ONa

f. grams of ZnI_2 (MM = 319.2.) in 2.50 moles of ZnI_2

III. Chemical Changes and Chemical Reactions

When a nail rusts in the presence of oxygen, or an engine burns gasoline, a chemical change takes place. When a chemical change occurs, a new substance is formed and a chemical reaction takes place. In chemistry, a chemical reaction is used to represent a chemical change. The initial substances, like iron and oxygen, are called **reactants** and the final substances produced, like the oxide of iron, are called **products**. The format used to represent a chemical reaction is:

Reactants ⟶ Products

A chemical reaction identifies the elements and compounds involved in the chemical change and may also include the energy required for the reaction to take place. For example, if carbon reacts with oxygen gas to produce carbon dioxide, energy is released. Whenever energy is **released** in a chemical reaction, the reaction is called an **exothermic reaction**.

$$C_{(s)} + O_{2(g)} \rightarrow CO_{2(g)} + \textbf{HEAT}$$

On the other hand, when hydrogen combines with iodine to form hydrogen iodide, energy is absorbed. Whenever energy is **absorbed** in a chemical reaction, the reaction is called an **endothermic reaction**. The following diagrams represent these examples.

$$H_{2(g)} + I_{2(g)} + \textbf{HEAT} \rightarrow 2\ HI_{(g)}$$

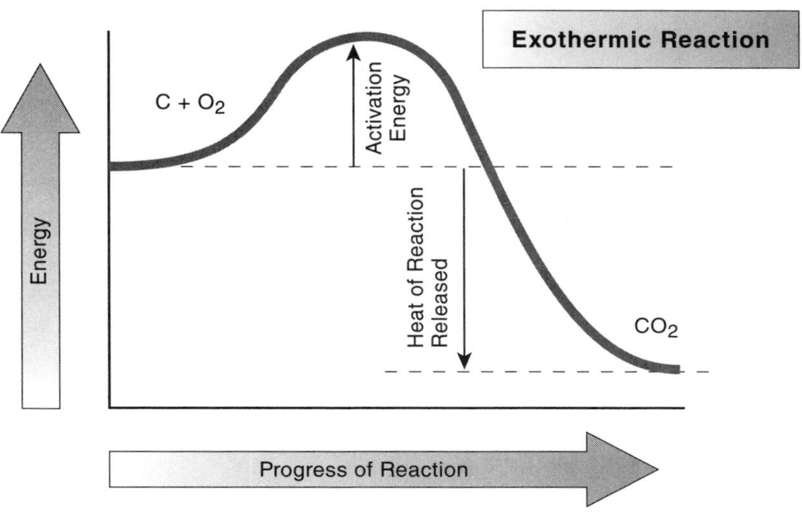

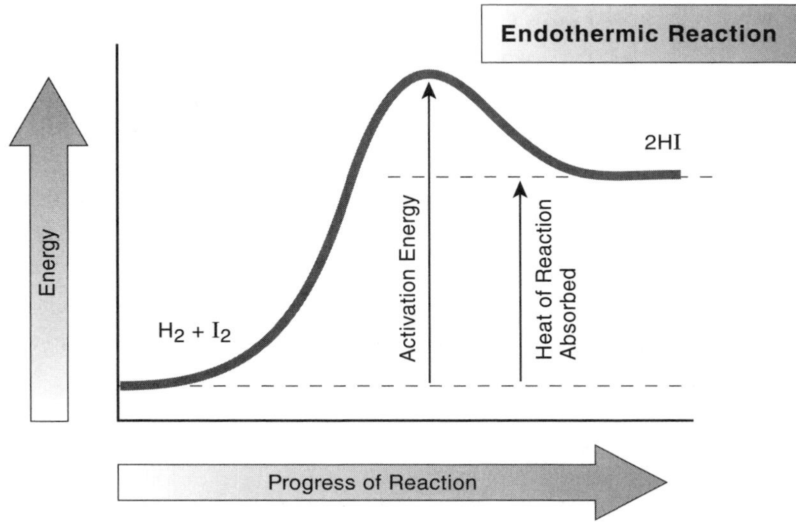

IV. Balancing Chemical Equations

In chemical reactions, matter is never created nor destroyed (Law of Conservation of Mass), matter is only transformed from one substance to another. This means that the same number of atoms present originally (reactants) must be there at the end (products). In the following chemical equation,

$$H_2 + Cl_2 \longrightarrow HCl \text{ (unbalanced)}$$

two H atoms are present on the left side and only one H atom is present on the right side. The same can be said for Cl. So **2** molecules of HCl are produced instead of just 1. The equation will be **balanced** by adding a **coefficient** of 2 in front of HCl.

$$H_2 + Cl_2 \longrightarrow 2\ HCl \text{ (balanced)}$$

a coefficient

If no coefficient is present, as is the case with H_2 and Cl_2, then it is understood that the coefficient is *one,* meaning only 1 molecule is present.

To balance chemical equations, a correct chemical formula is *never* changed since this changes the identity of the compound (subscripts are never added or changed).

For example,

$$H_2 + Cl_2 \longrightarrow \cancel{H_2Cl_2}$$

Guide to Balancing a Chemical Equation:

a. Balance those atoms that appear in only *one* of the formulas on both the right and left side of the equation.

b. Save for last those atoms that appear in more than one formula (on the same side of the equation). For example,

$$C + SO_2 \rightarrow CS_2 + CO$$

Start with S placing a 2 in front of SO_2, continue with O and C would be balanced last because it appears in two of the formulas (CS_2 and CO) on the right side.

$$5C + 2\ SO_2 \rightarrow CS_2 + 4\ CO$$

c. If there is an odd number of atoms on one side of the equation and an even number on the other side, and if those atoms appear only once on their respective side of the equation, then the coefficients will be the cross-multiplication product of the subscripts.

For example,

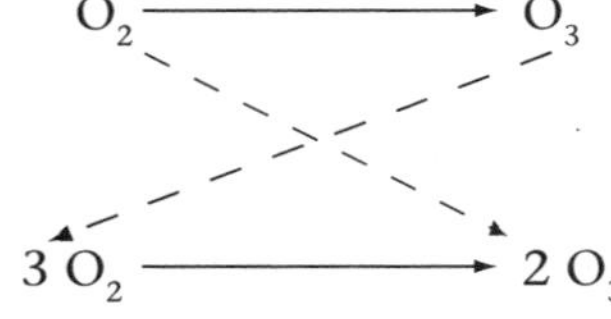

There are thus six O's on both sides of the equation.

d. If the same polyatomic ion is present on both sides of the equation, balance it first. In this case, the polyatomic ion should NOT be split into its elements, but should be balanced as one entity.

e. Check to see that the equation is completely balanced. Sometimes balancing one element will undo the balance of another. If this is the case, you must return to the other element and rebalance.

Example J: Balance the following chemical equation:

$$Mg + N_2 \rightarrow Mg_3N_2$$

The only atoms that are present are Mg and N, and since both Mg and N appear in only one formula on their respective side of the equation, you can pick either one to balance first.

Let's balance Mg first. There is one Mg on the left and three on the right, therefore, we need to put a coefficient of three in front of Mg.

$$\underline{3}\ Mg + N_2 \rightarrow Mg_3N_2$$

Let's balance N next. There are two N on the left and two on the right, therefore, N is already balanced.

A final check of the above chemical equation reveals that all atoms are balanced.

Example K: Balance the following chemical equation:

$$Fe + Cl_2 \rightarrow FeCl_3$$

The only atoms that are present are Fe and Cl and since both Fe and Cl appear in only one formula on their respective side of the equation, you can pick either one to balance first.

Let's balance Fe first. There is one Fe on the left and one on the right, therefore, Fe is already balanced.

Let's balance Cl next. There are two Cl on the left and three on the right. Since there is an odd-even combination (see guideline d above), the coefficients will be the cross-multiplication product of the subscripts.

$$Fe + \underline{3}\ Cl_2 \rightarrow \underline{2}\ FeCl_3$$

Having performed the above operation, Fe is now unbalanced (one on the left and two on the right). Fe is balanced as follows:

$$\underline{2}\ Fe + 3\ Cl_2 \rightarrow 2\ FeCl_3$$

A final check of the above chemical equation reveals that all atoms are balanced.

Example L: Balance the following **Combustion Reaction**.

$$C_2H_4 + O_2 \rightarrow CO_2 + H_2O$$

[A combustion reaction is a reaction in which a compound containing C and H is burned in the presence of O_2. The product of such a reaction is always CO_2 and H_2O.]

Balance either C or H first because each appears in only one of the formulas on their respective sides of the equation. Save O for last because it appears in two of the formulas on the right side.

1. Let's balance C first. There are two C on the left and one on the right. C is balanced as follows:

$$C_2H_4 + O_2 \rightarrow \underline{2}\ CO_2 + H_2O$$

2. Let's balance H next. There are four H on the left and two on the right. H is balanced as follows:

$$C_2H_4 + O_2 \rightarrow 2\ CO_2 + \underline{2}\ H_2O$$

3. Now balance O. There are two O on the left and six on the right. O is balanced as follows:

$$C_2H_4 + \underline{3}\ O_2 \rightarrow 2\ CO_2 + 2\ H_2O$$

A final check of the above chemical equation reveals that all atoms are balanced.

Example M: Balance the following chemical equation:

$$NaOH + PbCl_2 \rightarrow NaCl + Pb(OH)_2$$

Since the polyatomic ion "OH" is present on both sides of the equation, balance it first. Then balance any of the other atoms: Na, Pb, or Cl next. It doesn't matter which because all appear in only one of the formulas on their respective sides of the equation.

There is one "OH" on the left and two on the right. "OH" is balanced as follows:

$$\underline{2}\ NaOH + PbCl_2 \rightarrow NaCl + Pb(OH)_2$$

Let's balance Na next. There are two Na on the left and one on the right. Na is balanced as follows:

$$2\ NaOH + PbCl_2 \rightarrow \underline{2}\ NaCl + Pb(OH)_2$$

Let's balance Pb next. There is one Pb on the left and one on the right. Pb is already balanced.

Finally, let's balance Cl. There are two Cl on the left and two on the right. Cl is already balanced.

A final check of the above chemical equation reveals that all atoms are balanced.

Example N: Balance the following **Neutralization Reaction**:

$$H_3PO_4 + Mg(OH)_2 \rightarrow Mg_3(PO_4)_2 + H_2O$$

[A neutralization reaction is a reaction in which an acid reacts with a base. One of the products of such a reaction is H_2O.]

When balancing neutralization reactions, it is easier to consider H_2O as if it were HOH → H and polyatomic ion "OH." Rewriting the above equation, we have:

$$H_3PO_4 + Mg(OH)_2 \rightarrow Mg_3(PO_4)_2 + HOH$$

Polyatomic ions "PO_4" and "OH" are present on both sides of the equation. Let's balance those first. Then balance H and Mg.

There is one "PO_4" on the left and two on the right. "PO_4" is balanced as follows:

$$\underline{2}\ H_3PO_4 + Mg(OH)_2 \rightarrow Mg_3(PO_4)_2 + HOH$$

Let's balance "OH" next. There are two "OH" on the left and one on the right. "OH" is balanced as follows:

$$2\ H_3PO_4 + Mg(OH)_2 \rightarrow Mg_3(PO_4)_2 + \underline{2}\ HOH$$

Let's balance H next. There are 6 H on the left and 2 on the right (only consider <u>H</u>OH). H is balanced as follows:

$$2\ H_3PO_4 + Mg(OH)_2 \rightarrow Mg_3(PO_4)_2 + \underline{6}\ HOH$$

Finally, let's balance Mg. There is one Mg on the left and three on the right. Mg is balanced as follows:

$$2\ H_3PO_4 + \underline{3}\ Mg(OH)_2 \rightarrow Mg_3(PO_4)_2 + 6\ HOH$$

A final check of the above chemical equation reveals that all atoms are balanced.

Problem 4. Balance the following chemical equations:

a. $Na + Cl_2 \rightarrow NaCl$

b. $K + O_2 \rightarrow K_2O$

c. $Al + F_2 \rightarrow AlF_3$

d. $CO_2 + H_2O \rightarrow H_2CO_3$

e. $Cl_2O_3 + H_2O \rightarrow HClO_2$

f. $P_4O_{10} + H_2O \rightarrow H_3PO_4$

g. $Na_2CO_3 \rightarrow Na_2O + CO_2$

h. $KClO_3 \rightarrow KCl + O_2$

i. $H_2SO_3 \rightarrow H_2O + SO_2$

j. $HNO_2 \rightarrow N_2O_3 + H_2O$

k. $C_3H_8 + O_2 \rightarrow CO_2 + H_2O$

l. $C_5H_{12} + O_2 \rightarrow CO_2 + H_2O$

m. $C_5H_8 + O_2 \rightarrow CO_2 + H_2O$

n. $Na_3PO_4 + BaCl_2 \rightarrow Ba_3(PO_4)_2 + NaCl$

o. $Na_2CO_3 + AgNO_3 \rightarrow Ag_2CO_3 + NaNO_3$

p. $CaBr_2 + AgNO_3 \rightarrow AgBr + Ca(NO_3)_2$

q. $FeCl_3 + KOH \rightarrow Fe(OH)_3 + KCl$

r. $V(NO_3)_3 + KOH \rightarrow KNO_3 + V(OH)_3$

s. $HCl + NaOH \rightarrow NaCl + H_2O$

t. $HCl + Mg(OH)_2 \rightarrow MgCl_2 + H_2O$

u. $H_2SO_4 + NH_4OH \rightarrow (NH_4)_2SO_4 + H_2O$

v. $H_2SO_4 + Mg(OH)_2 \rightarrow MgSO_4 + H_2O$

Problem 5. When each of the above equations is balanced, what is the sum of all the coefficients?

V. Stoichiometry (Mass Relationships Involving Chemical Reactions) (OPTIONAL)

The quantitative relationship between the substances involved in a chemical reaction is called *stoichiometry*.

The following balanced chemical equation,

$$C_3H_8 + 5\ O_2 \rightarrow 3\ CO_2 + 4\ H_2O \text{ (eq. 1)}$$

tells us that when 1 mole of C_3H_8 is reacted with 5 moles of O_2, 3 moles of CO_2 and 4 moles of H_2O are produced. Thus, the following relationships can be used:

$$1 \text{ mole } C_3H_8 = 5 \text{ moles } O_2 = 3 \text{ moles } CO_2 = 4 \text{ moles } H_2O$$

A. Mole-to-Mole Conversion

Process:

$$\text{Mole A} \xrightarrow[\text{from balanced equations}]{\text{use coefficients}} \text{Mole B}$$

Example O: Consider eq. 1. How many moles of C_3H_8 are needed to react with 15.0 moles of O_2?

$$1 \text{ mole } C_3H_8 = 5 \text{ moles } O_2$$

$$? \ C_3H_8 = 15.0 \text{ moles } O_2\left(\frac{1 \text{ mole } C_3H_8}{5 \text{ moles } O_2}\right) = 3.00 \text{ moles } C_3H_8$$

Example P: Consider eq. 1. How many moles of H_2O are produced when 10.0 moles of C_3H_8 is reacted with the appropriate amount of O_2?

$$1 \text{ mole } C_3H_8 = 4 \text{ moles } H_2O$$

$$? \text{ moles } H_2O = 10.0 \text{ moles } C_3H_8\left(\frac{4 \text{ moles } H_2O}{1 \text{ mole } C_3H_8}\right) = 40.0 \text{ moles } H_2O$$

B. Mole-to-Gram Conversion

Process:

$$\text{Mole A} \xrightarrow[\text{from balanced equations}]{\text{use coefficients}} \text{Mole B} \xrightarrow[\text{of B}]{\text{use FM}} \text{Grams B}$$

Step 1 | Step 2

Example Q: Consider eq. 1. How many grams of O_2 (FM = 32.0) are needed to react with 4.00 moles of C_3H_8?

$$1 \text{ mole } C_3H_8 = 5 \text{ moles } O_2 \qquad 1 \text{ mole } O_2 = 32.0 \text{ g } O_2$$

$$? \text{ g } O_2 = 4.00 \text{ moles } C_3H_8\underbrace{\left(\frac{5 \text{ moles } O_2}{1 \text{ mole } C_3H_8}\right)}_{\text{Step 1}}\underbrace{\left(\frac{32.0 \text{ g } O_2}{1 \text{ mole } O_2}\right)}_{\text{Step 2}} = 640. \text{ g } O_2$$

C. Gram-to-Mole Conversion

Process:

$$\text{Grams A} \xrightarrow[\text{of A}]{\text{use FM}} \text{Mole A} \xrightarrow[\text{from balanced equations}]{\text{use coefficients}} \text{Mole B}$$

Step 1 Step 2

Example R: Consider eq. 1. How many moles of C_3H_8 are needed to produce 100 g of H_2O (FM = 18.0)?

$$1 \text{ mole } C_3H_8 = 4 \text{ mol } H_2O \qquad 1 \text{ mole } H_2O = 18.0 \text{ g } H_2O$$

$$\text{moles } C_3H_8 = 100.\text{ g } H_2O\left(\frac{1 \text{ mole } H_2O}{18.0 \text{ g } H_2O}\right)\left(\frac{1 \text{ mole } C_3H_8}{4 \text{ moles } H_2O}\right) = 1.39 \text{ moles of } C_3H_8$$

Step 1 Step 2

D. Gram-to-Gram Conversion

Process:

$$\text{Grams A} \xrightarrow[\text{of A}]{\text{use FM}} \text{Mole A} \xrightarrow[\text{from balanced equations}]{\text{use coefficients}} \text{Mole B} \xrightarrow[\text{of B}]{\text{use FM}} \text{Grams B}$$

Step 1 Step 2 Step 3

Example S: Consider eq. 1. How many grams of C_3H_8 (FM = 44.0) are needed to react with 100. g of O_2 (FM = 32.0)?

$$1 \text{ mole } C_3H_8 = 5 \text{ moles } O_2$$

$$1 \text{ mole } C_3H_8 = 44.0 \text{ g } C_3H_8 \qquad 1 \text{ mole } O_2 = 32.0 \text{ g } O_2$$

$$\text{g C} = 100.\text{ g } O_2\left(\frac{1 \text{ mole } O_2}{32.0 \text{ g } O_2}\right)\left(\frac{1 \text{ mole } C_3H_8}{5 \text{ moles } O_2}\right)\left(\frac{44.0 \text{ g } C_3H_8}{1 \text{ mole } C_3H_8}\right) = 27.5 \text{ g } C_3H_8$$

Step 1 Step 2 Step 3

For the next 5 questions use the balanced equation given below:

$$5\,C + 2\,SO_2 \rightarrow CS_2 + 4\,CO$$

Problem 6. How many moles of C are needed to react with 6.00 moles of SO_2?

Problem 7. How many moles of CO are produced from the reaction of 10.0 moles of C?

Problem 8. How many grams of SO_2 are needed to react with 5.00 moles of C?

Problem 9. How many grams of C are needed to produce 100. g of CO?

Problem 10. How many grams of C are needed to react with 100. g of SO_2?

ANSWERS

1. a. 42.0 b. 319.2 c. 16.0 d. 68.1 e. 114.5 f. 389.9

2. a. 1.00 b. 1.17 c. 81.0 d. 112.

3. a. 1.95 b. 1.57 c. 1.75 d. 48.0 e. 136. f. 798.

4. a. $2\ Na + Cl_2 \rightarrow 2\ NaCl$
   b. $4\ K + O_2 \rightarrow 2\ K_2O$
   c. $2\ Al + 3\ F_2 \rightarrow 2\ AlF_3$
   d. $CO_2 + H_2O \rightarrow H_2CO_3$
   e. $Cl_2O_3 + H_2O \rightarrow 2\ HClO_2$
   f. $P_4O_{10} + 6\ H_2O \rightarrow 4\ H_3PO_4$
   g. $Na_2CO_3 \rightarrow Na_2O + CO_2$
   h. $2\ KClO_3 \rightarrow 2\ KCl + 3\ O_2$
   i. $H_2SO_3 \rightarrow H_2O + SO_2$
   j. $2\ HNO_2 \rightarrow N_2O_3 + H_2O$
   k. $C_3H_8 + 5\ O_2 \rightarrow 3\ CO_2 + 4\ H_2O$
   l. $C_5H_{12} + 8\ O_2 \rightarrow 5\ CO_2 + 6\ H_2O$
   m. $C_5H_8 + 7\ O_2 \rightarrow 5\ CO_2 + 4\ H_2O$
   n. $2\ Na_3PO_4 + 3\ BaCl_2 \rightarrow Ba_3(PO_4)_2 + 6\ NaCl$
   o. $Na_2CO_3 + 2\ AgNO_3 \rightarrow Ag_2CO_3 + 2\ NaNO_3$
   p. $CaBr_2 + 2\ AgNO_3 \rightarrow 2\ AgBr + Ca(NO_3)_2$
   q. $FeCl_3 + 3\ KOH \rightarrow Fe(OH)_3 + 3\ KCl$
   r. $V(NO_3)_3 + 3\ KOH \rightarrow 3\ KNO_3 + V(OH)_3$
   s. $HCl + NaOH \rightarrow NaCl + H_2O$
   t. $2\ HCl + Mg(OH)_2 \rightarrow MgCl_2 + 2\ H_2O$
   u. $H_2SO_4 + 2\ NH_4OH \rightarrow (NH_4)_2SO_4 + 2\ H_2O$
   v. $H_2SO_4 + Mg(OH)_2 \rightarrow MgSO_4 + 2\ H_2O$

5. a. 5 b. 7 c. 7 d. 3 e. 4 f. 11
   g. 3 h. 7 i. 3 j. 4 k. 13 l. 20
   m. 17 n. 12 o. 6 p. 6 q. 8 r. 8
   s. 4 t. 6 u. 6 v. 5

6. 15.0

7. 8.00

8. 128

9. 53.6

10. 46.8

Chemical Reactions

Name

Student Number

Date Instructor

1. Calculate the molar mass of

   a. C_2H_6 b. $Mg(NO_3)_2$

   c. K_2SO_4 d. C_4H_{10}

2. How many moles are in 4.25 g of C_2H_6?

3. How many grams of $Mg(NO_3)_2$ in 0.0250 moles of $Mg(NO_3)_2$?

4. Calculate the number of moles of K_2SO_4 in 149 g of K_2SO_4.

5. How many moles of C_4H_{10} are in 300. g of C_4H_{10}?

6. Balance the following chemical equations:

   a. $C_4H_{10}O + O_2 \rightarrow CO_2 + H_2O$

   b. $Mg + N_2 \rightarrow Mg_3N_2$

   c. $Na + Cl_2 \rightarrow NaCl$

   d. $K + O_2 \rightarrow K_2O$

   e. $Al + F_2 \rightarrow AlF_3$

   f. $BaO + H_2O \rightarrow Ba(OH)_2$

   g. $Fe_2O_3 + CO_2 \rightarrow Fe_2(CO_3)_3$

   h. $P_4O_{10} + H_2O \rightarrow H_3PO_4$

7. Consider the following balanced equation: $C_5H_{12} + 8\ O_2 \rightarrow 5\ CO_2 + 6\ H_2O$

   a. How many moles of O_2 are needed to react with 0.725 moles of C_5H_{12}?

   b. If excess C_5H_{12} reacts with 50.0 g O_2, how many moles of CO_2 are formed?

   c. If 100. g of H_2O are produced, how many grams of O_2 reacted?

5

Solutions

Certain homogeneous mixtures called solutions are encountered on a daily basis. A solution consists of at least one substance dissolved in a second substance; for example, salt water. Liquid solutions are the most common, but there are also gases or solid solutions. Beer is a solution in which a liquid (alcohol), a solid (malt), and a gas (carbon dioxide) are dissolved in the solvent, water. Other examples of solutions are air, smoke, sea water, milk, and blood.

I. Components of a Solution

A solution has two components: the **solute** and the **solvent**. The substance that is dissolved is called the solute, and the dissolving medium is the solvent. In the case of salt water, salt is the solute and water is the solvent.

II. Concentration of Solutions

To prepare a **dilute** solution of sugar in water, a few grams of sugar are added to water and stirred. If more sugar is added to the solution, the solution becomes more **concentrated**. The process may be repeated until the solution reaches **saturation**.

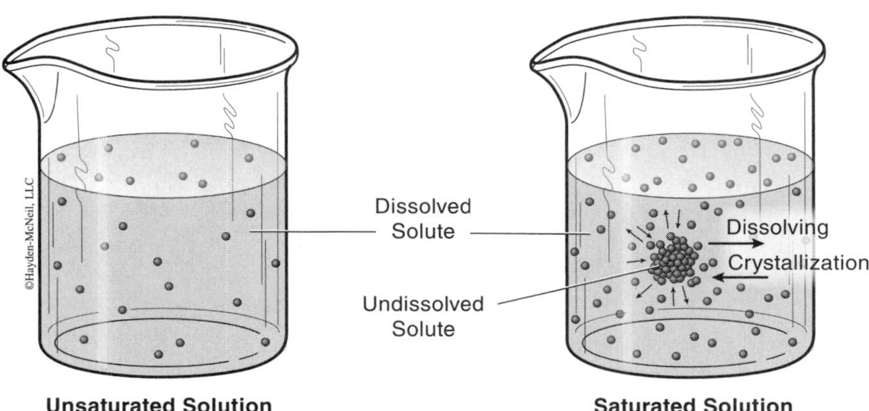

The solubility of a solid in a liquid is the maximum amount of that solid that dissolves in that liquid. At 25°C, the solubility of sugar is 67.5 g per 100 g of water. If more sugar is added, the excess solid will not dissolve and will sink to the bottom of the flask. When a solvent contains all the solute it can hold at a given temperature, the solution is considered to be **saturated**. Any solution containing a lesser amount of solute is **unsaturated**. If the temperature is increased, the solubility of most solids in water increases. The solution could be allowed to cool slowly, producing a solution that is **supersaturated**. Supersaturated solutions are not stable solutions. Crystals are grown from supersaturated solutions.

III. Water

A. Water as a Solvent

Water is a very important solvent and it is the solvent used most frequently. Water is a **polar** solvent and is, therefore, an excellent solvent for **polar solutes**. A general rule states: "**like dissolves like**." That is, polar solvents will dissolve polar solutes and nonpolar solvents will dissolve nonpolar solutes. For example, nonpolar liquids like carbon tetrachloride will dissolve nonpolar substances like iodine. On the other hand, ionic compounds like NaCl are soluble in polar solvents like water.

How water dissolves ionic compounds is as follows. The solid crystal is held together by ionic bonds which are attractions between positive and negative ions. When an ionic solid such as NaCl is added to water, the ions at the surface of the crystal become surrounded by water molecules. Electrostatic attraction is the force that naturally exists between charged species. The negative ions (the chloride ions) attract the positive ends of the water molecules (the hydrogens). By the same token, the positive ions of the crystal (the sodium ions) attract the negative end of water (the oxygen). Each ion attracts two or three water molecules so that the water molecules remove the ions from the solid crystal. These ions are **hydrated** or solvated by water. In other words, the ions are pulled out of the solid crystal and become trapped in cages of water. This process, called **dissolution**, is illustrated below and it can be represented by:

$$NaCl_{(s)} \xrightarrow{H_2O} Na^+_{(aq)} + Cl^-_{(aq)}$$

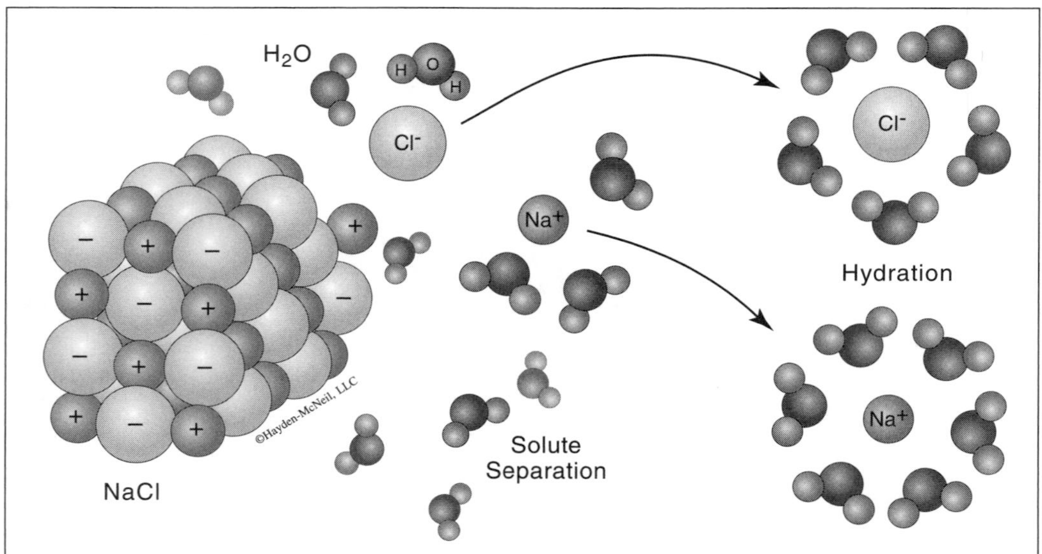

B. Properties of Water

Water is the most abundant substance on Earth and the most abundant substance in your body. Water is essential and central to metabolic processes. Water is a solvent for many molecules in living organisms primarily because it is a polar molecule. As we had previously mentioned, the general rule of solubility "like" dissolve "like" means that polar solutes will dissolve in polar solvents like water. The unique properties of water allow it to serve as the essential basis for life.

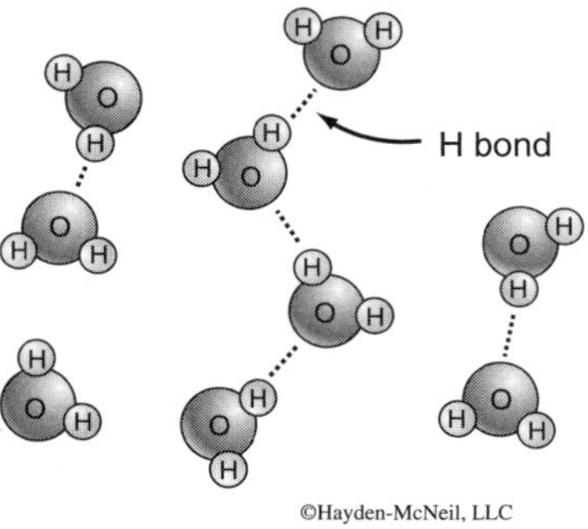

Hydrogen bond diagram

Water is polar, it is "V" shaped and **hydrogen bonds** can form between neighbor water molecules. Water expands as it freezes from liquid to solid; as a consequence the density of liquid water is higher than the density of ice. Most substances have higher density in the solid state than in the liquid state, but since ice is less dense than liquid water, it can float and aquatic life survives under an ice covered ocean or lake during winter. Hydrogen bonds between neighbor water molecules are also responsible for another unusual property of water. Water has an extraordinarily **high value of specific heat or capacity to absorb energy**. This enables water to undergo minor changes in temperature compared to the environment. Also hydrogen bonds in water generate its **very high heat of vaporization** so water can act to moderate Earth's climate. Life is based on the properties of water.

IV. Electrolytes

The ions produced in this way can migrate from one place to another, maintaining their charge. Because of this, solutions of ions can **conduct electricity**. Substances that conduct electricity are called **electrolytes**. A common laboratory experiment, illustrated below, demonstrates this process.

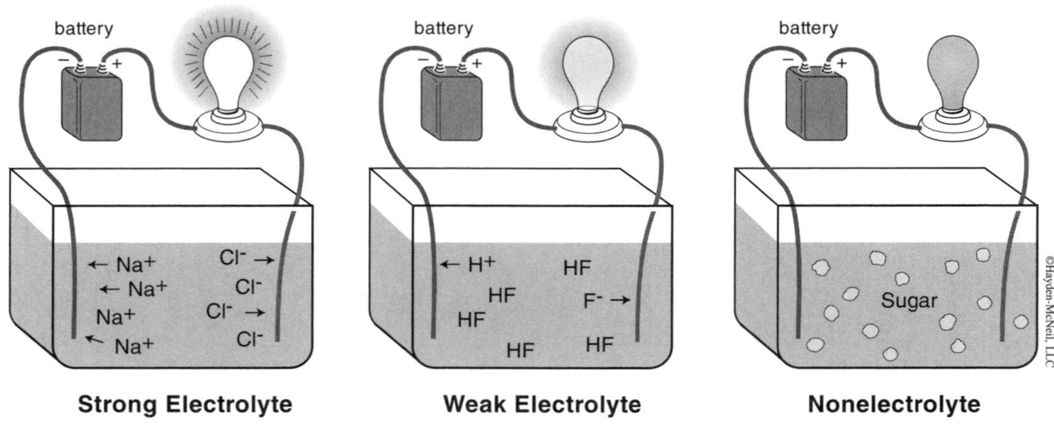

Hydrated sodium ions are positively charged, hydrated chloride ions are negatively charged. Therefore, they conduct electricity, and by completing the circuit, an electric light bulb lights up. Substances that do not conduct electricity are called **nonelectrolytes**. Distilled water and sugar in water are nonelectrolytes. The light bulb does not light up if only distilled water is present. However, if tap water is tested in this same way, what happens to the light bulb? Indeed, tap water contains enough ions to conduct electricity and it is classified as a **weak electrolyte**. Using tap water, the light bulb will have a dim light. HF is also a weak electrolyte.

Problem 1. State whether each of the following solutes will be soluble in water or in a nonpolar solvent like carbon tetrachloride or benzene:

a. LiCl, ionic

b. NaOH, ionic

c. vegetable oil, nonpolar

d. NaBr, salt

Problem 2. Indicate the ionization processes (if any) occurring in the previous exercise. Also predict the presence of electrolytes or nonelectrolytes in each case.

V. Concentration Calculations

The amount of solute dissolved in a given quantity of solvent is called the **concentration**. Concentration may be expressed in a quantitative manner by several methods. **Percent concentration** and **molarity** are two very useful methods of expressing concentration.

Percent Concentration. There are two common ways of representing percent concentration:

A. Mass/Volume Percent—% (m/v)

Percent m/v refers to the number of grams of solute in 100. mL of solution.

Example A: If 10. g of sugar is dissolved in enough water so that the total volume is 100. mL, what is the concentration of the solution?

$$\% = \frac{10.\text{ g of sugar}}{100.\text{ mL of solution}} \times 100 = 10.\%(\text{m/v})$$

$$\text{In general: } \% = \frac{\text{g of solute}}{\text{mL of solution}} \times 100 = (\text{m/v})$$

Example B: How many grams of KCl are needed to prepare 500. mL of a 1.5 percent (m/v) KCl solution?

$$500.\text{ mL} \times \frac{1.5\text{ g KCl}}{100.\text{ mL}} = 7.5\text{ g KCl}$$

B. Volume/Volume Percent—% (v/v)

Percent v/v refers to the number of mL of solute in 100. mL of solution.

Example C: If 10. mL of alcohol is dissolved in enough water so that the total volume is 100. mL, what is the concentration of the solution?

$$\% = \frac{10.\text{ mL of alcohol}}{100.\text{ mL of solution}} \times 100 = 10.\%(\text{v/v})$$

Problem 3.

a. How many grams of NaF are needed to prepare 250. mL of a 3.50% m/v solution?

b. How many grams of KBr are needed to prepare 375 mL of a 5.50% m/v solution?

c. How many mL of alcohol are needed to prepare 550. mL of a 15.0% v/v solution?

d. How many mL of carbon tetrachloride are needed to prepare 750. mL of a 4.50% v/v solution?

e. Calculate the percent concentration m/v of a solution prepared by dissolving 57.5 g of LiOH in a total of 350. mL of solution.

f. Calculate the percent v/v of a solution prepared by dissolving 15 mL of benzene in chloroform if the total volume of the solution is 75 mL.

g. Calculate the percent concentration v/v of a solution prepared by dissolving 330. mL of ethyl acetate in 500. mL of water.

C. Molarity

Molarity refers to the number of moles of solute dissolved in 1 L of solution. The unit for molarity is moles/liter and the symbol is M.

$$\mathrm{M} = \frac{\text{moles of solute}}{\text{liter of solution}}$$

(OPTIONAL)

Example D: What is the molarity of a solution made by dissolving 75 g of glucose, MM=180 g/mole, in enough water to have 550. mL of solution?

To find moles:

$$75\ \mathrm{g} \times \frac{1\ \text{mole glucose}}{180.0\ \text{g glucose}} = 0.42\ \text{mole glucose}$$

To find liters:

$$550.\ \mathrm{mL} \times \frac{1\ \mathrm{L}}{1000\ \mathrm{mL}} = 0.550\ \mathrm{L}$$

To find molarity:

$$\frac{0.42\ \text{mole glucose}}{0.55\ \mathrm{L}} = 0.76\ \mathrm{M}$$

Example E: The molar mass of NaOH is 40. If 100. g of NaOH are dissolved in enough water to prepare 2.00 liters of solution, what is the molarity of this solution?

To find moles:

$$100.\text{ g} \times \frac{1\text{ mole NaOH}}{40.\text{ g}} = 2.50\text{ moles of NaOH}$$

To find molarity:

$$\frac{2.50\text{ moles}}{2.00\text{ liters}} = 1.25\text{ M}$$

Problem 4. Calculate the molarity in each of the following solutions:

a. 20.0 g of KCl in 750. mL of solution. MM=74.6

b. 10.0 g of $MgSO_4$ in 550. mL of solution. MM=120.4

c. 15.0 g of LiBr in 750. mL of solution. MM=86.8

d. 25.0 g of KOH in 900. mL of solution. MM=56.1

e. 2.25 moles of HCl in 250. mL of solution.

Example F: How many grams of NaBr are needed to prepare 250. mL of a 3.0 M solution? The molar mass of NaBr is 103.

Since the solution is 3.0 M we have:

$$3.0\text{ M} = \frac{3.0\text{ moles NaBr}}{1\text{ liter}}$$

$$250.\text{ mL} \times \frac{1\text{ liter}}{1000.\text{ mL}} \times \frac{3.0\text{ moles NaBr}}{1\text{ liter}} \times \frac{103\text{ g NaBr}}{1\text{ mole NaBr}} = 77\text{ g of NaBr}$$

Problem 5. Calculate the number of grams of solute necessary to prepare the following solutions:

a. 500. mL of a 0.200 M NaCl solution.

b. 250. mL of a 0.125 M $C_6H_{12}O_6$ (glucose) solution.

c. 500. mL of a 0.400 M KOH solution.

Example G: The concentration of sodium chloride in blood serum is approximately 0.140 M. What volume of blood serum contains 2.00 g of NaCl?

First the molar mass of NaCl is calculated: 58.5 g = 1 mole

Then the moles present in 2.00 g of NaCl are determined:

$$2.00 \text{ g NaCl} \times \frac{1 \text{ mole NaCl}}{58.5 \text{ g NaCl}} = 0.0342 \text{ mole of NaCl}$$

Finally the volume is calculated:

$$0.0342 \text{ mole of NaCl} \times \frac{1 \text{ L}}{0.140 \text{ mole NaCl}} = 0.244 \text{ L} = 244 \text{ mL}$$

Problem 6. Calculate the number of milliliters of solution which contain:

a. 0.775 g of LiOH (MM=23.9) if the solution is 0.250 M.

b. 0.500 g of LiCl (MM=42.4) if the solution is 0.100 M.

c. 2.55 moles of NaOH if the solution is 6.00 M.

VI. Dilution

Solutions are frequently prepared by diluting more concentrated solutions rather than by weighing out pure solute. A common example of a dilution is the preparation of orange juice or lemonade from a concentrated product. Water is simply added and a more dilute product is obtained. In the lab, one can also dilute solutions. The number of moles of solute remains unchanged since no additional solute is added in the dilution process. A simple formula to be used in dilution problems is the following:

$$V_1C_1 = V_2C_2$$

V_1 and C_1 are the volume and concentration of the dilute solution, while

V_2 and C_2 are the volume and concentration of the concentrated solution.

Example H: How does one prepare 400. mL of a 3.50 M solution of acetic acid from a more concentrated (6.00 M) acetic acid solution?

Using the equation:

$$V_1C_1 = V_2C_2$$

$$(400.\ \text{mL})\ (3.50\ \text{M}) = V_2\ (6.00\ \text{M})$$

$$V_2 = \frac{400.\ \text{mL}(3.5\ \text{M})}{6.00\ \text{M}} = 233\ \text{mL}$$

Therefore, 233 mL of the concentrated acetic acid is placed in a large graduated cylinder, and water is added to reach a final volume of 400. mL. The solution is stirred. We have now 400. mL of a 3.50 M solution of acetic acid.

Problem 7.

a. A concentrated 10 M solution is available. How many milliliters of the stock 10 M solution are needed to prepare 200. mL of 0.2 M NaOH?

b. How would 250. mL of a 0.5% NaCl solution be prepared if a stock solution of 25% NaCl is available?

c. A concentrated solution of 15% KCl is available. What is the percent concentration of a diluted KCl solution prepared by combining 5.00 mL of the concentrated solution with 10.0 mL water?

d. How many milliliters of a 6.0 M HCl solution are needed to prepare 50.0 mL of a 0.50 M HCl solution?

VII. Solutions, Colloids, and Suspensions

There are three different types of mixtures. They are: true solutions, colloids, and suspensions.

A. A true **solution** is a homogeneous mixture in which the solute is small particles, such as atoms, ions, or small molecules. These particles are so small that they can pass through filters and semipermeable membranes. True solutions are transparent (not necessarily colorless). Salt water is an example of a true solution.

B. **Colloids** are mixtures having particles that are moderately large. Colloidal particles are small enough to pass through filters, but too large to pass through membranes. Colloids exhibit the **Tyndall Effect** when a beam of light shines through it. The large particles reflect the light and make the light beam visible; these large particles are acting as tiny mirrors that will reflect light. Fog is an example of a colloid.

C. **Suspensions** are heterogeneous mixtures that are very different from solutions or colloids. The solute particles are so large and heavy that they settle to the bottom of the container soon after mixing. These solute particles can be retained by both filters and semipermeable membranes.

The following table compares solutions, colloids, and suspensions:

	Solutions	Colloids	Suspensions
Solute Particles:	small particles (ions or molecules)	larger particles	very large particles (macromolecules)
Examples:	salted water, beer	starch and water, fog, smoke, sprays	calamine lotion
Characteristics:	Transparent. Particles cannot be separated by filters or semipermeable membranes.	Tyndall Effect. Particles can be separated by semipermeable membranes.	Opaque. Particles can be separated by filters.

VIII. Osmosis

The flow of a solvent across a semipermeable membrane from a solution of low solute concentration into a solution of higher solute concentration is called **osmosis**. A beaker with two compartments, A and B, separated by a semipermeable membrane could be used to illustrate osmosis. A semipermeable membrane, such as cellophane, contains tiny holes far too small to be seen but large enough to let solvent molecules pass through. Compartment A contains pure water, compartment B contains a solution of starch in water. The water molecules are so small that they can move freely back and forth through the membrane. There is a net flow of water molecules from compartment A to compartment B.

This passage of water molecules from the dilute to the more concentrated side of the semipermeable membrane is called **osmosis**. **Water** continues to diffuse back and forth across the membrane, and eventually, the height of the two compartments does not change any further. The height of solution B creates sufficient pressure to equalize the flow of water between compartment A and compartment B. **Osmotic pressure** is the pressure that prevents the flow of additional solvent into the more concentrated solution (from A to B).

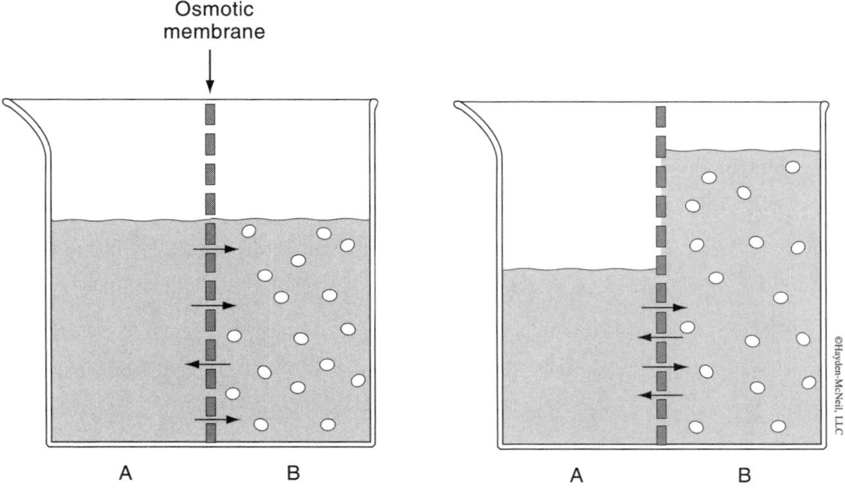

Osmotic pressure is very important in biological organisms because cell membranes are semipermeable membranes. Osmotic pressure depends on the number of particles in the solution. If a solution has the same osmotic pressure as a red blood cell it is called **isotonic**. Plasma is isotonic with red blood cells. This means that no osmotic pressure is generated across the cell membrane. Fluids that are placed intravenously in the body, like **0.9% NaCl** or **5% glucose** are called **isotonic solutions** (*iso* means equal to).

If a red blood cell is placed in pure water, the volume of the cell increases since water flows into the red blood cell. Pure water is **hypotonic** as compared to a red blood cell (*hypo* means lower than). The red blood cell continues to swell and it may eventually burst. This process is called **hemolysis**. A similar process occurs when dehydrated food, such as raisins or prunes, are placed in water. The water enters the cells and the food becomes swollen and enlarged.

Finally, if red blood cells are placed in a 10% glucose solution, since the red blood cell has a concentration equal to 5% glucose, the 10% glucose solution is **hypertonic** to the reference red blood cell (*hyper* means greater than). In this case, the cell will shrink as the water flows from the cell into the 10% glucose solution. This process is called **crenation**.

Problem 8. Indicate whether each of the following is isotonic, hypotonic, or hypertonic to red blood cells and whether hemolysis, crenation, or no change takes place in each case.

a. 0.9% NaCl   b. 2% glucose   c. 5% NaCl   d. pure water

IX. Dialysis

Dialysis uses a semipermeable membrane to separate dissolved ions and molecules from larger colloidal particles dispersed in the solution. These solute particles move through the membrane from a more concentrated to a less concentrated solution. Large solute particles, such as macromolecules of starch or proteins, cannot pass through the small openings of the semipermeable membrane. They can be separated from small solute particles like glucose and urea using a dialysis bag.

Kidney function occurs in the following manner: the waste products of the blood dialyze out through a semipermeable membrane and enter collective tubes that carry urine to the urethra; large protein molecules and cells are retained in the blood.

The kidneys' main functions are filtration, reabsorption, and secretion. Secretion rids the body of excess ions, foreign substances, and waste products. When the kidneys are not working properly, **hemodialysis** is used.

In hemodialysis, an artificial kidney machine performs the same filtration process. The patient's blood is circulated through a long tube of cellophane membrane suspended in an isotonic solution, and after it is purified it is returned to the patient's vein. The cellophane membrane retains all the large molecules (like proteins) but allows the small ones (like toxic wastes) to pass through.

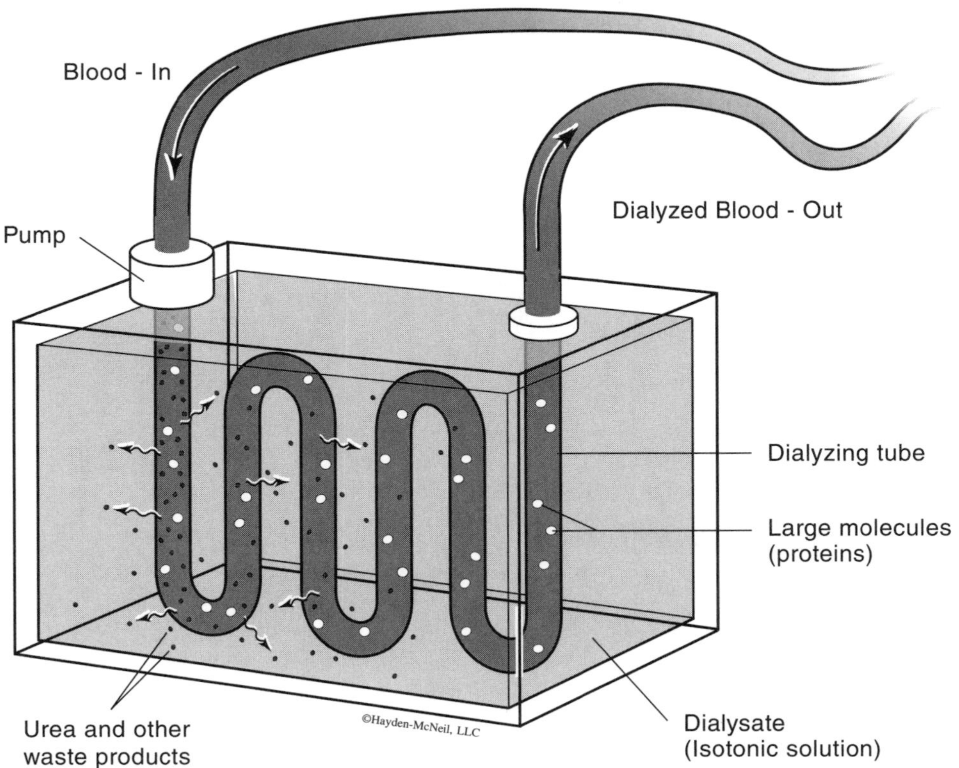

ANSWERS

1. a. soluble in water
   b. soluble in water
   c. soluble in nonpolar solvent
   d. soluble in water

2. a. $LiCl_{(solid)} \rightarrow Li^{+}_{(aq)} + Cl^{-}_{(aq)}$ (strong electrolyte)
   b. $NaOH_{(solid)} \rightarrow Na^{+}_{(aq)} + OH^{-}_{(aq)}$ (strong electrolyte)
   c. none (nonelectrolyte)
   d. $NaBr_{(solid)} \rightarrow Na^{+}_{(aq)} + Br^{-}_{(aq)}$ (strong electrolyte)

3. a. 8.75 g   b. 20.6 g   c. 82.5 mL   d. 33.8 mL
   e. 16.4%   f. 20.%   g. 39.8%

4. a. 0.357 M   b. 0.151 M   c. 0.230 M   d. 0.495 M   e. 9.00 M

5. a. 5.85 g   b. 5.62 g   c. 11.2 g

6. a. 130 mL   b. 118 mL   c. 425 mL

7. a. 4 mL
   b. To 5 mL of the 25% solution add 245 mL of water
   c. 5.0%
   d. 4.2 mL

8. a. isotonic, no change
   b. hypotonic, hemolysis
   c. hypertonic, crenation
   d. hypotonic, hemolysis

Solutions

5 Assignment

Name

Student Number

Date Instructor

1. Water is a __________ (polar/nonpolar) solvent and therefore may dissolve ________ (nonpolar/ionic) compounds.

2. Which of the following compounds are more soluble in water than in CCl_4? Underline the correct choices.

   I_2 KCl HBr C_6H_6 Kr Cl_2 Na_2SO_4

3. Classify each of the following as an electrolyte or a nonelectrolyte.

   a. $C_6H_{12}O_6$ b. $MgCl_2$ c. CH_3OH

4. What happens if a crystal of sugar is added to each of the following solutions?

   a. A supersaturated sugar solution

   b. An unsaturated sugar solution

   c. A saturated sugar solution

5. A solution containing 2.40 g sucrose in 50.0 mL of solution has a percent (m/v %) concentration of __________ .

6. The volume needed to obtain 10.0 grams of NaCl from a 5.00% (m/v) solution is ____________.

7. A solution is prepared by dissolving 50.0 g $C_6H_{12}O_6$ (FM = 180) in enough water so that the total volume is 400. mL.

   Calculate:

   a. the mass/volume percent of $C_6H_{12}O_6$ in the solution

   b. the molarity of $C_6H_{12}O_6$ in the solution

8. Calculate the number of moles of K_2SO_4 (174.2 g/mole) in 300. mL of a 3.00 M K_2SO_4 solution.

9. Calculate the number of grams of ZnI_2 (319.2 g/mole) needed to prepare 0.500 L of a 0.500 M ZnI_2 solution.

10. 25.0 mL of 10.0% NH_4Cl solution is diluted to 500. mL. The final concentration of the NH_4Cl solution is ____________.

11. How many mL of alcohol are needed to prepare 250. mL of 6.0% (v/v) solution?

12. If 25.0 mL of water is added to 50.0 mL of 6.00 M HCl solution, what is the final molarity of HCl in the solution?

13. What was the initial concentration of 100. mL of a KBr solution, if after adding water to dilute it, 300. mL of a 4.00% solution was obtained?

14. Particles can be separated from the solvent by filtration in which of the following? Underline the correct choice(s).

    colloids   solutions   suspensions

15. A solution that has an osmotic pressure that is less than that of the blood is __________ (hypotonic, isotonic, hypertonic) and will _______ (hemolyse, crenate, not affect) red blood cells.

16. Indicate whether each of the following solutions is isotonic, hypotonic, or hypertonic to red blood cells and whether hemolysis, crenation, or no change takes place in each case.

    a. 5% glucose   b. 2% NaCl   c. 1% glucose

17. Colloidal particles __________ (can/cannot) diffuse through a cellular membrane.

18. If a 2.0% glucose solution and a 5.0% solution are separated by a semipermeable membrane _________ (glucose, water, neither) flows from the 2.0% glucose solution to the 5.0% glucose solution.

6

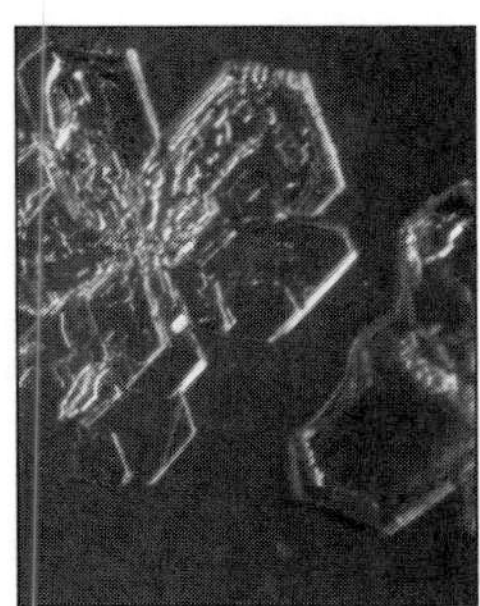

Acids, Bases, and Salts

Acids and bases are encountered in everyday life. Some common acids are lemon juice and vinegar. Acids produce hydronium ions (H_3O^+) in aqueous solution. Some common bases are ammonia, often found in household cleansers, and sodium hydroxide (NaOH), commonly called lye and the main component of the drain cleaner, Drano.

I. Characteristics of Acids and Bases

Acids	Bases
a. Produce hydrogen (H^+) or hydronium (H_3O^+) ions when dissolved in water.	a. Produce OH^- in aqueous solutions.
b. Taste sour.	b. Taste bitter.
c. Turn blue litmus paper red. (Litmus paper is used as an indicator to identify acidic or basic substances.)	c. Turn red litmus paper blue.
d. Are electrolytes. (Electrolytes are substances that conduct electricity.)	d. Are electrolytes.
e. Neutralize bases. (A neutralization reaction occurs when an acid and a base react to produce salt and water.)	e. React with acids.
	f. Feel slippery or soapy.

II. General formula:

III. Strong and Weak Acids and Bases

Any substance that dissociates in water to produce ions, including acids and bases, is considered an electrolyte. If the substance dissociates completely (like strong acids and bases), it is considered a strong electrolyte, while a compound that dissociates less than 50% is considered a weak electrolyte (like weak acids and bases). Some examples of strong acids and bases are given below; any other acid or base not listed as strong will be considered weak.

Strong Acids and Strong Electrolytes	
HCl hydrochloric acid HBr hydrobromic acid HI hydroiodic acid	HNO_3 nitric acid H_2SO_4 sulfuric acid $HClO_4$ perchloric acid

Strong Bases and Strong Electrolytes	
LiOH lithium hydroxide NaOH sodium hydroxide KOH potassium hydroxide RbOH rubidium hydroxide CsOH cesium hydroxide	$Ca(OH)_2$ calcium hydroxide $Sr(OH)_2$ strontium hydroxide $Ba(OH)_2$ barium hydroxide

Ammonia (NH_3) is a weak base. The ammonia molecule has no hydroxide ion, but when dissolved in water, it reacts with the water molecule to produce hydroxide (OH^-) ions.

$$\mathrm{H{-}\ddot{N}(H){-}H} + \mathrm{HOH} \rightleftharpoons \mathrm{H{-}N^{+}(H)_2{-}H} + \mathrm{OH^-}$$

Problem 1. Complete the following table:

		Check One			
Aqueous Solution	**Strong or Weak Electrolyte**	**Strong Acid**	**Weak Acid**	**Strong Base**	**Weak Base**
H_2CO_3 carbonic acid					
H_3BO_3 boric acid					
KOH potassium hydroxide					
H_2SO_4 sulfuric acid					
$Fe(OH)_3$ Iron (III) hydroxide					
$HC_2H_3O_2$ acetic acid					
NH_4OH ammonium hydroxide					
HF Hydrofluoric acid					

Problem 2. Complete the following table:

Substance	Strong Electrolyte	Weak Electrolyte
$HBrO_2$		
NaOH		
HNO_3		
HCl		
Tap water		

IV. Ionization of Water

Even though pure water is considered a nonelectrolyte, a water molecule can react with another water molecule to produce a hydronium ion and a hydroxide ion.

$$H_2O + H_2O \rightleftharpoons \underset{\text{hydronium}}{H_3O^+} + \underset{\text{hydroxide}}{OH^-}$$

The above equation is often simplified as follows:

$$H_2O \rightleftharpoons H^+ + OH^-$$

The double arrow indicates that this is an **equilibrium** (the forward and reverse reactions are taking place at the same rate and the concentration of all the components does not change as long as nothing is done to the system) and for every mole of water molecules, only 1×10^{-7} moles dissociate producing the same concentration of hydrogen ions and hydroxide ions. The molar concentration (Molarity) of H^+ and OH^- in pure water at 25°C is:

$$[H^+] = 1 \times 10^{-7}\ M = 0.0000001\ M \qquad [OH^-] = 1 \times 10^{-7}\ M = 0.0000001\ M$$

V. pH and pOH

The pH scale was developed by chemists to simplify expressing acid and base concentrations. The pH scale typically has values that range from 0 to 14.

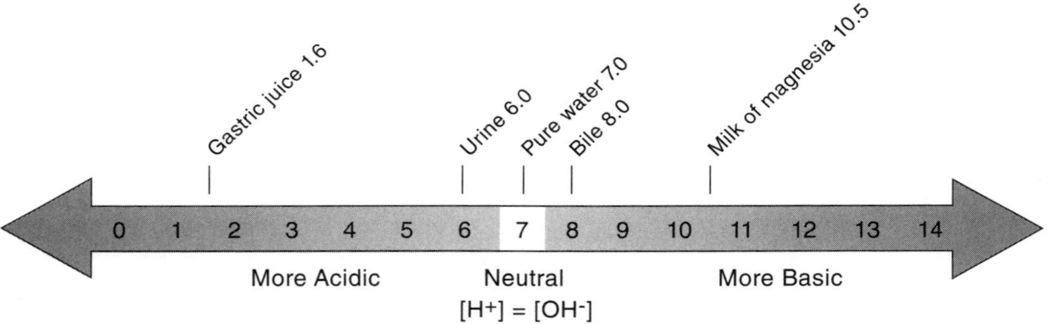

A solution with a pH less than 7 is considered acidic. If the pH is greater than 7, the solution is basic. When the pH is 7, the solution is neutral.

Problem 3. Using the data given in the above pH scale diagram, answer the following questions:

a. Is urine acidic, basic, or neutral?

b. Gastric juice turns blue litmus paper what color?

c. What is more acidic, water or urine?

d. For something to be considered an acid, what should its pH be?

Mathematically, pH is defined as the negative logarithm of the hydronium ion molar concentration, while pOH is defined as the negative logarithm of the hydroxide ion molar concentration:

$$pH = -\log [H^+] \qquad pOH = -\log [OH^-]$$

The following table gives a comparison of pH and pOH values and their corresponding [H^+] and [OH^-] values. Notice that pH + pOH = 14.

pH	pOH	[H^+]	[OH^-]	
0	14	10^0 M	10^{-14} M	acidic
1	13	10^{-1} M	10^{-13} M	
2	12	10^{-2} M	10^{-12} M	
3	11	10^{-3} M	10^{-11} M	
4	10	10^{-4} M	10^{-10} M	
5	9	10^{-5} M	10^{-9} M	
6	8	10^{-6} M	10^{-8} M	
7	7	10^{-7} M	10^{-7} M	neutral
8	6	10^{-8} M	10^{-6} M	basic
9	5	10^{-9} M	10^{-5} M	
10	4	10^{-10} M	10^{-4} M	
11	3	10^{-11} M	10^{-3} M	
12	2	10^{-12} M	10^{-2} M	
13	1	10^{-13} M	10^{-1} M	
14	0	10^{-14} M	10^0 M	

Problem 4. Complete the following table:

pH	**pOH**	**[H^+]**	**[OH^-]**	**Acidic, Basic, or Neutral**
	13			
		10^{-3} M		
8				
			10^{-7} M	
	8			
0				

VI. Neutralization (Acid–Base) Reactions

When acids and bases react with each other they produce a salt and water. Neutralization occurs when there are equal quantities of the acid and base. The following is an example of a neutralization (acid–base) reaction. [Note: The products of all neutralization reactions are a salt and water.]

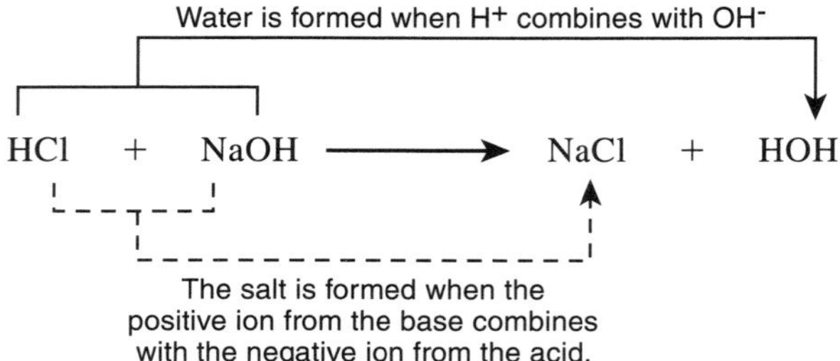

The following is a step-by-step process used to complete and balance neutralization reactions.

Step 1. To obtain the products, salt and water, the positive ion (hydrogen) from the acid and the negative ion (hydroxide) from the base are combined to produce water. The remaining ions, calcium and nitrate, are joined.

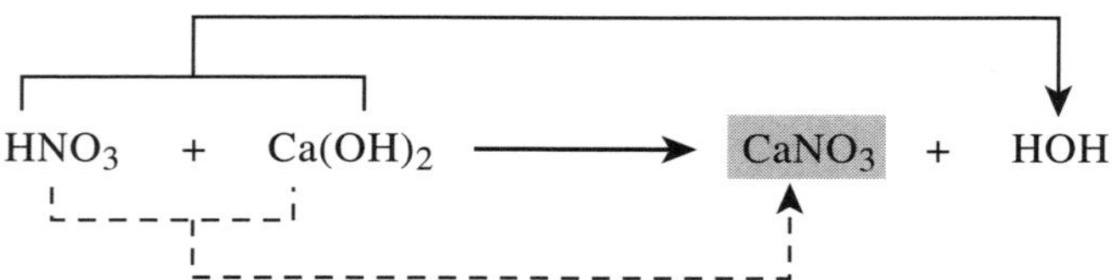

Step 2. Next, make sure that the salt formed has the correct formula. Calcium is a +2 ion (cation) and nitrate is a –1 ion (anion).

Write the charge for each individual ion.

$$Ca^{2+}\ NO_3^-$$

Step 3. If the charge on the cation is not equal to the charge on the anion, subscripts need to be used to achieve electrical neutrality. Two nitrate ions will be needed for every calcium ion.

$$Ca^{2+}NO_3^- \xrightarrow{\text{crosscharges}} Ca(NO_3)_2$$

Step 4. Rewrite the equation using the correct formula for the salt.

$$HNO_3 + Ca(OH)_2 \rightarrow Ca(NO_3)_2 + HOH$$

Step 5. Balance the chemical equation.

$$2\ HNO_3 + Ca(OH)_2 \rightarrow Ca(NO_3)_2 + 2\ HOH$$

Example A: Complete and balance the following reaction.

$$H_2SO_4 + NH_4OH \rightarrow$$

Step 1. Exchange partners.

$$H_2SO_4 + NH_4OH \rightarrow NH_4SO_4 + HOH$$

Step 2. For the salt, write the charge on each ion.

$$NH_4^+ \ SO_4^{2-}$$

Step 3. Balance charges.

$$NH_4^+ \ SO_4^{2-} \rightarrow (NH_4)_2SO_4$$

Step 4. Rewrite equation with the correct formula for the salt.

$$H_2SO_4 + NH_4OH \rightarrow (NH_4)_2SO_4 + HOH$$

Step 5. Balance the chemical equation.

$$H_2SO_4 + 2\ NH_4OH \rightarrow (NH_4)_2SO_4 + 2\ HOH$$

Problem 5. Complete and balance the following neutralization reactions:

a. $HCl + Ba(OH)_2 \rightarrow ?$

b. $H_3PO_4 + NaOH \rightarrow ?$

c. $H_2SO_4 + Ca(OH)_2 \rightarrow ?$

d. $HI + LiOH \rightarrow ?$

e. $H_3PO_4 + NH_4OH \rightarrow ?$

f. $HNO_3 + NaOH \rightarrow ?$

g. $H_3PO_4 + Ca(OH)_2 \rightarrow ?$

h. $HNO_3 + Mg(OH)_2 \rightarrow ?$

VII. Buffers

Even in small amounts, when an acid or base is added to water, the pH changes drastically. However, when a small amount of acid or base is added to a buffered solution, there is very little change in pH. A buffer solution is thus defined as a solution whose pH remains relatively constant when either acids or bases are added to it. Buffers, however, do not have an unlimited capacity to resist pH changes.

Buffers are of tremendous biological importance. For example, blood is a solution that is buffered at a pH = 7.35 – 7.45. If the pH of blood deviates above or below this narrow range, it can cause drastic changes in respiration, metabolism, and can even cause death!

Since a buffer must be able to react with excess acid or excess base it must have two components, one to react with the acid and one to react with the base. Most common buffers consist of a **weak** acid and its salt or a **weak** base and its salt.

For example,

Weak Acid	Salt Derived from Acid
H_2CO_3 carbonic acid	$NaHCO_3$
H_3PO_4 phosphoric acid	KH_2PO_4
H_3BO_3 boric acid	LiH_2BO_3
$HC_2H_3O_2$ acetic acid	$NaC_2H_3O_2$

Weak Base	Salt Derived from Weak Base
NH_3 ammonia	NH_4Cl

Problem 6. Indicate whether each of the following substances would make a buffer solution.

a. H_2SO_4 and $NaHSO_4$

b. HCl and LiCl

c. HF and KF

d. HClO and KClO

e. NH_3 and NH_4Br

f. HNO_3 and $NaNO_3$

VIII. How Buffers Maintain a Constant pH

The carbonic acid/bicarbonate blood buffer is a particularly interesting example since it is related to respiration. As an end product of cellular metabolism, carbon dioxide is constantly being produced. Some of the carbon dioxide (CO_2) is carried by red blood cells to the lungs, where it is eliminated. This occurs by binding the carbon dioxide molecule to the heme group in hemoglobin. Other carbon dioxide molecules dissolve in the aqueous medium of the blood, where it can react with water molecules to produce carbonic acid (H_2CO_3).

$$CO_2 + H_2O \rightleftharpoons H_2CO_3$$

$$\underset{\text{weak acid}}{H_2CO_3} \xrightleftharpoons{H_2O} H^+ + \underset{\text{salt derived from weak acid}}{HCO_3^-}$$

Buffer System

Since carbonic acid is a weak acid, it can dissociate into hydrogen ions and bicarbonate ions, HCO_3^-.

When base (OH^-) is added to a buffer solution, the OH^- reacts with the weak acid of the buffer (H_2CO_3) producing bicarbonate ions (see forward reaction in the equilibrium below, #1). On the other hand, if acid (H^+) is added to a buffer solution, the H^+ reacts with the bicarbonate ions HCO_3^- of the buffer, producing carbonic acid (see reverse reaction in the equilibrium below, #2). So, a buffer solution contains two components, one that can neutralize excess acid (in this case HCO_3^-) and another component that can neutralize excess base (H_2CO_3).

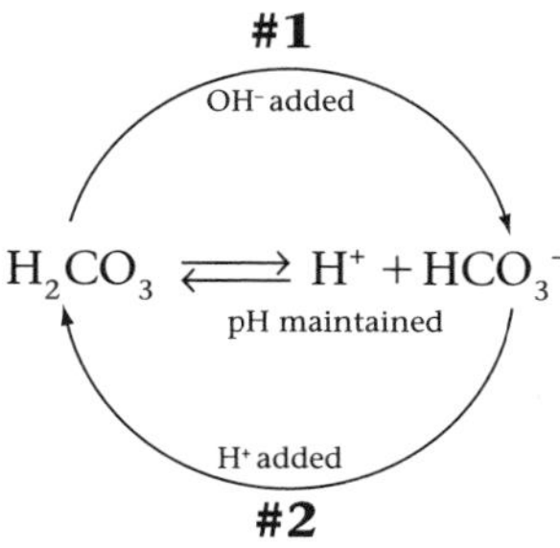

IX. Acidosis and Alkalosis

The pH of the blood is maintained by a series of reactions at equilibrium (the forward and reverse reactions are taking place at the same rate and the concentration of all the components does not change as long as nothing is done to the system). Even though blood is buffered, this capacity is limited. Concentrations of acid or base which exceed this capacity can result in acidosis or alkalosis. If the pH of the blood drops below approximately 7.35, acidosis occurs. If it is caused by respiratory problems, we call it **respiratory acidosis.** This occurs if the body retains higher than normal levels of CO_2, because of a defect of the respiratory center in the medulla of the brain, improper gas diffusion (due to a poorly ventilated room, where CO_2 is elevated), or from incomplete exhalation (for example, emphysema).

Le Châtelier's Principle states that if an external stress is applied to a system at equilibrium, the system reacts in such a way as to partially relieve that stress. For example, an increase in concentration of any one component causes the equilibrium to shift to the opposite side. Conversely, a decrease in the concentration of any component causes the equilibrium to shift to the side to which the component was removed.

Respiratory Acidosis: CO_2 ↑ pH ↓ $[H^+]$ ↑	
Symptoms:	Breathing suppression, disorientation, weakness, coma
Causes:	Lung diseases such as pneumonia, bronchitis, emphysema, and asthma, poorly ventilated room, cardiopulmonary arrest, stroke, or nervous system disorders
Chemistry Involved:	increase in $[CO_2]$ $CO_2 + H_2O \rightleftharpoons H_2CO_3 \overset{H_2O}{\rightleftharpoons} \boxed{H^+} + HCO_3^-$ equilibrium shifts to remove CO_2 thus causing the production of more H^+ which causes the pH to decrease
Treatment:	Correction of disorder; infusion of bicarbonate

Respiratory alkalosis may be produced by hyperventilation, resulting in too much CO_2 being exhaled. To compensate for the decrease of CO_2 level in the blood plasma, dissolved carbonic acid decomposes to CO_2 and water.

Respiratory Alkalosis: CO_2 ↓ pH ↑ $[H^+]$ ↓	
Symptoms:	Increased rate and depth of breathing, numbness, light-headedness
Causes:	Hyperventilation due to anxiety, fever, hysteria, exercise
Chemistry Involved:	decrease in $[CO_2]$ $CO_2 + H_2O \rightleftharpoons H_2CO_3 \xrightleftharpoons{H_2O} \boxed{H^+} + HCO_3^-$ equilibrium shifts to produce more CO_2 thus causing the removal of H^+ which causes the pH to increase
Treatment:	Elimination of anxiety-producing state, breathing into paper bag

Metabolic acidosis occurs when the blood pH drops due to an increased acid level. Acids are produced by metabolic reactions or ingested faster than they can be eliminated through the kidneys. Some medical conditions that may result in metabolic acidosis include: diabetes mellitus, kidney failure, diarrhea, aspirin overdose, alcoholism, and starvation (as in crash dieting).

Metabolic Acidosis: $[H^+]$ ↑ pH ↓	
Symptoms:	Increased ventilation, fatigue, confusion
Causes:	Renal disease, diarrhea, alcoholism, starvation, diabetes mellitus, kidney failure
Chemistry Involved:	If acids produced by metabolic reactions or ingestion are not neutralized fast enough by blood buffers or eliminated by the kidney, then $[H^+]$ increases thus causing a decrease in pH
Treatment:	Oral dose of sodium bicarbonate, dialysis for renal failure, insulin treatment for diabetes

If the body loses an excess of acid or retains too much base, the resulting condition is called **metabolic alkalosis.** Some of the causes may be vomiting (loss of stomach acid), ingesting excess base (too much antacid medication), or kidney problems.

Metabolic Alkalosis: $[H^+]$ ↓ pH ↑	
Symptoms:	Depressed breathing, apathy, confusion
Causes:	Vomiting, ingestion of excess alkali
Chemistry Involved:	If the body loses too much acid or if too much base is ingested, then $[H^+]$ decreases, thus causing a increase in pH
Treatment:	Infusion of saline solution, treatment of underlying diseases

ANSWERS

1.

		Check One			
Substance	**Strong or Weak Electrolyte**	**Strong Acid**	**Weak Acid**	**Strong Base**	**Weak Base**
H_2CO_3	weak		X		
H_3BO_3	weak		X		
KOH	strong			X	
H_2SO_4	strong	X			
$Fe(OH)_3$	weak				X
$HC_2H_3O_2$	weak		X		
NH_4OH	weak				X
$HF_{(aq)}$	weak		X		

2.

Substance	Strong Electrolyte	Weak Electrolyte
$HBrO_2$		X
NaOH	X	
HNO_3	X	
HCl	X	
Tap water		X

3. a. acidic b. red c. urine d. less than 7

4.

pH	pOH	$[H^+]$	$[OH^-]$	Acid, Base, or Neutral
1	13	10^{-1} M	10^{-13} M	acidic
3	11	10^{-3} M	10^{-11} M	acidic
8	6	10^{-8} M	10^{-6} M	basic
7	7	10^{-7} M	10^{-7} M	neutral
6	8	10^{-6} M	10^{-8} M	acidic
0	14	10^{0} M	10^{-14} M	acidic

5. a. $2\ HCl + Ba(OH)_2 \rightarrow BaCl_2 + 2\ H_2O$
   b. $H_3PO_4 + 3\ NaOH \rightarrow Na_3PO_4 + 3\ H_2O$
   c. $H_2SO_4 + Ca(OH)_2 \rightarrow CaSO_4 + 2\ H_2O$
   d. $HI + LiOH \rightarrow LiI + H_2O$
   e. $H_3PO_4 + 3\ NH_4OH \rightarrow (NH_4)_3PO_4 + 3\ H_2O$
   f. $HNO_3 + NaOH \rightarrow NaNO_3 + H_2O$
   g. $2\ H_3PO_4 + 3\ Ca(OH)_2 \rightarrow Ca_3(PO_4)_2 + 6\ H_2O$
   h. $2\ HNO_3 + Mg(OH)_2 \rightarrow Mg(NO_3)_2 + 2\ H_2O$

6. a. no, H_2SO_4 is a strong acid
   b. no, HCl is a strong acid
   c. yes, HF is a weak acid and KF is a salt derived from HF
   d. yes, HClO is a weak acid and KClO is a salt derived from HClO
   e. yes, NH_3 is a weak base and NH_4Br is a salt derived from NH_3
   f. no, HNO_3 is a strong acid

Acids, Bases, and Salts

Name

Student Number

Date Instructor

1. For each of the following properties, indicate whether it is characteristic of acids, characteristic of bases, or characteristic of both acids and bases.

   a. bitter taste ________ b. water solutions conduct electricity ________

   c. slippery ________ d. turns blue litmus paper red ________

   e. sour taste ________ f. produce H^+ ions when dissolved in H_2O ________

   g. produce OH^- ions when dissolved in H_2O ________

2. Classify each of the following as a strong acid, a weak acid, a strong base, or a weak base.

   a. $HC_2H_3O_2$ ________ b. $Zn(OH)_2$ ________

   c. HNO_3 ________ d. RbOH ________

   e. HCl ________ f. HF ________

   g. NH_4OH ________ h. LiOH ________

   i. H_2SO_4 ________ j. $Co(OH)_3$ ________

3. Complete the following table.

pH	pOH	[H^+]	[OH^-]	Acidic, Basic, or Neutral
6				
	10			
			1×10^{-5} M	
11				
		1×10^{-5} M		
	12			
7				
	2			

4. Balance the following neutralization reactions.

a. $HBr + NaOH \rightarrow NaBr + HOH$

b. $H_2SO_4 + NH_4OH \rightarrow (NH_4)_2SO_4 + HOH$

c. $Mg(OH)_2 + HCl \rightarrow MgCl_2 + HOH$

d. $Al(OH)_3 + HCl \rightarrow AlCl_3 + HOH$

5. Complete and balance the following neutralization reactions.

a. $HCl + KOH \rightarrow$

b. $H_3PO_4 + NaOH \rightarrow$

c. $Ba(OH)_2 + HNO_3 \rightarrow$

d. $H_2SO_4 + Mn(OH)_3 \rightarrow$

6. Give an example of a buffer system. Explain how it works.

7. Which of the following pairs of compounds, when dissolved in water, make a buffer solution?

   a. HCl and NaCl
   b. H_3PO_4 and NaH_2PO_4
   c. HNO_2 and $NaNO_2$
   d. NH_3 and NH_4Cl
   e. NaOH and Na_2SO_4
   f. HNO_3 and $NaNO_3$

8. Which of the following occurs when HCl is mixed with an excess of buffer solution?

   a. the pH increases slightly
   b. the pH decreases slightly
   c. the pH stays exactly the same
   d. the pH increases significantly
   e. the pH decreases significantly

9. Which of the following occurs when NaOH is mixed with an excess of buffer solution?

   a. the pH increases slightly
   b. the pH decreases slightly
   c. the pH stays exactly the same
   d. the pH increases significantly
   e. the pH decreases significantly

10. Which of the following occurs when HCl is mixed with a solution that is not a buffer solution?

    a. the pH increases slightly

    b. the pH decreases slightly

    c. the pH stays exactly the same

    d. the pH increases significantly

    e. the pH decreases significantly

11. Which of the following occurs when NaOH is mixed with a solution that is not a buffer solution?

    a. the pH increases slightly

    b. the pH decreases slightly

    c. the pH stays exactly the same

    d. the pH increases significantly

    e. the pH decreases significantly

7

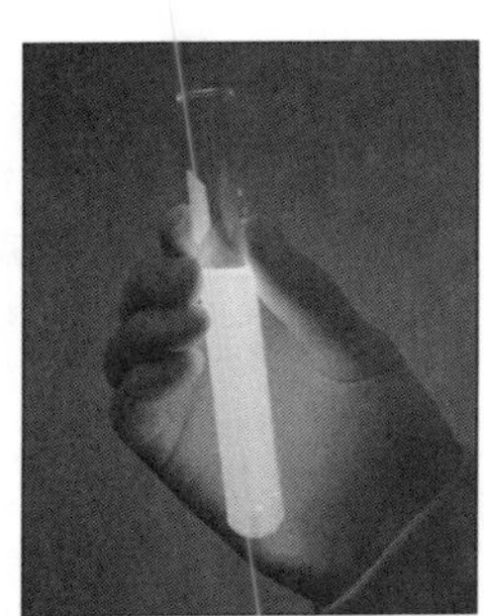

Nuclear Chemistry

At the end of the 19th century a French scientist, Henri Becquerel, discovered that certain rocks affected unexposed photographic film just like X-rays do. He realized that this rock, which contained uranium, gave off some form of radiation. He and others, among them Pierre and Marie Curie, studied this effect and nuclear chemistry began. The term radioactivity was coined by Marie Curie, who won two Nobel Prizes in her extensive research career. She discovered two new elements, radium and polonium, and determined that unstable isotopes caused this radioactivity.

I. Radioactive Isotopes

Remember that protons and neutrons are found in the nucleus of any atom, while electrons occupy the region outside the nucleus. The atomic number represents the number of protons and the mass number is the sum of protons and neutrons. Isotopes of any element vary in the number of neutrons, therefore having different masses. Most isotopes in nature are stable, but close to 40 isotopes are unstable.

These unstable isotopes are considered radioactive because they undergo nuclear decay, releasing radioactive particles or energy from the nucleus. As a consequence, these radioactive elements may change into new elements. Alpha, beta, and gamma radiation may be emitted as the nuclear change takes place. Unlike chemical changes, which only involve the valence electrons in an atom, nuclear reactions occur in the nucleus of the atom. Energy released in a nuclear reaction is much, much greater than that of a chemical reaction.

The **nuclide symbol** is used to represent the number of protons, neutrons, and electrons in an element.

MASS NUMBER:
ATOMIC NUMBER:

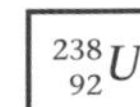

$^{238}_{92}U$

146 neutrons
92 protons
92 electrons

The number of neutrons is calculated by subtracting the **atomic number (subscript)** from the **mass number (superscript)**:

$$238 - 92 = 146$$

II. Types of Radiation

A. Alpha Particles

Different forms of radiation may be emitted from an unstable radioactive nucleus. Energy is released and a new, more stable nucleus is formed. The 3 types of radiation to be considered in this section are: alpha, beta, and gamma radiation. An **alpha particle** can be considered to be equivalent to the nucleus of a helium atom. Helium has 2 protons and 2 neutrons in its nucleus. If both of its electrons were removed, the result would be an alpha particle:

$$^{4}_{2}He \quad \text{or} \quad \alpha$$

Since there are two protons and no electrons, alpha particles are positively charged. Alpha particles are not very penetrating. Paper, clothing, or a few centimeters of air can effectively shield against alpha particles. However, if ingested or inhaled, alpha particles can be hazardous.

B. Beta Particles

Beta particles are high-speed electrons emitted from the nuclei of decaying radioisotopes. These electrons have a negative charge and a mass so small that it is approximately 0 amu.

$$^{0}_{-1}e \quad \text{or} \quad \beta$$

Beta particles may travel 2 or 3 meters through air. Heavy clothing, thick cardboard, or one-inch thick wood will provide protection from beta radiation.

C. Gamma Radiation

Gamma radiation is very much like X-rays. It has no charge, a very short wavelength, and high energy. Gamma radiation is the most penetrating form of radiation considered in this section. It travels great distances through air (500 meters). To be protected from a gamma emitter, thick sheets of lead or concrete are required.

Nuclear Radiation

Name	Charge	Symbol	Shield	Distance Traveled
alpha	positive	$^{4}_{2}He$ or α	paper or clothing	2–4 cm
beta	negative	$^{0}_{-1}e$ or β	heavy clothing	2–3 m
gamma	neutral	γ	lead or concrete	500 m

III. Radiation Safety

There are three ways to keep exposure to radiation at a minimum: (1) maintain distance as possible from the source, (2) use adequate shielding, or (3) minimize th of exposure. The **greater** the distance from the radioactive source, the **lower** the int of the radiation. For example, if the distance from the radioactive source is doubled, intensity is decreased by one fourth or $(1/2)^2$.

The table shown below illustrates this point:

Distance from source:	**1 m**	**2 m**	**3 m**
Intensity of radiation:	$(1/1)^2 = \mathbf{1}$	$(1/2)^2 = \mathbf{1/4}$	$(1/3)^2 = \mathbf{1/9}$

IV. Nuclear Reactions

A. Alpha Emission

When a radioactive element spontaneously breaks down and emits an alpha particle, a new element is formed. The original radioactive element is called the parent isotope, and the new element is called the daughter isotope. This process is called radioactive decay and can be represented with a **nuclear equation**.

Example A: Write the nuclear equation for an atom of ${}^{238}_{92}U$ emitting an α particle.

The atom of the new element will have 2 fewer protons; therefore, the atomic number (subscripts) will decrease from 92 to 90. This means that the identity of the atom has changed from uranium to thorium. (Check the atomic numbers for uranium and thorium in the periodic table.) **The mass number has decreased by 4**:

PARENT → DAUGHTER + RADIATION

$${}^{238}_{92}U \rightarrow {}^{234}_{90}Th + {}^{4}_{2}He$$

${}^{238}_{92}U$ has become ${}^{234}_{90}Th$

mass number 238 − 4 = 234

atomic number 92 − 2 = 90

Problems 1–7

Fill in the missing isotope for the alpha decay in each of the following nuclear reactions.

1. ${}^{150}_{64}Gd \rightarrow \alpha + ?$	5. $? \rightarrow {}^{255}_{100}Fm + \alpha$
2. ${}^{144}_{60}Nd \rightarrow \alpha + ?$	6. ${}^{174}_{72}Hf \rightarrow \alpha + ?$
3. ${}^{245}_{96}Cm \rightarrow \alpha + ?$	7. ${}^{238}_{94}Pu \rightarrow \alpha + ?$
4. $? \rightarrow {}^{206}_{82}Pb + \alpha$	

B. Beta Emission

If a neutron is transformed into a proton and an electron, a beta particle is produced. Beta radiation is the high energy electron emitted from the nucleus. When a beta particle is emitted, the result is an increase of one proton and a decrease of one neutron. Therefore, the **mass number remains the same but the atomic number is increased by one.** For example, carbon-14 is a beta emitter:

$$^{14}_{6}C \rightarrow {}^{14}_{7}N + {}^{0}_{-1}e$$

Remember: The sum of the masses (superscripts) are equal on the two sides of the equation. The same is true for the atomic numbers (subscripts).

Problems 8–12

Fill in the missing isotope for the beta decay in each of the following reactions.

8. $^{159}_{63}Eu \rightarrow {}^{0}_{-1}e + ?$
9. $^{141}_{56}Ba \rightarrow {}^{0}_{-1}e + ?$
10. $^{242}_{95}Am \rightarrow {}^{0}_{-1}e + ?$
11. $? \rightarrow {}^{0}_{-1}e + {}^{32}_{16}S$
12. $? \rightarrow {}^{0}_{-1}e + {}^{139}_{52}Te$

C. Gamma Radiation

There are a few instances of pure gamma emitters, but in most examples of radioactive decay, gamma rays may also be emitted during alpha or beta emission. The following examples will illustrate this point.

Example B:

$$^{11}_{5}B^{*} \rightarrow {}^{0}_{0}\gamma + {}^{11}_{5}B$$

$$^{131}_{53}I \rightarrow {}^{0}_{0}\gamma + {}^{0}_{-1}e + {}^{131}_{54}Xe$$

$^{11}_{5}B^{*}$ symbolizes a high energy state of the boron nucleus. In the first example, the element remains the same. Since gamma rays are not particles but high energy radiation, they will not affect the atomic number nor the mass number of the daughter nucleus. Unlike the parent isotope, the daughter isotope may be a stable isotope.

Problems 13–17

Fill in the missing product in the following nuclear reactions:

13. $^{40}_{19}K \rightarrow \beta + \gamma + ?$
14. $^{239}_{94}Pu \rightarrow \alpha + \gamma + ?$
15. $^{235}_{92}U \rightarrow \alpha + \gamma + ?$
16. $^{226}_{88}Ra \rightarrow \alpha + \gamma + ?$
17. $^{214}_{84}Po \rightarrow \alpha + \gamma + ?$

V. Radiation Measurement

A Geiger counter is a common instrument used to detect beta and gamma radiation. Radiation can be measured in different ways: the activity of the radioactive sample could be measured or the impact of radiation on biological tissues could be determined.

The units used to measure activity of a radioactive sample are curie or becquerel. The curie, Ci, is defined as the number of disintegrations that occur in one second for 1 gram of radium (or 3.7×10^{10} disintegrations per second). The curie was named after Marie Curie, a Polish scientist who discovered radioactive radium and polonium. Another unit of radiation activity is the becquerel, Bq, which represents one disintegration per second.

To measure the impact of radiation on biological tissues, the rad, the gray, the rem, or the sievert could be used. The rad (radiation absorbed dose) measures the amount of radiation absorbed by 1 gram of material such as biological tissues. The gray, Gy, equals 100 rads. The rem (radiation equivalents in humans) measures the biological effects of different types of radiation, that is biological damage. Rem dose will vary depending on the type of radiation (alpha, beta, gamma, X-ray, etc.). To determine the rem dose, the absorbed dose in rads is multiplied by a factor. The factor changes depending on the type of radiation absorbed (alpha, beta, gamma, X-rays). A sievert, Sv, equals 100 rems.

Measurement	Unit	SI Unit
Activity	curie 3.7×10^{10} disintegrations/sec	becquerel 1 disintegration/sec
Absorbed radiation	rad	gray = 100 rads
Biological damage	rem = rad × factor	sievert

VI. Half-life

The rate of decay for a radioactive isotope varies considerably. The half-life of a radioisotope is constant and independent of the sample size. **The time that it takes for half of any sample to decay is called the half-life.**

Half-lives of Several Radioisotopes				
Isotope	$^{60}_{27}Co$	$^{32}_{15}P$	$^{14}_{6}C$	$^{131}_{51}I$
Half-life	5 years	14 days	5730 years	8 days
Use	chemotherapy	detect tumors	archaeological dating	treatment for hyperthyroidism

NOTE: $^{238}_{92}U$ has a half-life of 4.5 billion years. Very old rock samples can be dated based on their ^{238}U and ^{206}Pb content. The oldest rock found on earth (in Greenland) was dated 3.7 billion years. The solar system has an estimated age of 4.6 billion years based on dating meteorites.

Example C:

Barium-122 has a half-life of 2 minutes. A fresh sample weighing 80 g was obtained. If it takes 10 minutes to set up an experiment using barium-122, how much barium-122 will be left when the experiment begins?

Every half-life, 2 minutes, half of the original amount will undergo nuclear decay:

Time:	start	2 min	4 min	6 min	8 min	10 min
Mass:	80 g	40 g	20 g	10 g	5 g	**2.5 g**

At the end of 10 minutes (5 half-lives) only 2.5 g are left; the rest has decayed.

Example D:

If 10 mg of iodine-131 is given to a patient, how much is left after 24 days? The half-life of iodine-131 is 8 days.

Since the half-life is 8 days, 24 days corresponds to 3 half-lives. After one half-life 5 mg are left; after two half-lives, 2.5 mg; and after 3 half-lives 1.25 mg remains.

Carbon-14 has a half-life of 5730 years and is used to date archaeological objects.

All living organisms have a constant carbon-12/carbon-14 ratio. When the organism dies carbon-12 levels remain constant but carbon-14 decays. The changing carbon-12/carbon-14 ratio can be used to determine the date of the artifact. For example, fresh charcoal made from a tree contains carbon-14 which will give a radioactive count of **13.60** disintegrations per minute per gram of carbon.

Example E:

Prehistoric cave paintings were found in Spain. A piece of charcoal found in the ancient cave in Altamira, Spain gave **1.70** disintegrations per minute per gram of carbon. From this information, determine the age of the cave paintings.

After one half-life the number of disintegrations will go from 13.60 to 6.80; after two half-lives it is 3.40 and after three half-lives 1.70. Therefore, 3 half-lives have elapsed since the paintings were done. Since the half-life of carbon-14 is 5730 years, the paintings are about $5730 \times 3 = 17{,}190$ years old.

Problems 18–23

18. Iodine-131 is used to destroy thyroid tissue in the treatment of an overactive thyroid. The half-life of iodine-131 is 8 days. If a hospital receives a shipment of 200 g of iodine-131, how much I-131 would remain after 32 days?

19. The half-life of carbon-14 is 5730 years. A piece of linen found today contains carbon-14 and gives an activity of 15 counts per minute per gram of carbon. If an anthropologist found an ancient piece of linen believed to date back to the Neolithic period which gave only 7.5 counts per minute per gram of carbon, how old is the ancient linen?

20. Technetium-99m is used for brain scans. If a laboratory receives a shipment of 200 g of this isotope and after 24 hours only 12.5 g of this isotope remain, what is the half-life of technetium-99m?

21. Mercury-197 is used for kidney scans and has a half-life of 3 days. If the amount of mercury-197 needed for a study is 1.0 gram and the time allowed for shipment is 15 days, how much mercury-197 will need to be ordered?

22. The half-life of strontium-90 is 25 years. How much strontium-90 will remain after 100 years if the initial amount is 4.0 g?

23. If the half-life of uranium-232 is 70 years, how many half-lives will it take for 10 g of it to be reduced to 1.25 g?

ANSWERS

1. $^{146}_{62}Sm$
2. $^{140}_{58}Ce$
3. $^{241}_{94}Pu$
4. $^{210}_{84}Po$
5. $^{259}_{102}No$
6. $^{170}_{70}Yb$
7. $^{234}_{92}U$
8. $^{159}_{64}Gd$
9. $^{141}_{57}La$
10. $^{242}_{96}Cm$
11. $^{32}_{15}P$
12. $^{139}_{51}Sb$
13. $^{40}_{20}Ca$
14. $^{235}_{92}U$
15. $^{231}_{90}Th$
16. $^{222}_{86}Rn$
17. $^{210}_{82}Pb$
18. 12.5 g
19. 5730 years
20. 6 hours
21. 32 g
22. 0.25 g
23. 3 half-lives

Nuclear Chemistry

7 Assignment

____
Name

____
Student Number

____
Date *Instructor*

1. Rank alpha, beta, and gamma radiation in order of increasing penetrating ability.

2. Beta particles resemble ______________________.

3. Alpha particles are analogous to ______________________.

4. What type of shielding material is necessary to protect you from:

   a. α-radiation ____________________

   b. β-radiation ____________________

   c. γ-radiation ____________________

5. If you are 5 meters from a radiation source, the intensity of the radiation you are exposed to is _______ times that of a person 20 meters from the same radiation source.

6. Complete the following nuclear equations.

   a. $^{28}Al \rightarrow$ _______ $+ \beta$

   b. _______ $\rightarrow {}^{234}Th + \alpha$

   c. $^{210}Bi \rightarrow$ _______ $+ \alpha$

   d. $^{35}S \rightarrow$ _______ $+ \beta$

7. Give the nuclear equation for the alpha decay of ^{226}Ra.

8. ^{60}Co is used in radiation therapy and emits both beta and gamma radiation. Give the nuclear equation for the decay of ^{60}Co.

9. Strontium-85, used for bone scans, has a half-life of 64 days. A 120 g sample of strontium-85 is stored for 192 days. How many grams of the strontium-85 remains?

10. Iodine-131, used to diagnose and treat thyroid conditions, has a half-life of 8 days. How many days does it take for the amount of iodine-131 in the sample to decrease from 80 g to 5 g?

11. The half-life of ^{83}Sr is 32 hours. In how many days will a 40 mg sample of ^{83}Sr be reduced to 2.5 mg?

12. ^{24}Na is used to study the blood circulation and has a half-life of 15 hours. If you have 100 mg of this radioisotope today, how many milligrams will remain after 75 hours?

8

Gases

Of the three states of matter—solid, liquid, and gas—the gaseous state is the one most studied and the best understood. The gaseous state will be discussed, as well as some of the variables that describe the behavior of gases.

I. Properties of Gases

All gases have similar properties when they have the same temperature and pressure. Among the properties of gases are the following:

- Gases have an indefinite shape, and they will expand to completely fill any container.
- Gas particles are far apart from each other, with mostly empty space surrounding these gas particles. About 99.9% of a helium balloon is empty space and less than 0.1% of the balloon is occupied by helium atoms.
- Gases may be compressed, since there is so much empty space between particles.
- Gas particles are in constant motion (kinetic energy). The average speed of an oxygen molecule is 1000 miles per hour at room temperature.
- When gas particles collide with each other or with the walls of the container, they bounce back. These elastic collisions explain why gas molecules do not settle to the bottom of the container.

II. Common Gases

Gases are usually covalent substances with low molecular weights. The following substances exist as gases under normal laboratory conditions:

Elements – N_2, O_2, H_2, F_2, Cl_2, noble gases (He, Ne, Ar, Kr, Xe, Rn)

Compounds – CO, CO_2, NH_3, HCl, N_2O (laughing gas)

III. Gas Variables

Gas particles move so fast, and they are so far apart, that the attractive forces between particles are too weak to hold them together.

A. Volume (V)

Most of the space in a gas-filled container is empty space; however, the gas particles move around throughout this whole space. Therefore, the volume of the gas is considered to be the same as the volume of the container.

The most common unit for volume is the liter.

B. Temperature (T)

Kinetic energy is directly related to the speed of gas particles. Temperature has been found to vary with the kinetic energy of particles. If the temperature of a gas is lowered, then the particles slow down. Conversely, if the temperature is increased, the particles of the gas move faster.

Kelvin is the unit of temperature that must be used when dealing with gases. The relationship between the Kelvin scale, also known as absolute temperature, and the Celsius scale is shown below:

$$K = °C + 273$$

C. Moles (n)

Another important variable to consider when dealing with gases is how much of a gas is inside a container. We usually measure this amount in moles (n).

D. Pressure (P)

The particles of a gas are very disordered, moving randomly and rapidly. As the particles of gas strike the walls of the container, pressure is exerted. These collisions produce the pressure of the gas. The greater the number of collisions per unit time, the greater the pressure.

Atmospheric pressure may be measured using a barometer, where a long column of mercury is used. Modern barometers use electronics to measure atmospheric pressure. The pressure inside a container may be measured using another device called a manometer. Mechanical devices (gas gauges) are used to measure pressure in multiple devices such as respirators, autoclaves, fire extinguishers, and gas cylinders. Another common device, also using a manometer, but to measure the pressure of a liquid rather than a gas, is the blood pressure gauge.

Pressure is often expressed in units of atmosphere (atm) or millimeters of mercury (mmHg). Often the unit torr, which is equal to a millimeter of mercury, is used.

Pressure at sea level is close to one atmosphere (1 atm). Below sea level, pressure is greater than 1 atm, while at higher elevations, the pressure is less than 1 atm.

$$1 \text{ atm} = 760 \text{ torr} = 760 \text{ mmHg}$$

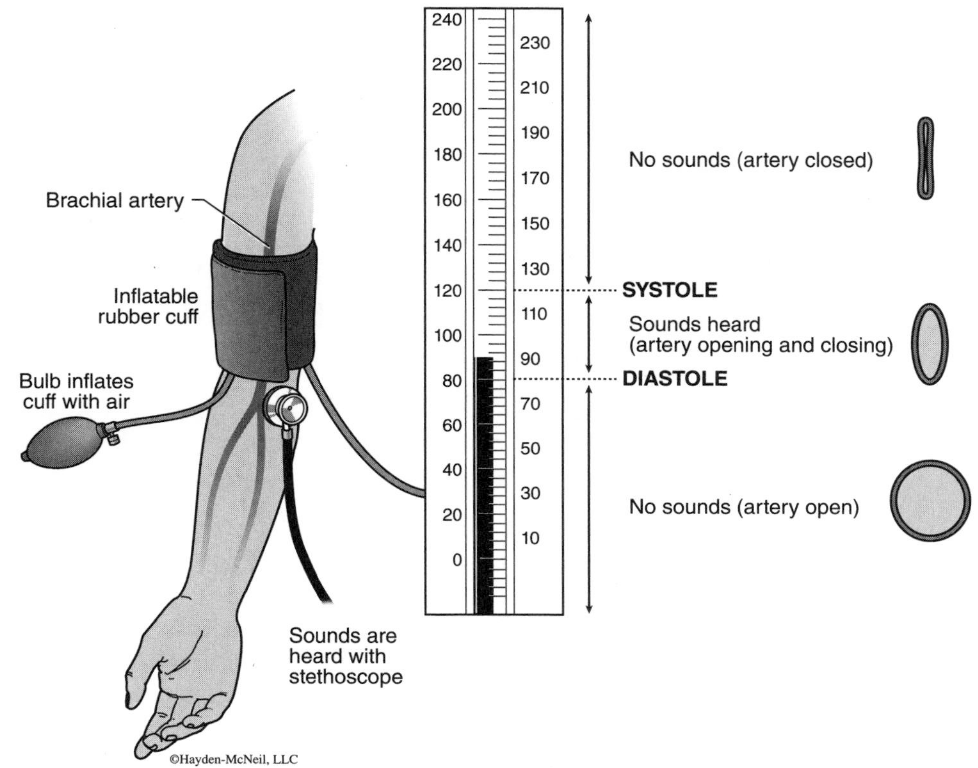

Gas Variables

Variable	Units
Pressure (P)	atm, torr, or mmHg
Temperature (T)	K
Volume (V)	mL or L
Amount (n)	mole

E. Conversions

Example A: 1.7 atm = _____ torr

$$? \text{ torr} = 1.7 \text{ atm} \left(\frac{760 \text{ torr}}{1 \text{ atm}}\right) = 1292 \text{ torr}$$

Example B: 100 torr = _____ mmHg

$$? \text{ mmHg} = 100 \text{ torr} \left(\frac{760 \text{ mmHg}}{760 \text{ torr}}\right) = 100 \text{ mmHg}$$

Example C: 76 mmHg = _____ atm

$$? \text{ atm} = 76 \text{ torr} \left(\frac{1 \text{ atm}}{760 \text{ torr}}\right) = 0.10 \text{ atm}$$

Example D: 58 °C = _____ K

$? K = 58 + 273 = 331 K$

Example E: 500 K = ____ °C

$? °C = 500 - 273 = 227 °C$

Problem 1. Perform the following conversions:

a. If the atmospheric pressure in Denver is 630 torr, then what is the pressure in atmospheres?

b. If the pressure at 100 ft below the surface of the ocean is 4 atm, then what is the pressure in mmHg and torr?

c. If the temperature in a hot air balloon is 150 °C, what is that temperature in the Kelvin scale?

d. If the temperature in an underwater air tank is 280 K, what is that temperature in the Celsius scale?

IV. Relationships Among Pressure, Volume, and Temperature

In observing the behavior of gases, a number of relationships have been established.

1. **P–V Relationship (holding n and T constant)**

The relationship between pressure and volume will be examined, while keeping all other variables constant. If the **volume** of a gas is **increased**, the **pressure decreases**, and if the **volume** of the gas is **decreased**, then the **pressure** must **increase**. Pressure and volume are said to be inversely proportional. The product of volume times pressure is a constant.

$$P \times V = \text{constant}$$

If the letter **k** is used to represent a constant, then the equation may be rewritten:

$$P \times V = k$$

For example, if the volume of the gas is cut by half, its pressure will double.

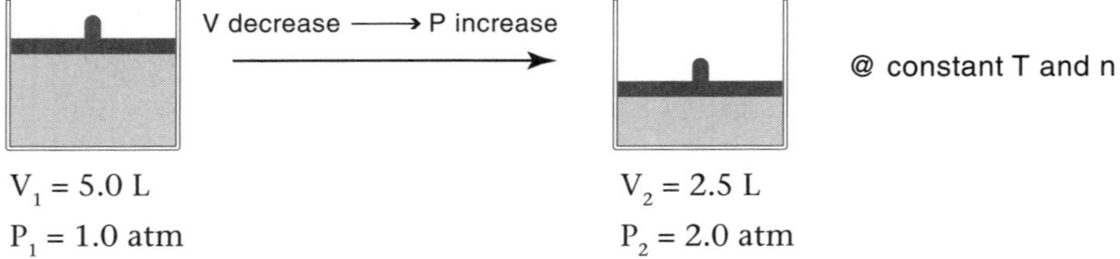

When we breathe in, the diaphragm contracts and moves down. As the diaphragm contracts, the volume of the rib cage increases and the pressure inside the lungs becomes lower than the outside pressure. Thus, air flows from the higher pressure area into the lungs. The process is reversed when we breathe out: the diaphragm is relaxed and moves up. The resulting **volume** of the rib cage **decreases**, which causes the **pressure** to **increase** and air flows out of the lungs.

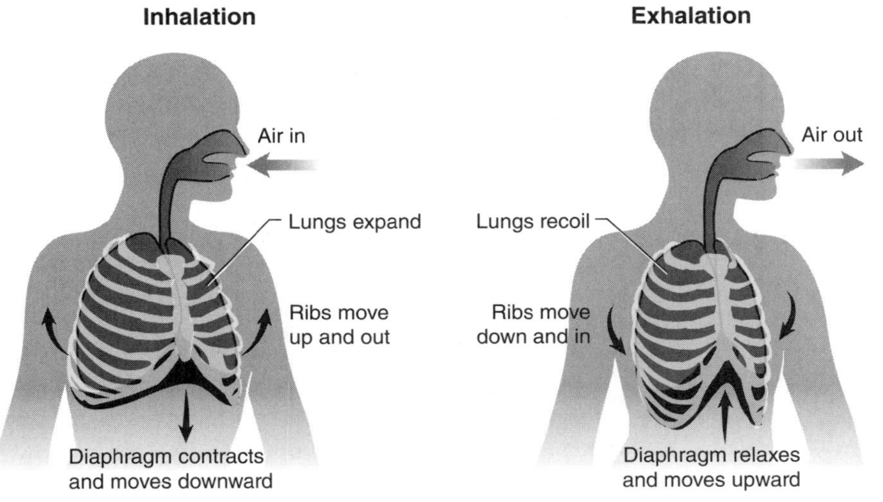

2. **P–T Relationship (holding n and V constant)**

If the **temperature** of a gas is **increased**, the molecules of the gas move faster. This faster motion causes the gas particles to hit the walls of the container more frequently, thereby **increasing** the **pressure** of the gas. Therefore, pressure and temperature are directly proportional—when one increases, the other one also increases—and vice versa.

$$P \propto T$$

$$P = kT$$

(k is a constant)

For example, if the pressure of a gas is reduced to half its original value, then the absolute temperature (Kelvin scale) is also halved.

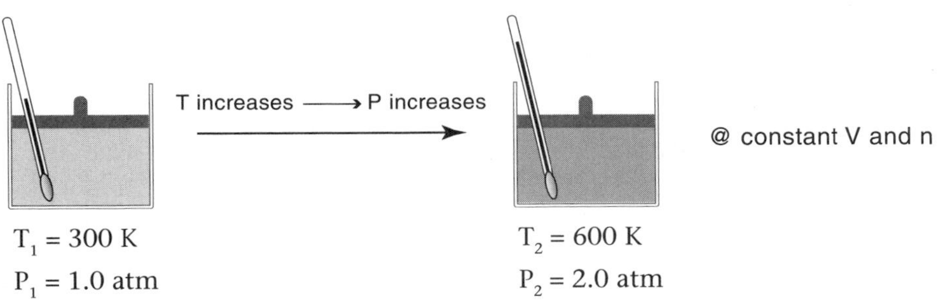

3. **V–T Relationship (holding n and P constant)**

If the **temperature** of a gas is **increased**, while keeping the pressure and the number of particles constant, then the **volume** of the gas will also **increase**. Volume and temperature are said to be directly proportional. For example, if the absolute temperature of the gas is doubled, its volume will also double.

$$V \propto T$$

$$V = kT$$

(k is a constant)

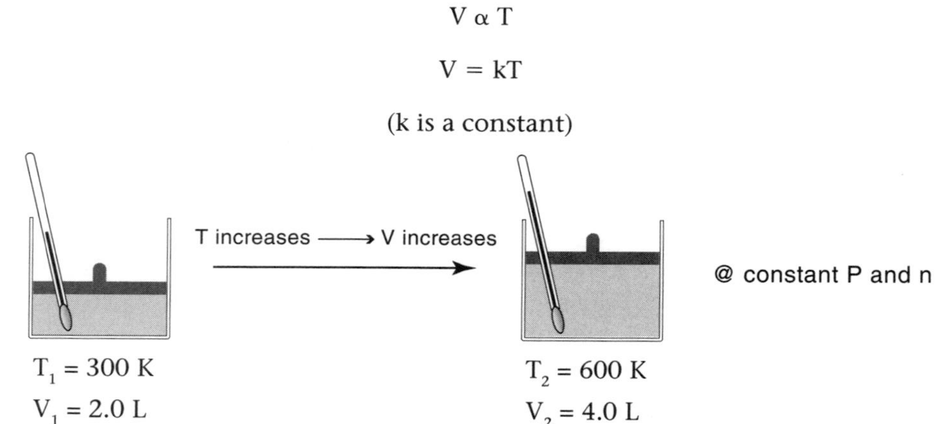

Problem 2. Answer the following questions.

a. How can the volume of a constant amount of gas at 760 torr be increased?

b. As air (at room temperature) is inhaled, what happens to the volume of the lungs?

c. A mischievous kid places a filled Mylar balloon in the freezer. What happens to the appearance of the balloon?

d. Increasing the pressure of a constant amount of gas at 0°C causes what change in the volume of the gas?

e. What would be the new volume of 5 liters of gas if its pressure decreases from 2 atm to 1 atm, and its absolute temperature triples from 100 to 300 K?

4. **V – n Relationship (holding P and T constant)**

Have you ever blown up a balloon? As you add air to the balloon, it expands (the volume increases). As **particles** are added to a flexible container (while keeping the pressure and temperature constant), the **volume** of the container will **increase**.

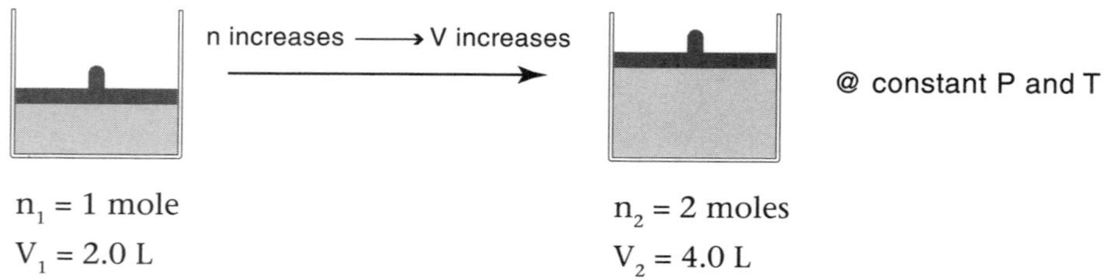

$n_1 = 1$ mole
$V_1 = 2.0$ L

$n_2 = 2$ moles
$V_2 = 4.0$ L

Example F: At constant temperature, if the number of moles of gas increases, the volume of the gas will _______ (increase/decrease).

Since the volume and moles are directly proportional, if one increases the other one will also *increase*. On the other hand, if the number of moles of a gas increases, at constant pressure and volume, the temperature will *decrease*.

5. **The Ideal Gas Law**

Combining the three previous relationships, [P = k/V, P = kT, and V = kT], provides a relationship for gases which is called the Ideal Gas Law. This relationship is valid for not only any pressure, volume, and temperature but also for any amount of gas or mixture of gases.

$$PV = nRT \text{ (R = gas constant)}$$

V. Dalton's Law of Partial Pressures

Many gases are composed of a mixture of gases. Air is such a mixture whose composition is: 78% N_2, 21% O_2, ~1% CO_2, and H_2O.

In a mixture of gases, each gas exerts the pressure it would exert if it were the only gas in the container. Dalton's law states that, at constant volume and temperature, the total pressure exerted by a mixture of ideal gases is the sum of the partial pressures of those gases.

$$P_T = P_1 + P_2 + P_3 + \ldots.$$

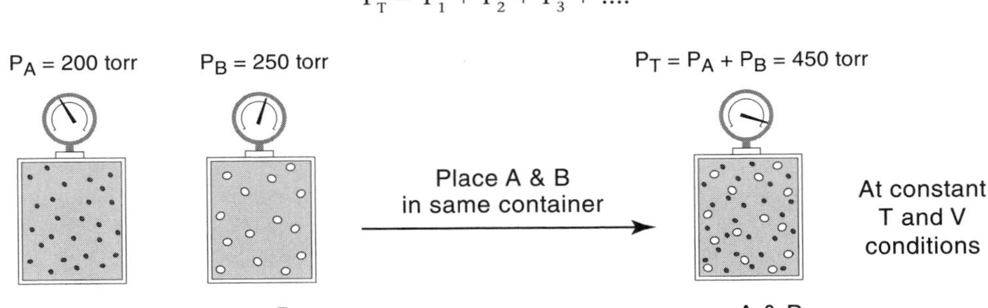

Example G: An anesthetic consists of a mixture of cyclopropane gas and oxygen. If this mixture has a total pressure of 825 torr, what is the partial pressure of oxygen in the anesthetic if the partial pressure of cyclopropane is 73 torr?

$$P_T = P_{cyclopropane} + P_{oxygen}$$

$$825 \text{ torr} = 73 \text{ torr} + P_{oxygen}$$

$$P_{oxygen} = 825 - 73 = 752 \text{ torr}$$

Problem 3. Solve the following problems:

a. Assume that the exhaled breath of a patient is composed of O_2, N_2, and CO_2. If the atmospheric pressure is 755 mmHg and the partial pressure of O_2 is 110 mmHg and that of N_2 is 617 mmHg, then what is the partial pressure of CO_2 (in mmHg)?

b. To a tank already containing helium at 1.5 atm and oxygen at 2.0 atm, an unknown amount of carbon dioxide is added until the total pressure is 4.0 atm. Given this information, what is the partial pressure of carbon dioxide?

c. If a gas tank used by a scuba diver contains He and O_2 having a partial pressure of 5.5 atm and 1.5 atm, respectively, then what is the total pressure inside the tank?

Gas exchange in the alveoli (air sacs) of the lungs is dependent on the difference in pressure of individual gases. The pressure of oxygen in fresh air (as inhaled) is approximately 150 torr, while venous blood (that which has traveled through the body) has an oxygen pressure of close to 100 torr. This difference of 50 torr allows for diffusion of oxygen molecules from the alveolus to red blood cells. In contrast, the level of carbon dioxide in venous blood is 40 torr, while there is less than 1 torr pressure of CO_2 in inhaled air. Consequently, carbon dioxide molecules will transfer from the blood into the alveoli to be exhaled in the next breath.

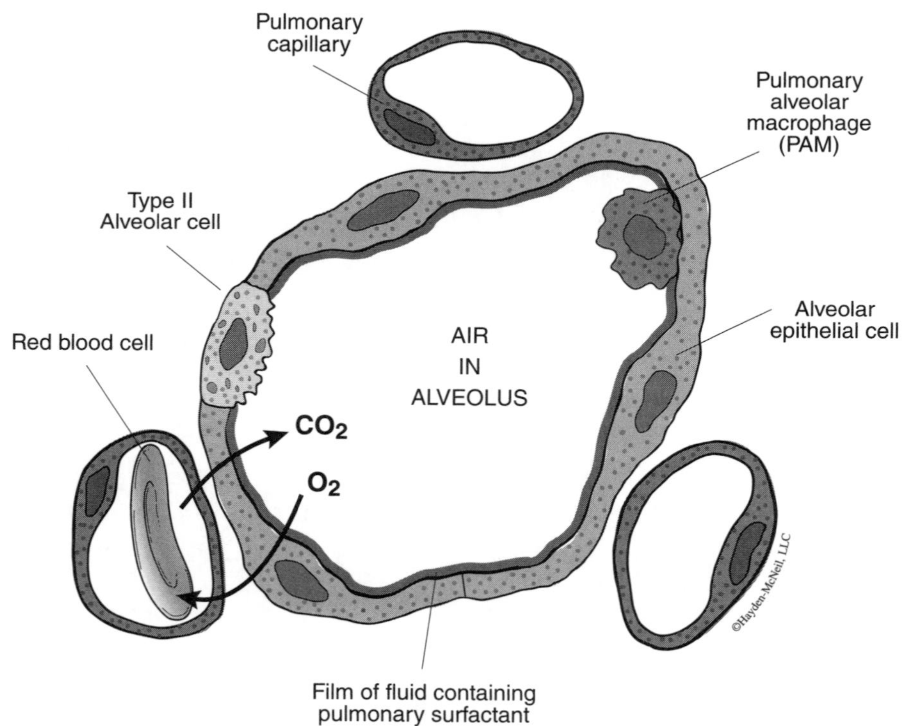

VI. Henry's Law

Henry's law states that the solubility of a gas in a liquid is directly related to the pressure of that gas above the liquid. Hyperbaric chambers (a chamber in which pressures 2 to 3 times greater than atmospheric pressure are applied to patients) illustrates Henry's law. These chambers, which are used for carbon monoxide poisonings, burns, and some cancer treatments, produce an increase in gas solubility (particularly oxygen) due to higher applied pressures. Patients undergoing treatment in hyperbaric chambers must undergo decompression (pressure reduction) at a rate that slowly reduces the concentration of gas in the blood. If decompression is applied too rapidly, the released gas not only can appear in the joints or tissues and cause severe pain, but it can also form bubbles in the blood that can produce life-threatening blood clots. Deep sea divers must also undergo slow decompression.

VII. Blood Gases

If a patient is possibly experiencing respiratory acidosis or alkalosis, blood pH determination is essential for a satisfactory biochemical diagnosis. However, rather than determining the pH of blood, it is more feasible to determine the concentration of CO_2 gas in blood plasma to determine the severity of respiratory acidosis or alkalosis.

When the concentration of CO_2 is elevated, the equilibrium of the carbonic acid/hydrogen carbonate buffer is shifted, and higher concentrations of H_2CO_3 are produced, which then produces more hydrogen ion. This increased hydrogen ion in effect lowers the pH of the blood.

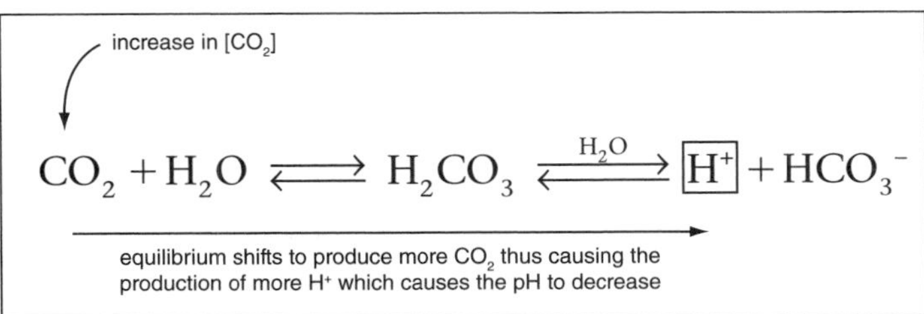
increase in [CO2]
CO2 + H2O ⇌ H2CO3 ⇌(H2O) H+ + HCO3−
equilibrium shifts to produce more CO2 thus causing the production of more H+ which causes the pH to decrease

ANSWERS

1. a. 0.829 atm

   b. 3040 torr; 3040 mmHg

   c. 423 K

   d. 7 °C

2. a. by applying heat to the gas (V α T @ constant n and P)

   b. the volume of the lungs increase (V α n @ constant P and T)

   c. the balloon gets deflated (V α T @ constant n and P)

   d. the volume decreases (P α 1/V @ constant n and T)

   e. 30 liters

3. a. 28 mmHg

   b. 0.5 atm

   c. 7.0 atm

Gases Assignment 8

____
Name

____
Student Number

____
Date *Instructor*

1. a. As the volume of a gas sample increases, the pressure of the sample ______________ (increases, decreases, remains the same) if the temperature and moles are constant.

   b. As the volume of a gas sample increases, the temperature of the sample ______________ (increases, decreases, remains the same) if the pressure and moles are constant.

   c. If the moles in a gas sample are decreased, while keeping the volume and pressure constant, the temperature ______________ (increases, decreases, remains the same).

   d. If the temperature of a gas does not change and its volume is cut in half, its pressure is ___________ (halved, doubled, remains the same).

   e. If the pressure of a gas is held constant and the temperature is increased from 350 K to 700 K, the volume of the gas will __________ (increase/decrease) by a factor of ________.

   f. At constant volume, if the temperature of a gas is increased, the molecules move __________ (faster/slower) and the pressure of the gas ________ (increases/decreases).

2. What is the pressure, in atmospheres, of a gas pressure of 300 torr?

3. What is the pressure, in mmHg, of a sample of gas at 0.75 atm?

4. A mixture of hydrogen, oxygen, and carbon dioxide has a total pressure of 750 torr. If the pressure of oxygen and carbon dioxide are 200 torr and 300 torr respectively, what is the pressure of hydrogen?

5. a. Oxygen moves from the alveoli in the lungs into the bloodstream because the partial pressure in the alveoli is ______ (higher/lower) than the pressure in the blood.

   b. Oxygen diffuses from the blood into the tissues because its partial pressure is ______ (higher/lower) in the tissues.

   c. Carbon dioxide diffuses from the tissues into the blood because the partial pressure of carbon dioxide is ______ (higher/lower) in the tissues than it is in the blood.

6. List three applications of hyperbaric chambers.

7. In hyperbaric chambers the pressure is ______ (higher than, lower than, the same as) atmospheric pressure.

8. Deep-sea divers must undergo decompression. If a scuba diver experiences a pressure of 4 atm under the sea, this will ______ (increase/decrease) the solubility of nitrogen in his blood and nitrogen narcosis could result.

9. In respiratory acidosis, the concentration of carbon dioxide in blood plasma is ________ (higher/lower) than normal and the pH of the blood is ________ (higher/lower) than normal.

9

Hydrocarbons

Organic chemistry is the study of **carbon**-containing compounds. Carbon atoms have a unique ability to form long chains where hundreds of carbon atoms may attach to each other. Covalent compounds containing carbon and hydrogen are called **hydrocarbons**.

I. Hydrocarbons

A. Bonding

Hydrogen is a very small atom with one electron in its valence shell, and can only fit a maximum of two electrons; therefore it forms only one covalent bond. Carbon has four valence electrons and needs four more electrons to have an octet. Carbon, therefore, forms four covalent bonds.

The simplest hydrocarbon is formed when a carbon atom bonds to four hydrogen atoms, producing the compound methane, CH_4.

$$\begin{array}{ccccc} & & H & & \\ & & | & & \\ H & - & C & - & H \\ & & | & & \\ & & H & & \end{array}$$

two-dimensional structure of methane

The four bonds around carbon can be arranged in several ways:

4 single bonds	1 double bond and 2 single bonds	2 double bonds	1 triple bond and 1 single bond
$\begin{array}{c} \vert \\ -C- \\ \vert \end{array}$	$\begin{array}{c} \vert \\ -C= \end{array}$	$=C=$	$-C\equiv$

If all the bonds in a hydrocarbon are single bonds, the compound is classified as an **alkane**. If the hydrocarbon skeleton contains at least one double bond, it is considered an **alkene**; if there is a triple bond in the hydrocarbon, it is an **alkyne**.

B. Properties of Hydrocarbons

Since the two elements found in hydrocarbons, carbon and hydrogen, have similar electronegativity values, the covalent bond formed between these two elements is nonpolar. Therefore these compounds are nonpolar and hence, are not soluble in water. Hydrocarbons are also nonelectrolytes and very flammable substances.

C. Types of Hydrocarbons

Hydrocarbon chains are classified according to their structure. If they contain only single bonds they are **saturated hydrocarbons**, alkanes. **Unsaturated hydrocarbons**, on the other hand, contain double or triple bonds between carbon atoms. Alkenes and alkynes are unsaturated hydrocarbons.

II. Alkanes

A. Structures of Alkanes

Although the structure of methane is usually written as flat or two-dimensional, the actual three-dimensional shape of methane shows a tetrahedral arrangement where the carbon atom bonds equally to 4 hydrogen atoms. In this three-dimensional arrangement, all hydrogen atoms are equidistant and 109.5° apart from each other.

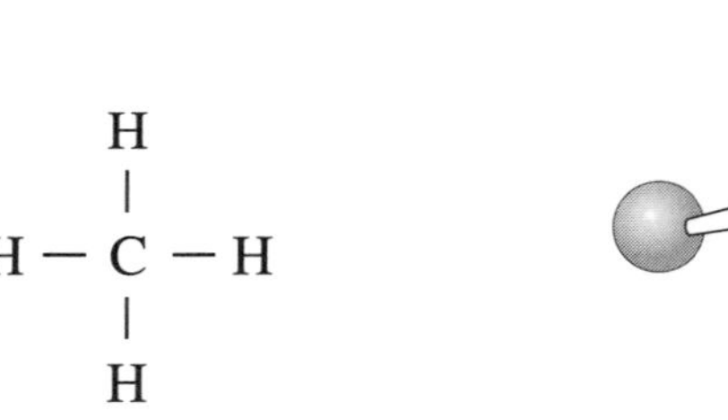

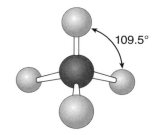

2-D structure of methane   3-D structure of methane

Formulas for hydrocarbons can be represented in several ways: structural, condensed, and molecular formulas. The molecular formula shows the total number of atoms of each element in a compound, but not how the atoms are arranged or attached to each other.

Structural, Condensed, and Molecular Formulas for Simple Alkanes

<table>
<tr><th>Carbon Backbone</th><th>Structural Formula</th><th>Condensed Formula</th><th>Molecular Formula</th></tr>
<tr><td>— C —</td><td>H
|
H — C — H
|
H</td><td>CH_4</td><td>CH_4</td></tr>
<tr><td>C — C</td><td>H H
| |
H — C — C — H
| |
H H</td><td>$CH_3—CH_3$</td><td>C_2H_6</td></tr>
<tr><td>C — C — C</td><td>H H H
| | |
H — C — C — C — H
| | |
H H H</td><td>$CH_3—CH_2—CH_3$</td><td>C_3H_8</td></tr>
<tr><td>C — C — C — C</td><td>H H H H
| | | |
H — C — C — C — C — H
| | | |
H H H H</td><td>$CH_3—CH_2—CH_2—CH_3$</td><td>C_4H_{10}</td></tr>
<tr><td>C — C — C — C — C</td><td>H H H H H
| | | | |
H — C — C — C — C — C — H
| | | | |
H H H H H</td><td>$CH_3CH_2CH_2CH_2CH_3$</td><td>C_5H_{12}</td></tr>
</table>

The previous table indicates that there is a simple pattern to these structures. Longer continuous chains are formed by adding one carbon atom at a time. The table above shows the first five members of the alkane series. The table below shows the name of the first ten members of the **alkane** series. Note that they all end in "**ane**." Furthermore, the molecular formula is C_nH_{2n+2}, where "n" is the number of carbons.

The Alkane Series

# of C	Name	# of C	Name
1	meth**ane**	6	hex**ane**
2	eth**ane**	7	hept**ane**
3	prop**ane**	8	oct**ane**
4	but**ane**	9	non**ane**
5	pent**ane**	10	dec**ane**

Later these names will be compared with those of alkenes and alkynes, where the stem of the name will be identical, and the only change will occur in the ending. The system used for naming these compounds is called the IUPAC system, where IUPAC stands for the International Union of Pure and Applied Chemistry.

3-D structure of ethane
CH_3CH_3

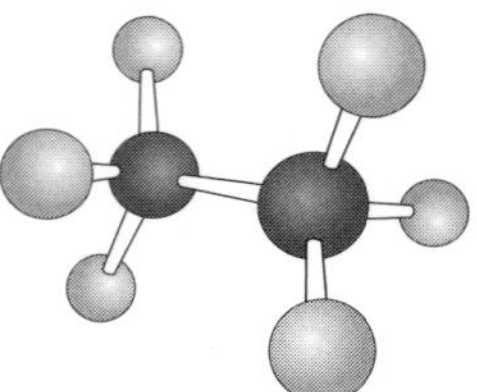

3-D structure of propane
$CH_3CH_2CH_3$

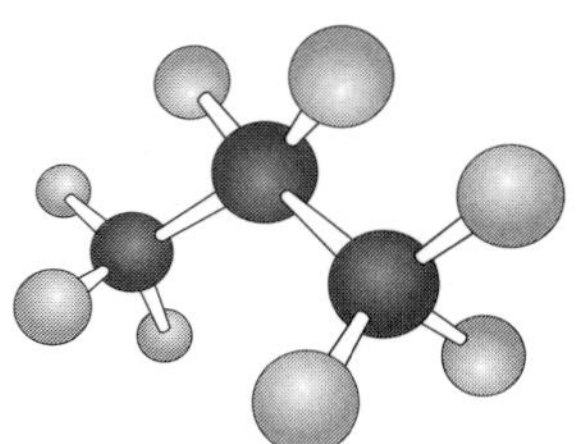

The three-dimensional figure for propane shows that continuous chains are NOT straight chains. They actually zigzag due to the 109.5° angles. However it is usually more convenient to use flat, two-dimensional structural formulas to represent these molecules.

Example A: Consider an **alkane** of molecular formula C_5H_{12}. How many different arrangements of atoms are possible? (Hint: C must have 4 bonds and H only one bond.)

```
    H   H   H   H   H
    |   |   |   |   |
H - C - C - C - C - C - H
    |   |   |   |   |
    H   H   H   H   H
```

1. A **continuous chain** of 5 C atoms.

```
          H
          |
      H \ C / H
          |
    H     |   H   H
    |     |   |   |
H - C  -  C - C - C - H
    |     |   |   |
    H     H   H   H
```

2. One C atom branches out from a **continuous chain** of 4 C atoms.

```
          H
          |
      H \ C / H
          |
    H     |   H
    |     |   |
H - C  -  C - C - H
    |     |   |
    H     |   H
          |
      H / C \ H
          |
          H
```

3. Two C atoms branch out from a **continuous chain** of 3 C atoms.

There are only 3 possible structures for C_5H_{12}. Any other arrangements are actually repetitions of these.

Compounds that have the same molecular formula but different structures are called ***structural isomers.***

B. Nomenclature of Alkanes

Alkanes are named according to the number of carbon atoms in the **longest continuous chain** or **parent chain**. To name an alkane, the parent chain must be located first. If there is branching (side groups attached to the parent chain), then the chain is numbered so that the branch (or branches) get the **lowest** possible number and this number becomes part of the name. Branches are called **alkyl groups** and end in "**yl**." A side chain containing one carbon atom is called meth**yl**, while one with two carbon atoms is called eth**yl**, and so forth.

Alkyl Groups

Methyl	Ethyl	Propyl	Isopropyl
$—CH_3$	$—CH_2—CH_3$	$—CH_2—CH_2—CH_3$	CH_3 | $— CH — CH_3$

Example B: Give the structures and names for the two isomers of C_4H_{10}. (Try drawing these structures without looking at the answers.)

i.

$CH_3—CH_2—CH_2—CH_3$

a continuous chain

ii.

a branch

CH_3
|
$CH_3 — CH — CH_3$

a branched carbon chain

i. Since this chain has 4 carbons the compound is called **butane.**

ii. The parent chain has 3 carbons with one methyl group attached to the carbon in position 2. The compound is **2-methyl propane.**

Example C: Name the isomers for C_5H_{12} as shown in Example A.

i. $CH_3\text{-}CH_2\text{-}CH_2\text{-}CH_2\text{-}CH_3$

A continuous chain of 5 carbon atoms is called **pentane**.

ii.

$$\begin{array}{c} \phantom{CH_3 - {}}CH_3 \\ \phantom{CH_3 - {}}| \\ CH_3 - CH - CH_2 - CH_3 \end{array}$$

A continuous chain of 4 carbon atoms with a methyl group attached to the C at position 2. The name is **2-methylbutane**.

iii.

$$\begin{array}{ccc} & CH_3 & \\ & | & \\ CH_3 - & C & - CH_3 \\ & | & \\ & CH_3 & \end{array}$$

A 3 carbon atom parent chain with two methyl groups attached at carbon 2. The name of this compound is **2,2-dimethylpropane.**

Example D: Name the following compound:

$$\begin{array}{c} CH_3 \\ | \\ CH_3CH_2CH_2CHCH_3 \end{array}$$

The longest continuous chain consists of 5 carbon atoms, therefore the parent chain is pentane and the branch is attached to the **second** carbon in the chain. In order to give the branch the LOWEST possible number the chain is numbered from **right to left**.

$$\begin{array}{ccccccccc} & & & & & & CH_3 & & \\ & & & & & & | & & \\ CH_3 & - & CH_2 & - & CH_2 & - & CH & - & CH_3 \\ 5 & & 4 & & 3 & & 2 & & 1 \end{array}$$

2-methylpentane

Example E: Name the following compound:

$$\begin{array}{l} CH_3 \\ | \\ CH_3CH_2CH_2CH_2CHCH_2CHCH_2CH_3 \\ | \\ CH_2 \\ | \\ CH_2 \\ | \\ CH_3 \end{array}$$

The **longest continuous chain** is found, and since it contains 10 carbons, it is called decane (note the 9 carbons that appear horizontally). Next, the parent chain is numbered so that the **branches are assigned the lowest possible numbers**. If the carbon chain is numbered starting at the lower right of the structure, the ethyl group then is attached to carbon 4, while the methyl group is attached to carbon 6. (Counting from the left and down will result in branches at carbons 6 and 8, which are higher numbers.)

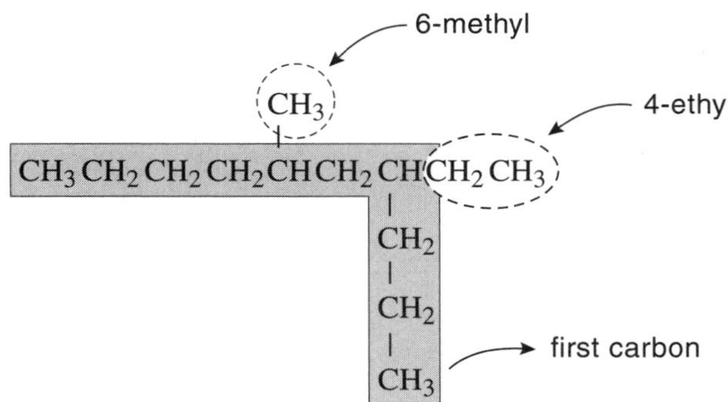

The name is: **4-ethyl-6-methyldecane**

Example F: Name the following compound:

$$
\begin{array}{lllll}
 & & & & CH_2-CH_2-CH_3 \\
 & & & & | \\
CH_3-CH_2- & CH & -CH_2- & C & -CH_3 \\
 & | & & | & \\
 & CH_3 & & CH_2-CH_3 &
\end{array}
$$

The longest continuous chain contains 8 carbons (not 6). **Alphabetically**, <u>e</u>thyl comes before <u>m</u>ethyl (the prefix *di* is not included in alphabetization). As numbered, branches are at 3, 5, 5. (Numbering in the opposite direction would have led to branches at 4, 4, 6.)

$$
\begin{array}{llllllll}
 & & & & 6 & & 7 & 8 \\
1 & 2 & 3 & 4 & 5 & CH_2- & CH_2- & CH_3 \\
 & & & & | & & & \\
CH_3- & CH_2- & CH- & CH_2- & C & -CH_3 & & \\
 & & | & & | & & & \\
 & & CH_3 & & CH_2-CH_3 & & &
\end{array}
$$

The name is **5-ethyl-3,5-dimethyloctane**

C. Haloalkanes

When a halogen is present in a compound, it is called a halogenated hydrocarbon, haloalkane, or alkyl halide. The following are the names given to halogens when attached to an alkyl group.

fluoro –F	chloro –Cl	bromo –Br	iodo –I

6 7 8 9 10 $CH_2-CH_2-CH_2-CH_2-CH_3$ 5 | $I-C-CH_2-CH_2-CH_3$ | $CH_2-CH_2-CH_2-CH_3$ 4 3 2 1	F Br | | $CH_3-CH-CH-CH_3$ 4 3 2 1
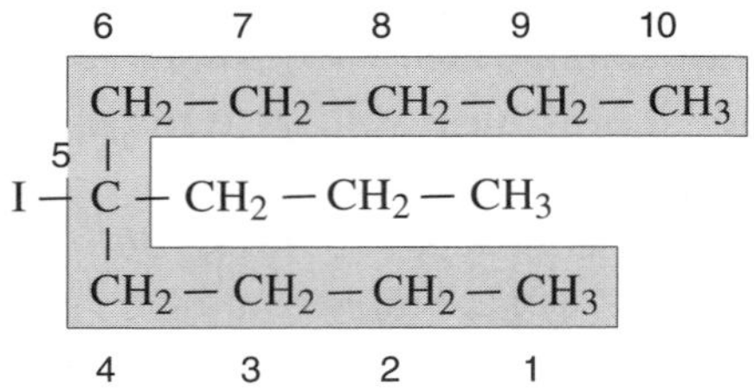 Iodo comes alphabetically before propyl. As numbered, branches are at 5, 5. Numbering in the other direction would have lead to branches at 6, 6. The name is **5-iodo-5-propyldecane.**	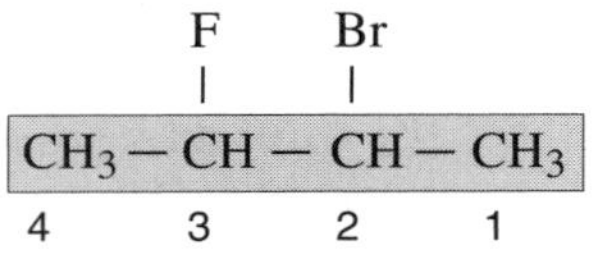 Regardless of direction for numbering the parent chain, the branches are at positions 2 and 3. However, since bromo comes alphabetically before fluoro, it is assigned the lower number and is also written first. The name is **2-bromo-3-fluorobutane.**

D. Cycloalkanes

Alkanes can be found as rings or cyclic structures. These are called **cycloalkanes**. The general molecular formula for cycloalkanes is C_nH_{2n}, where "n" represents the number of carbons.

Cycloalkanes

Carbon Skeleton	Structural Formula	Geometric Formula	Molecular Formula
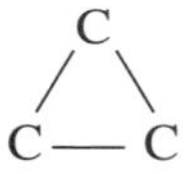 CYCLOPROPANE	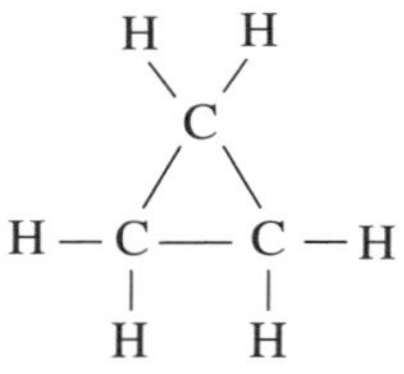	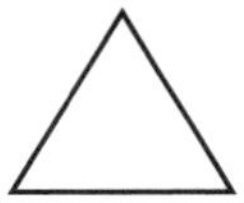 For cyclic compounds, each corner represents a carbon atom and hydrogens are not shown.	C_3H_6
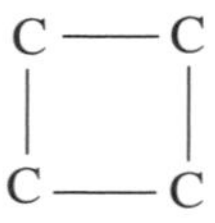 CYCLOBUTANE	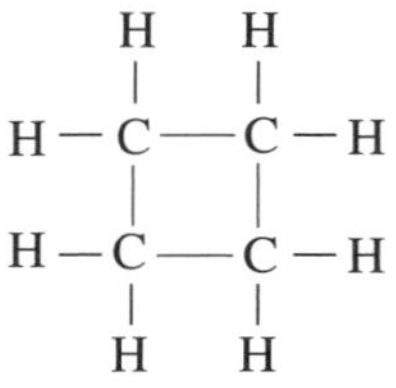		C_4H_8
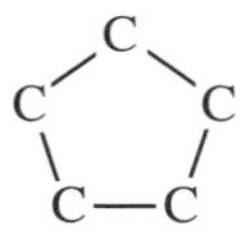 CYCLOPENTANE	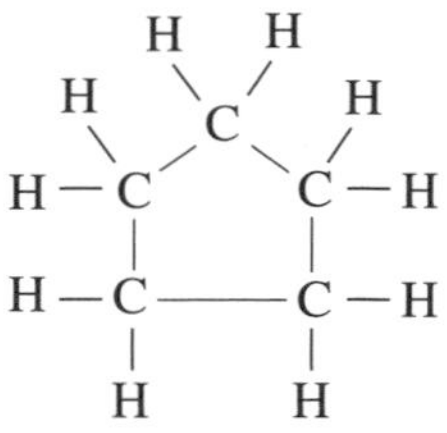	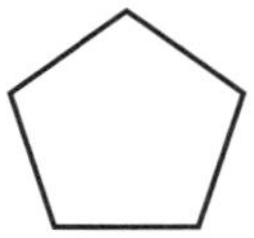	C_5H_{10}

To name cycloalkanes, the parent chain will always be the ring structure. Its name reflects the number of carbon atoms included in the ring. The name is preceded by the word *cyclo*. When only one branch is present, the branch is named, followed by the name of the parent cyclic structure. When two branches are present, the ring is numbered so that the substituent (the branch) that occurs first alphabetically is assigned position 1, and the second branch is numbered from whichever direction gives the lower possible number. For three or more substituents, the numbering is such that the branches have the lowest possible numbers.

Nomenclature of Cycloalkanes

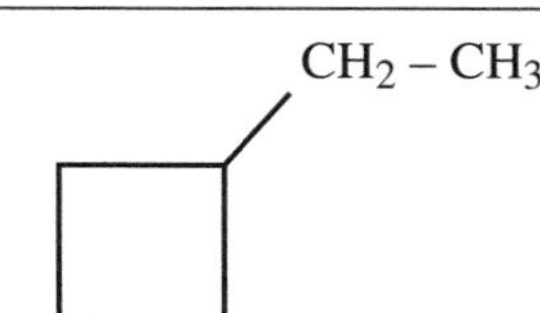 Parent is cyclobutane and there is an ethyl branch. The name is **ethylcyclobutane.**	CH_3 (3); 1 $CH - CH_3$ | CH_3 The #1 position is given to the isopropyl group because it occurs first alphabetically, then the numbering proceeds in a direction that leads to the lowest branch location. The name is **1-isopropyl-3-methylcyclohexane.**
CH_2CH_3 (4); 2 CH_3; 1 CH_3 Ethyl comes before <u>m</u>ethyl alphabetically, therefore it is written first. The numbering results in the lowest branch locations. The name is **4-ethyl-1,2-dimethylcyclohexane.**	CH_3 (4); 2 1 CH_3; CH_3 CH_3 There are four methyl branches at locations 1,1,2,4. The numbering used leads to the lowest branch locations. The name is **1,1,2,4-tetramethylcyclopentane.**

Problem 1. Name the following compounds:

a. $CH_3 - CH_2$ (\| $CH_2 - CH_2 - C(CH_3)_2 - CH_3$)

$$\begin{array}{l} CH_3-CH_2 \qquad\quad CH_3 \\ \qquad\quad | \qquad\qquad\quad | \\ \qquad\; CH_2-CH_2-C-CH_3 \\ \qquad\qquad\qquad\quad\;\; | \\ \qquad\qquad\qquad\;\; CH_3 \end{array}$$

b. 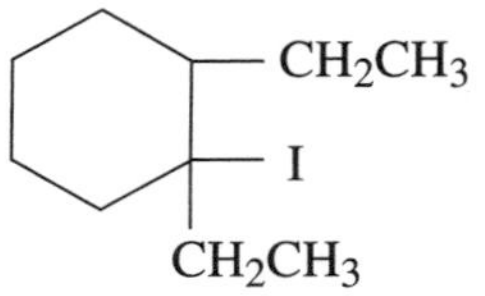 (cyclohexane ring) — CH_2CH_3, — I, — CH_2CH_3

c. 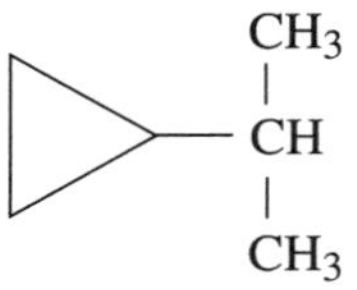 (cyclopropane ring) — CH, with CH_3 above and CH_3 below

d.

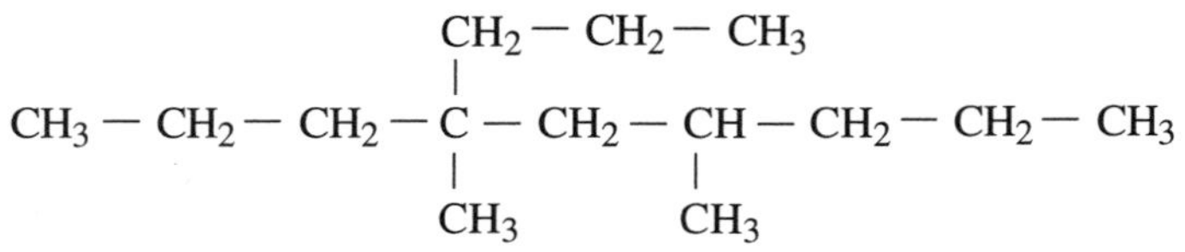

$$
\begin{array}{c}
CH_2-CH_2-CH_3 \\
| \\
CH_3-CH_2-CH_2-C-CH_2-CH-CH_2-CH_2-CH_3 \\
| \qquad\qquad | \\
CH_3 \qquad\quad CH_3
\end{array}
$$

e.

$$
\begin{array}{c}
CH_3 \\
| \\
CH_3-CH_2-CH_2-CH_2-C-Br \\
| \\
CH_2-CH_3
\end{array}
$$

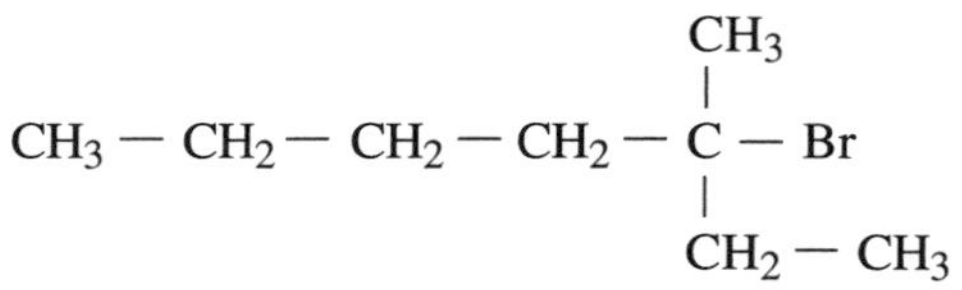

Problem 2. Draw structures for the following compounds and give their molecular formula:

a. 1,1,3-tribromocyclobutane

b. 2-methylpentane

c. 3-ethylhexane

d. 1-ethyl-4-isopropylcyclohexane

e. 2-bromo-3,3-dimethylbutane

f. propylcyclopentane

Problem 3. How many different isomers can be drawn for C_6H_{14}? Name the isomers.

Problem 4. How many isomers can be drawn for C_4H_9Cl? Name the isomers.

E. Reactions of Alkanes

i. Combustion of Hydrocarbons

$$C_xH_y + O_2 \rightarrow CO_2 + H_2O$$

Any hydrocarbon (C_xH_y) when burned in the presence of O_2 will yield CO_2 and H_2O.

The following is an example of a balanced equation for the complete combustion of a hydrocarbon.

$$CH_4 + 2\ O_2 \rightarrow CO_2 + 2\ H_2O$$

Problem 5. Complete and balance the following combustion reactions:

a. $CH_3CH_2CH_3 + O_2 \longrightarrow$

b. $C_5H_{12} + O_2 \longrightarrow$

c. heptane + $O_2 \longrightarrow$

d. 2,4-dimethylpentane + $O_2 \longrightarrow$

ii. Halogenation of Alkanes and Alkyl Halides

$$-\overset{|}{\underset{|}{C}}-H + X_2 \xrightarrow{\text{UV or } \Delta} -\overset{|}{\underset{|}{C}}-X + HX$$

The reactant in these reactions can either be an alkane or alkyl halide. A hydrogen atom is replaced by one of the two atoms of a halogen molecule (X_2 = F_2, Cl_2, Br_2, or I_2). This reaction only takes place in the presence of ultraviolet light (UV) or heat (Δ). If neither UV light nor heat is present, there is no reaction.

The following is an example of a halogenation reaction.

$$H-\overset{H}{\underset{H}{\overset{|}{\underset{|}{C}}}}-H + Br_2 \xrightarrow{\text{UV}} H-\overset{H}{\underset{H}{\overset{|}{\underset{|}{C}}}}-Br + HBr$$

Problem 6. Complete and balance the following halogenation reactions:

a. $CH_3\text{—}CH_3 + Br_2 \xrightarrow{\text{UV}}$

b. ⬡ $+ Br_2 \xrightarrow{\Delta}$

c. $CH_3Cl + Cl_2 \xrightarrow{\Delta}$

d. ⬠ $+ Cl_2 \xrightarrow{\text{UV}}$

III. Alkenes

Alkenes are **unsaturated hydrocarbons**. They contain at least one double bond. This double bond results from the sharing of 4 electrons, or two pairs of electrons, between two carbon atoms. If only one double bond is present, the general molecular formula for alkenes in C_nH_{2n}, where "n" is the number of carbons.

A. Nomenclature of Alkenes

The longest continuous chain containing the C=C double bond must be the parent chain. Its name will end in "ene." The number that indicates the position of the double bond is placed in front of the parent name, except for ethene and propene, where no numbers are necessary since the double bond can only be found at the end of the carbon chain.

The chain is numbered in a way that gives the lowest possible number to the double bond.

As with alkanes the location and name of each branch is listed in alphabetical order and, if there are two or more identical branches, prefixes are used to indicate how many (di, tri, tetra).

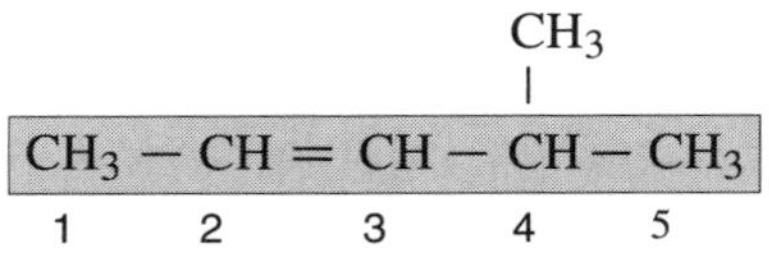 $CH_3-CH=CH-CH(CH_3)-CH_3$ (carbons numbered 1 2 3 4 5) The parent chain is called pentene. The chain was numbered to give the double bond the lowest possible number. The position of the double bond, which denotes the location of the first carbon in the double bond, is placed in front of the parent name. The position and type of branch is also placed in front of the parent name. The name is **4-methyl-2-pentene.**	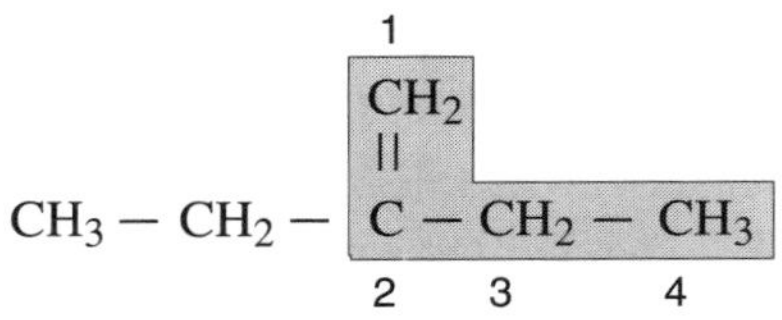 $CH_3-CH_2-C(=CH_2)-CH_2-CH_3$ (carbons numbered 1 (CH_2), 2, 3, 4) The longest continuous carbon chain that contains the double bond is shown above. An ethyl group is attached to carbon 2. The name is **2-ethyl-1-butene.**

Because the carbon atoms in double bonds are not able to rotate, the groups attached to the double bond remain fixed on one or the other side of the double bond. This situation leads to *cis-trans* isomers, where the only difference in structure is the position of atoms about the double bond. For example, 1,2-dibromopropene has both *cis* and *trans* isomers. These isomers have different boiling points: *cis*-1,2-dibromopropene boils at a higher temperature than *trans*-1,2-dibromopropene.

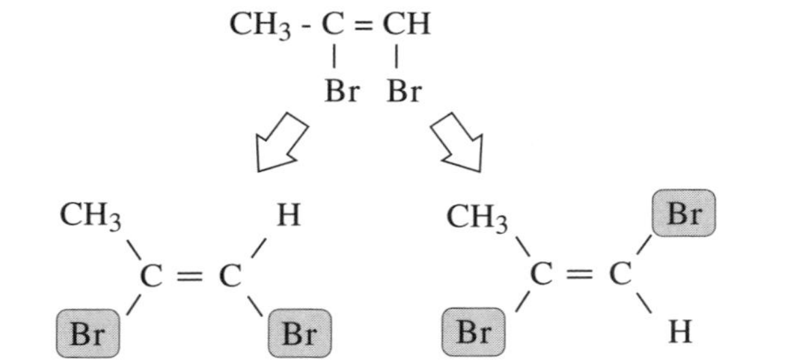

$CH_3-C(Br)=CH(Br)$

cis-1,2-dibromopropene: CH_3 and Br on one carbon, H and Br on the other

Br's are on same side of double bond

trans-1,2-dibromopropene: CH_3 and Br on one carbon, Br and H on the other

Br's are on opposite side of double bond

No *cis-trans* isomers occur if either carbon atom in the double bond is attached to identical groups or atoms. For example, 2-bromopropene:

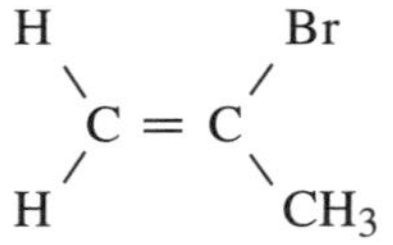

$(H)_2C=C(Br)(CH_3)$

no *cis-trans* isomers are possible because two of the same atom (i.e., H's) are present on one carbon atom.

2-Butene is another example of a compound that has *cis-trans* isomers.

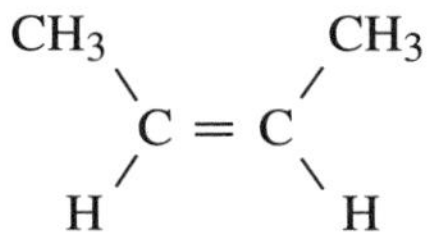

```
CH3         CH3          CH3          H
   \       /                \       /
    C = C                    C = C
   /       \                /       \
  H         H              H         CH3
```

cis-2-butene 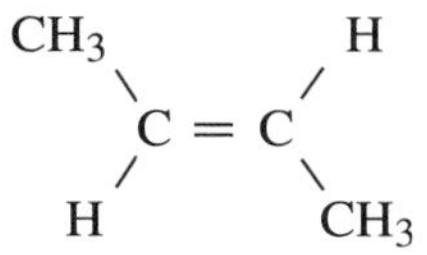   *trans*-2-butene

Problem 7. Indicate whether each of the following can exist as* cis-trans *isomers. If so, draw and name each isomer.

a. $CH_3 - CH = CH_2$ b. $CHBr = CHBr$

Problem 8. Draw the structural formula for both* cis *and* trans *isomers of 3-hexene.

B. Nomenclature of Cycloalkenes

To name cycloalkenes, the parent chain is always the ring structure. Its name reflects the number of carbon atoms included in the ring. The ring is numbered so that the double bond occupies positions 1 and 2 and branches have the lowest possible number. Since the double bond is in positions 1 and 2, its location is not included in front of the parent name.

CH_2CH_3 (4), 1, 2, CH_3, CH_3	1, 2, 4, 3, CH_3, CH_3 CH_3
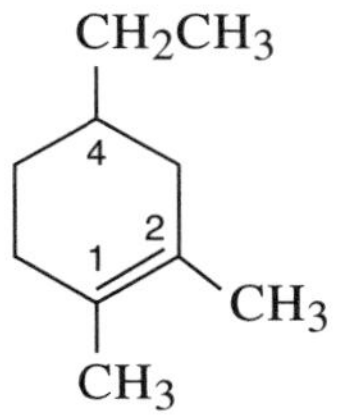 The positions 1 and 2 of the double bond were placed so that the branches had the lowest possible numbers (counterclockwise). The name is	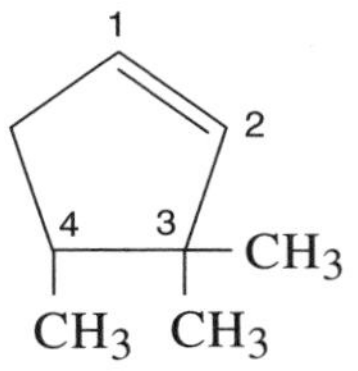 The positions 1 and 2 of the double bond were placed so that the branches had the lowest possible numbers (clockwise). The name is
4-ethyl-1,2-dimethylcyclohexene.	**3,3,4-trimethylcyclopentene.**

Problem 9. Name each of the following compounds:

a. $CH_3-\underset{CH_3}{\overset{Br}{\underset{|}{\overset{|}{C}}}}-CH=CH_2$

b. $\overset{CH_3}{\underset{H}{}}\!\!>C=C<\!\!\overset{CH_2-CH_3}{\underset{H}{}}$

c. $CH_3-CH=\overset{CH_2-CH_3}{\overset{|}{CH}}$

d. $CH_3-\underset{CH_2-CH_3}{\underset{|}{CH}}-CH=\overset{I}{\overset{|}{CH}}$

e. Cyclohexene ring with CH_2-CH_3 on one double-bond carbon and $CH_3-CH-CH_3$ on the adjacent ring carbon

f. Cyclooctene ring with CH_2-CH_3, CH_3, CH_3 substituents

Problem 10. Draw structures for the following alkenes:

a. 3-propylcyclopentene
b. 3,3,6-trimethylcyclohexene
c. *trans*-2-pentene
d. 3-methyl-1-butene
e. 3,4-dimethyl-2-pentene
f. 3-bromo-3-methyl-1-butene

Problem 11. Draw and name 5 isomers of C_4H_8.

C. Reactions of Alkenes

The following is a generalized addition reaction of an alkene:

$$-\overset{|}{C}=\overset{|}{C}- \quad + \quad A-B \longrightarrow -\underset{A}{\underset{|}{\overset{|}{C}}}-\underset{B}{\underset{|}{\overset{|}{C}}}-$$

[The double bond is broken and atoms A and B are added, one to each carbon.]

1. **Hydrogenation**

$$-\overset{|}{C}=\overset{|}{C}- \quad + \quad H_2 \xrightarrow{\text{catalyst}} -\underset{H}{\underset{|}{\overset{|}{C}}}-\underset{H}{\underset{|}{\overset{|}{C}}}-$$

In a hydrogenation reaction, an alkene reacts with H_2 in the presence of a catalyst (e.g., Ni, Pt, or Pd). The product is an alkane.

The following are examples of hydrogenation reactions.

$$CH_3-\underset{|}{\overset{H}{C}}=CH_2 + H_2 \xrightarrow{Ni} CH_3-\underset{H}{\underset{|}{CH}}-\underset{H}{\underset{|}{CH_2}}$$

$$\text{cyclohexene} + H_2 \xrightarrow{Pd} \text{cyclohexane (with H, H added)}$$

2. **Halogenation**

$$-\overset{|}{C}=\overset{|}{C}- + X_2 \longrightarrow -\underset{X}{\underset{|}{\overset{|}{C}}}-\underset{X}{\underset{|}{\overset{|}{C}}}-$$

In a halogenation reaction, an alkene reacts with a halogen (i.e., $X_2 = F_2$, Cl_2, Br_2, or I_2). The product is a dihalogenated hydrocarbon.

The following is an example of a halogenation reaction.

$$CH_3-CH=CH_2 + Br_2 \longrightarrow CH_3-\underset{Br}{\underset{|}{CH}}-\underset{Br}{\underset{|}{CH_2}}$$

$$\text{cyclohexene} + I_2 \longrightarrow \text{cyclohexane (with I, I added)}$$

3. **Hydrohalogenation**

$$-\overset{|}{C}=\overset{|}{C}- + H-X \longrightarrow -\underset{H}{\underset{|}{\overset{|}{C}}}-\underset{X}{\underset{|}{\overset{|}{C}}}-$$

In a hydrohalogenation reaction, an alkene reacts with a hydrogen halide (i.e., HX = HF, HCl, HBr, or HI). The product is a halogenated hydrocarbon (alkyl halide).

Unlike the two previous examples, hydrogenation and halogenation, where the two atoms added across a double bond are identical, the two atoms in a hydrogen halide are not the same. This affects the way that HX adds to a double bond that is not symmetrical. A symmetrical alkene has the same number of hydrogen atoms attached to each carbon atom of the double bond. For asymmetrical alkenes, **Markovnikov's rule** is used to decide how HX is added to the double bond. This rule basically states that the H is added to the carbon that has the most H's. For example,

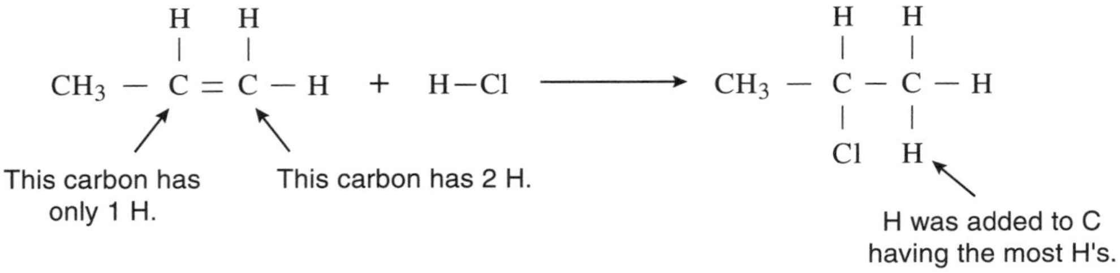

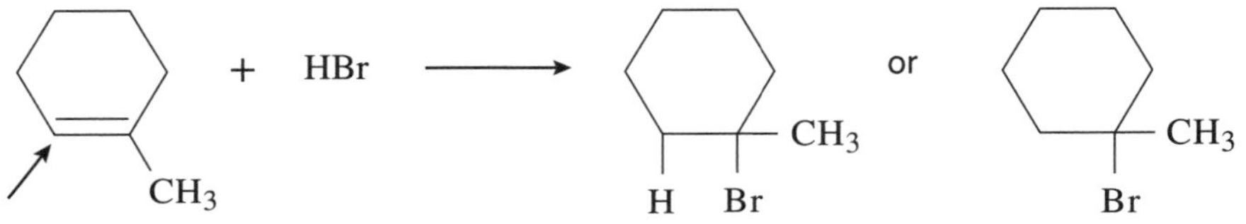

$$CH_3-\underset{\uparrow}{\overset{H}{\overset{|}{C}}}=\underset{\uparrow}{\overset{H}{\overset{|}{C}}}-H + H-Cl \longrightarrow CH_3-\underset{Cl}{\underset{|}{\overset{H}{\overset{|}{C}}}}-\underset{H}{\underset{|}{\overset{H}{\overset{|}{C}}}}-H$$

This carbon has only 1 H.

This carbon has 2 H.

H was added to C having the most H's.

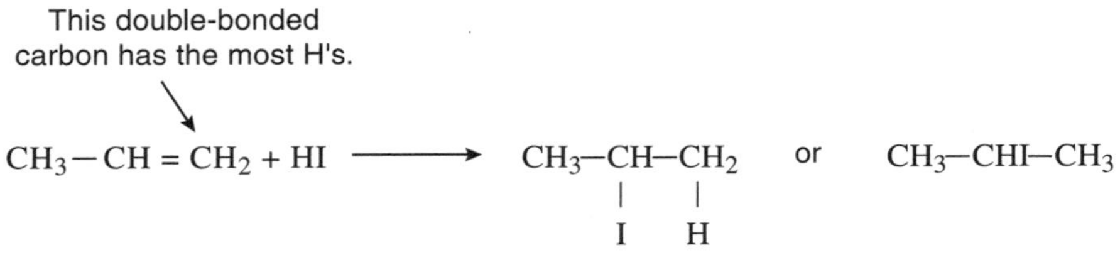

This double-bonded carbon has the most H's.

$$CH_3-CH=CH_2 + HI \longrightarrow CH_3-\underset{I}{\underset{|}{CH}}-\underset{H}{\underset{|}{CH_2}} \text{ or } CH_3-CHI-CH_3$$

1-methylcyclohexene + HBr ⟶ (cyclohexane ring with H and Br on adjacent carbons, CH_3 on the Br carbon) or (cyclohexane ring with Br and CH_3 on the same carbon)

4. **Hydration**

$$-\overset{|}{C}=\overset{|}{C}- + H-OH \xrightarrow{H^+} -\underset{H}{\underset{|}{\overset{|}{C}}}-\underset{OH}{\underset{|}{\overset{|}{C}}}-$$

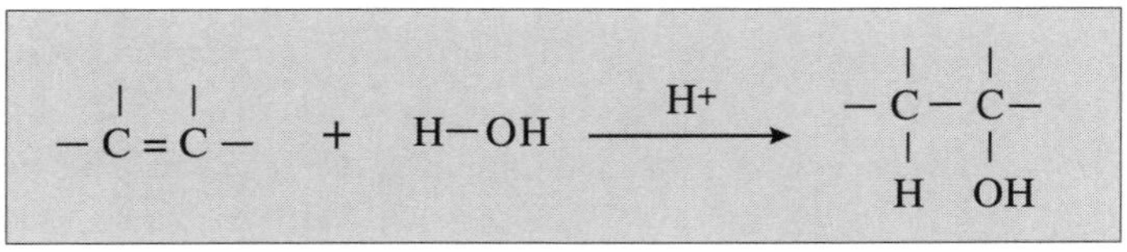

In a hydration reaction, an alkene reacts with water in the presence of an acid (H^+) catalyst. The product is an alcohol (an organic compound that contains a C−OH).

If the atoms that are being added are not identical, then Markovnikov's rule for asymmetrical alkenes must be used. For example,

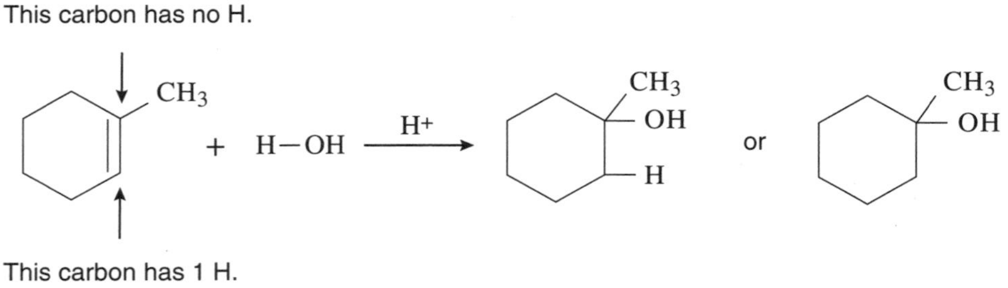

This carbon has no H.

1-methylcyclohexene (CH_3) + H−OH $\xrightarrow{H^+}$ (cyclohexane ring with CH_3 and OH on one carbon, H on the adjacent carbon) or (cyclohexane ring with CH_3 and OH on the same carbon)

This carbon has 1 H.

This double-bonded carbon has most H's

$$CH_3-CH=CH_2 + H-OH \xrightarrow{H^+} CH_3-\underset{\displaystyle OH}{CH}-\underset{\displaystyle H}{CH_2} \quad \text{or} \quad CH_3-\underset{\displaystyle OH}{CH}-CH_3$$

Problem 12. Complete and balance the following alkene addition reactions:

a. $CH_3-CH=CH_2 + H_2 \longrightarrow$

b. cyclohexene $+ \; H-OH \xrightarrow{H^+}$

c. 1-methylcyclopentene + $Br_2 \rightarrow$

d. 1-butene + HBr $\rightarrow$

e. 1- pentene + HI $\rightarrow$

IV. Alkynes

A. Nomenclature of Alkynes

The rules are basically the same as those for naming alkenes; however, the parent chain name is changed to end in "yne." If only one triple bond is present, the general molecular formula for alkynes is C_nH_{2n-2} where "n" represents the number of carbons.

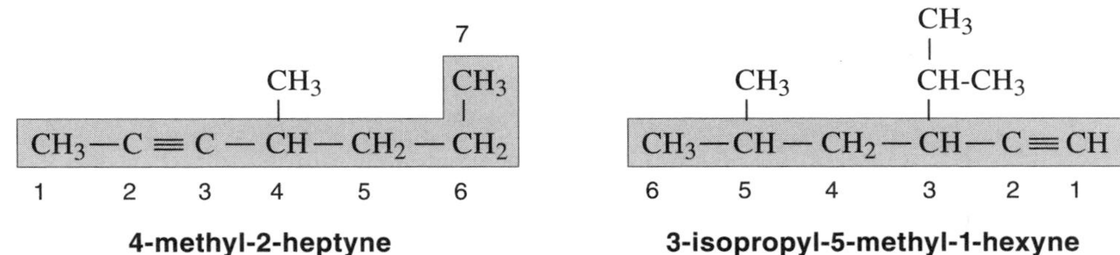

4-methyl-2-heptyne **3-isopropyl-5-methyl-1-hexyne**

Problem 13. Name each of the following alkynes:

a. $CH_3-\underset{\displaystyle CH_3}{\overset{\displaystyle Br}{C}}-C\equiv C-CH_3$

b. $CH_3-CH_2-CH_2-\underset{\displaystyle C\equiv CH}{CH}-CH_2-CH_3$

c. $CH_3-\underset{\displaystyle CH_2-CH_2-CH_3}{\overset{\displaystyle CH_2-CH_3}{C}}-C\equiv C-CH_3$

Problem 14. Draw structures for the following alkynes:

a. 3-hexyne
b. 3,3-dibromo-1-butyne
c. 4-bromo-3-chloro-1-hexyne
d. 4-isopropyl-4-methyl-2-heptyne

B. Hydrogenation of Alkynes

$$-C\equiv C- \quad + \quad 2\,H_2 \xrightarrow{\text{catalyst}} -\underset{\substack{|\\H}}{\overset{\substack{H\\|}}{C}}-\underset{\substack{|\\H}}{\overset{\substack{H\\|}}{C}}-$$

When an alkyne undergoes hydrogenation, the triple bond reacts with two molecules of H_2 in the presence of a catalyst (e.g., Ni, Pd, or Pt) to produce an alkane.

Problem 15. Name the products for the hydrogenation reactions for the following alkynes:

a. 3-hexyne + 2 $H_2 \rightarrow$
b. 1-butyne + 2 $H_2 \rightarrow$
c. 1-hexyne + 2 $H_2 \rightarrow$
d. 2-heptyne + 2 $H_2 \rightarrow$

V. Aromatic Hydrocarbons

Many aromatic hydrocarbons are derivatives of benzene, thus the parent name is often *benzene*. For example,

chlorobenzene

ethylbenzene

toluene

When two branches are present, the groups may be numbered to show their placement on the ring as previously discussed with other cyclic compounds. However, a common naming system is often used:

1,2-dichlorobenzene
o-dichlorobenzene

1-bromo-3-chlorobenzene
m-bromochlorobenzene

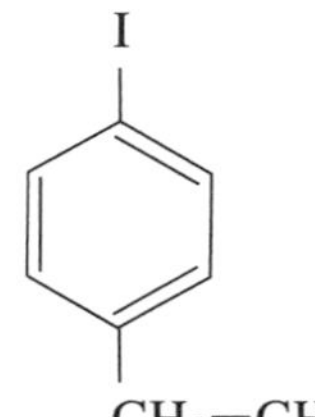

1-ethyl-4-iodobenzene
p-ethyliodobenzene

The prefix *ortho-* (abbreviated *o-*) is used when the two groups are in positions 1 and 2. The prefix *meta-* (abbreviated *m-*) is used when the two groups are in positions 1 and 3. The prefix *para-* (abbreviated *p-*) is used when the two groups are in positions 1 and 4.

Problem 16. Name each of the following aromatic compounds:

a. 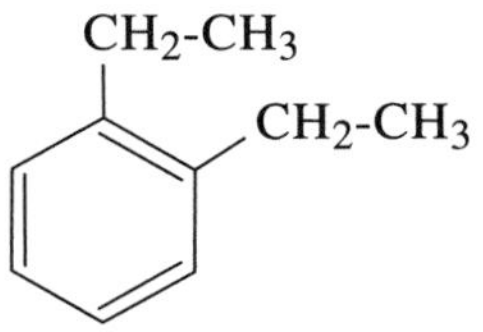 Benzene ring with CH_2-CH_3 and CH_2-CH_3 on adjacent carbons

b. 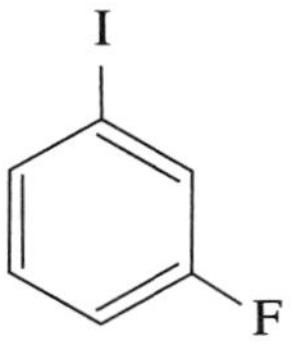 Benzene ring with I and F

c. 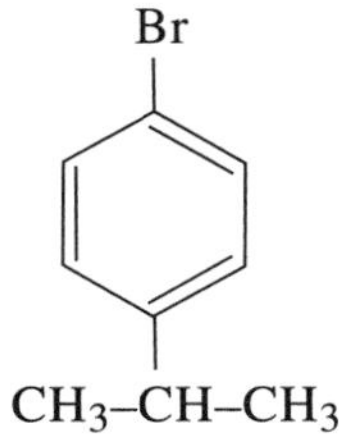 Benzene ring with Br and CH_3–CH–CH_3

ANSWERS

1. a. 2,2-dimethylhexane
   b. 1,2-diethyl-1-iodocyclohexane
   c. isopropylcyclopropane
   d. 4,6-dimethyl-4-propylnonane
   e. 3-bromo-3-methylheptane

2. a. Br, Br, Br (on cyclobutane ring)

   b. $H_3C - CH(CH_3) - CH_2 - CH_2 - CH_3$

   c. $CH_3 - CH_2 - CH_2 - CH(CH_2CH_3) - CH_2 - CH_3$

   d. $(CH_3)_2HC$ — cyclohexane — CH_2CH_3

   e. $CH_3 - C(CH_3)_2 - CH(Br) - CH_3$

   f. cyclopentane — $CH_2 - CH_2 - CH_3$

   Molecular formulas: a. $C_4H_5Br_3$ b. C_6H_{14} c. C_8H_{18} d. $C_{11}H_{22}$ e. $C_6H_{13}Br$ f. C_8H_{16}

3. Five isomers: hexane, 2-methylpentane, 3-methylpentane, 2,3-dimethylbutane and 2,2-dimethylbutane

4. Four isomers: 1-chlorobutane, 2-chlorobutane, 1-chloro-2-methylpropane, 2-chloro-2-methylpropane

5. a. $C_3H_8 + 5\ O_2 \longrightarrow 3\ CO_2 + 4\ H_2O$

   b. $C_5H_{12} + 8\ O_2 \longrightarrow 5\ CO_2 + 6\ H_2O$

   c. $C_7H_{16} + 11\ O_2 \longrightarrow 7\ CO_2 + 8\ H_2O$

   d. $C_7H_{16} + 11\ O_2 \longrightarrow 7\ CO_2 + 8\ H_2O$

6. a. $CH_3 - CH_3 + Br_2 \xrightarrow{UV} CH_3 - CH_2 - Br + HBr$

   b. cyclohexane $+\ Br_2 \xrightarrow{UV}$ cyclohexyl—Br $+\ HBr$

   c. $CH_3 - Cl \xrightarrow{UV} Cl - CH_2 - Cl + HCl$

   d. cyclopentane $+\ Cl_2 \xrightarrow{UV}$ cyclopentyl—Cl $+\ HCl$

7. a. no *cis-trans* isomers

   b. *cis*-1,2-dibromoethene *trans*-1,2-dibromoethene

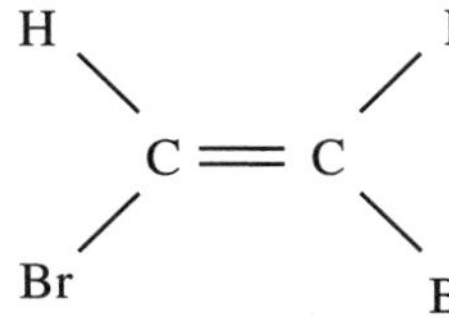

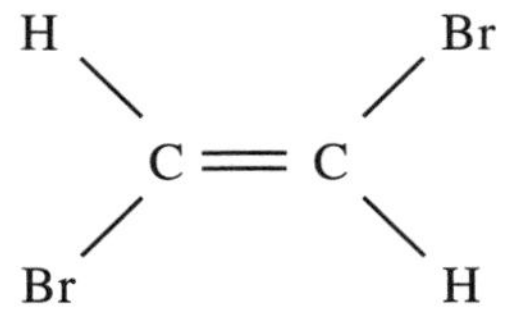

H, Br / C = C \ H, Br (cis: H and H on the same side; Br and Br on the same side)

H, Br / C = C \ Br, H (trans: H and Br top; Br and H bottom)

8.

cis-3-hexene: CH_3-CH_2 and CH_2-CH_3 on the same side of C = C, H and H on the other side

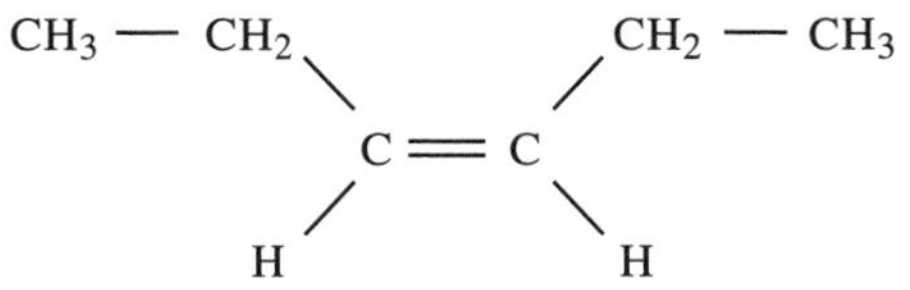

trans-3-hexene: CH_3-CH_2 and H on top of C = C; H and CH_2-CH_3 on the bottom

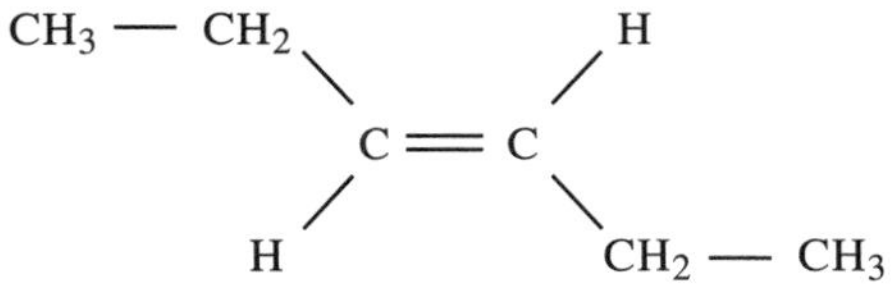

9. a. 3-bromo-3-methyl-1-butene b. cis-2-pentene

   c. 2-pentene d. 1-iodo-3-methyl-1-pentene

   e. 1-ethyl-3-isopropylcyclohexene f. 8-ethyl-3,4-dimethylcyclooctene

10. a. (cyclopentene ring)—$CH_2CH_2CH_3$

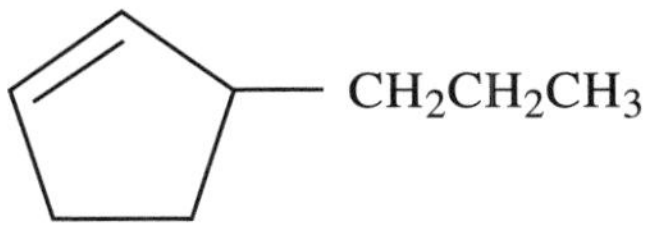

    b. H_3C—(cyclohexene ring)—(CH_3)(CH_3)

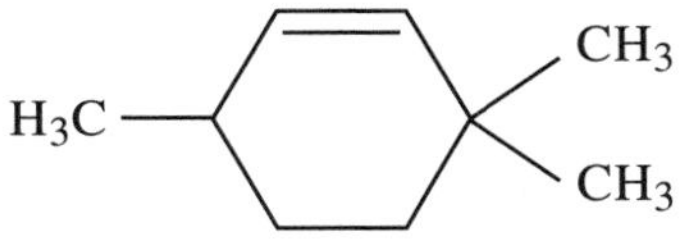

    c. CH_3, H / C = C \ H, CH_2-CH_3

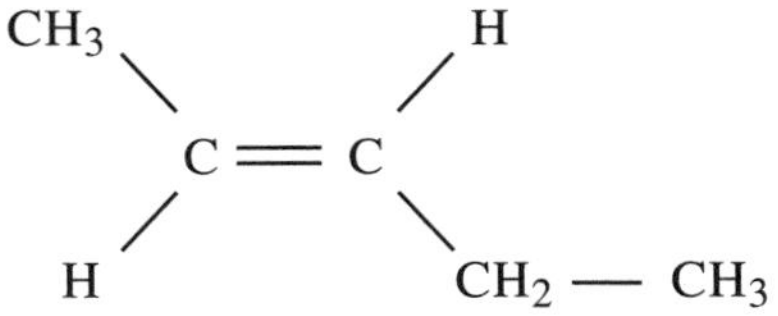

    d. $H_2C=CH-CH(CH_3)-CH_3$

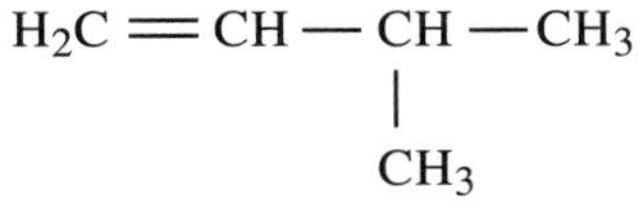

    e. $CH_3-CH(CH_3)-C(CH_3)=CH-CH_3$

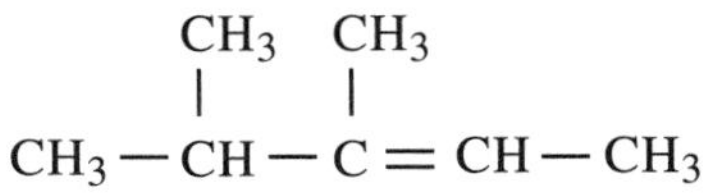

    f. $CH_3-C(CH_3)(Br)-CH=CH_2$

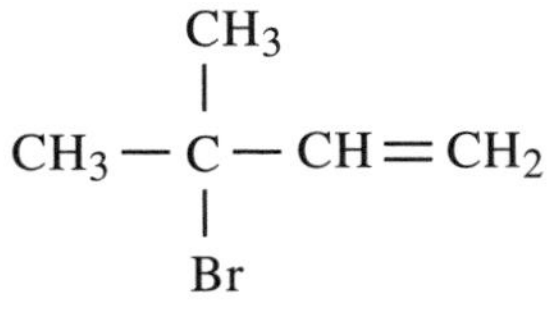

11.

cis-2-butene

$$\begin{array}{ccc} CH_3 & & CH_3 \\ & C=C & \\ H & & H \end{array}$$

trans-2-butene

$$\begin{array}{ccc} CH_3 & & H \\ & C=C & \\ H & & CH_3 \end{array}$$

1-butene

$CH_3-CH_2-CH=CH_2$

2-methylpropene:

$$\begin{array}{c} \quad\;\; CH_3 \\ \quad\;\; | \\ CH_3-C=CH_2 \end{array}$$

cyclobutane:

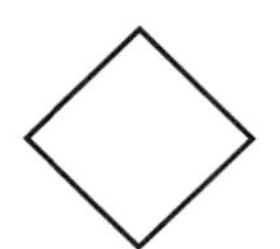

methylcyclopropane:

CH_3

12. a. $CH_3-CH=CH_2 + H_2 \xrightarrow{Ni} CH_3-CH_2-CH_3$

b. $+ \; H_2O \xrightarrow{H^+}$ OH

c. 1,2-dibromo-1-methylcyclopentane

d. 2-bromobutane

e. 2-iodopentane

13. a. 4-bromo-4-methyl-2-pentyne b. 3-ethyl-1-hexyne

c. 4-ethyl-4-methyl-2-heptyne

14. a. $CH_3-CH_2-C\equiv C-CH_2-CH_3$

b. $$\begin{array}{c} \qquad\qquad\quad Br \\ \qquad\qquad\quad | \\ HC\equiv C-C-CH_3 \\ \qquad\qquad\quad | \\ \qquad\qquad\quad Br \end{array}$$

c. $$\begin{array}{c} \qquad\quad Cl \quad\;\; Br \\ \qquad\quad | \qquad | \\ HC\equiv C-CH-CH-CH_2-CH_3 \end{array}$$

d. $$\begin{array}{c} \qquad\qquad\qquad\quad CH_3 \\ \qquad\qquad\qquad\quad | \\ H_3C-C\equiv C-C-CH_2-CH_2-CH_3 \\ \qquad\qquad\qquad\quad | \\ \qquad\qquad\quad H_3C-CH-CH_3 \end{array}$$

15. a. hexane b. butane c. hexane d. heptane

16. a. *o*-diethylbenzene or 1,2-diethylbenzene

b. *m*-fluoroiodobenzene or 1-fluoro-3-iodobenzene

c. *p*-bromoisopropylbenzene or 1-bromo-4-isopropylbenzene

Hydrocarbons

Assignment 9

Name

Student Number

Date Instructor

1. Write names for the following organic compounds.

a. 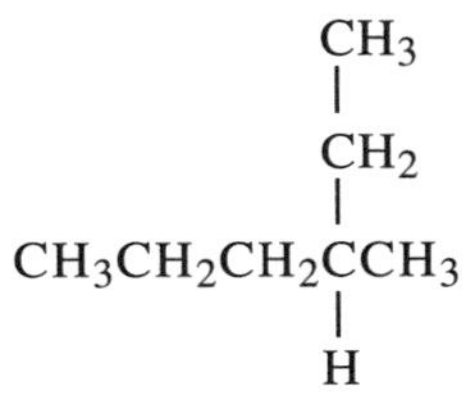
CH_3
CH_2
$CH_3CH_2CH_2CCH_3$
H

b. 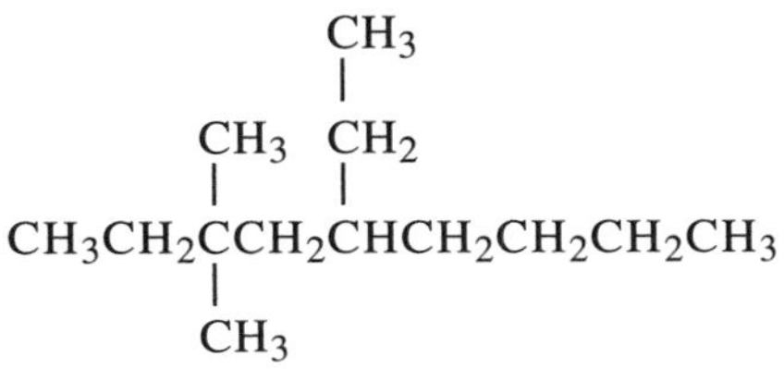
CH_3
CH_3 CH_2
$CH_3CH_2CCH_2CHCH_2CH_2CH_2CH_3$
CH_3

c. 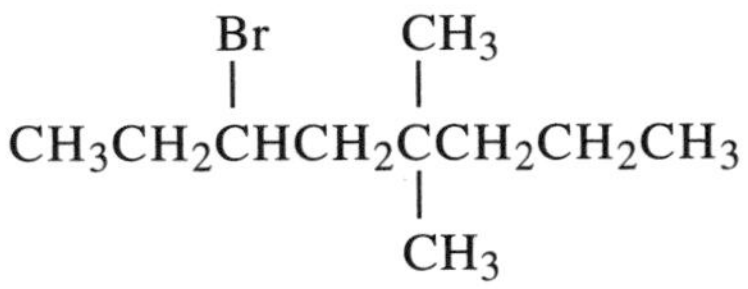
Br CH_3
$CH_3CH_2CHCH_2CCH_2CH_2CH_3$
CH_3

d. 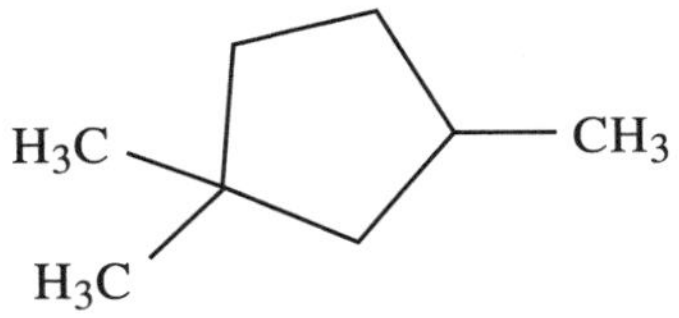
H_3C CH_3
H_3C

e. 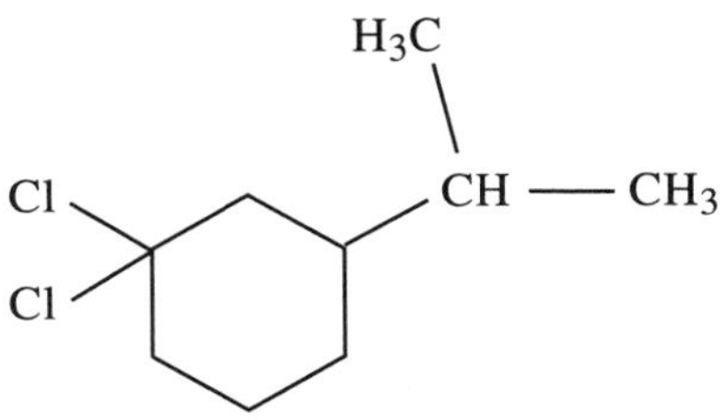
H_3C
Cl CH — CH_3
Cl

f. 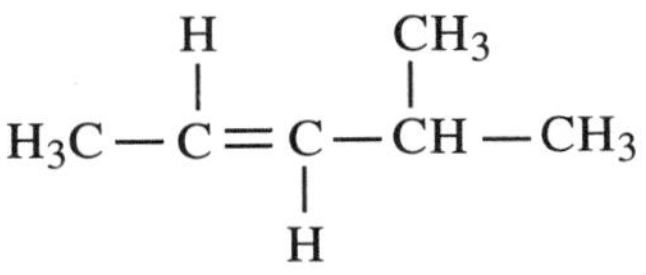
H CH_3
$H_3C-C=C-CH-CH_3$
H

g. 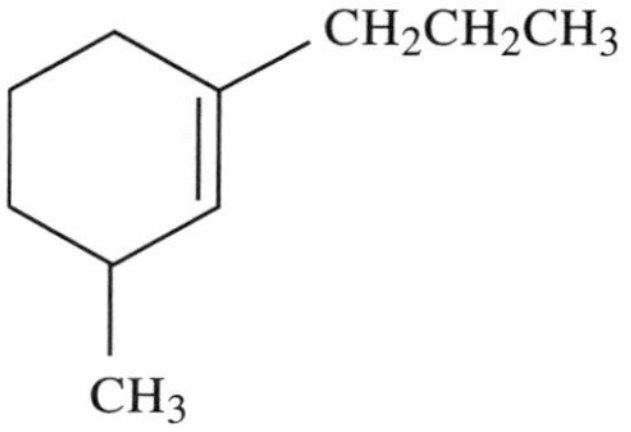 $CH_2CH_2CH_3$ CH_3

h. 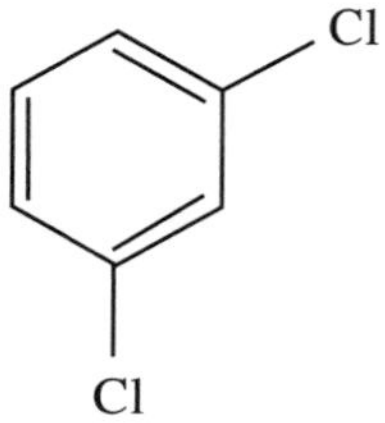 Cl Cl

i. 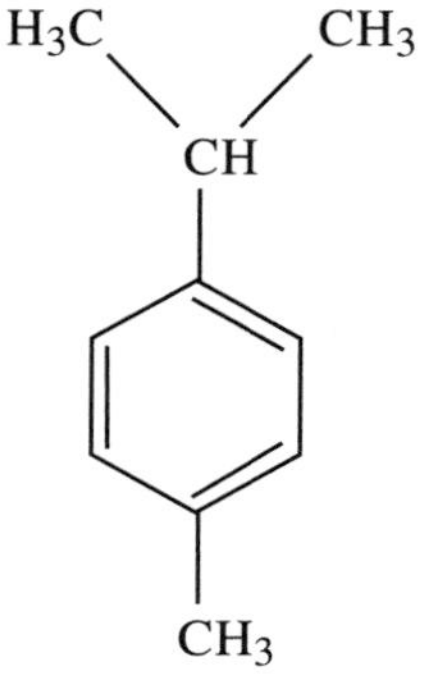 H_3C CH_3 CH CH_3

j. 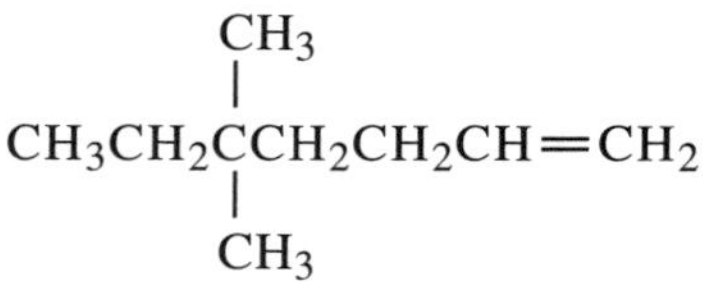 $CH_3CH_2C(CH_3)_2CH_2CH_2CH{=}CH_2$

$$\begin{array}{c} CH_3 \\ | \\ CH_3CH_2CCH_2CH_2CH{=}CH_2 \\ | \\ CH_3 \end{array}$$

k. 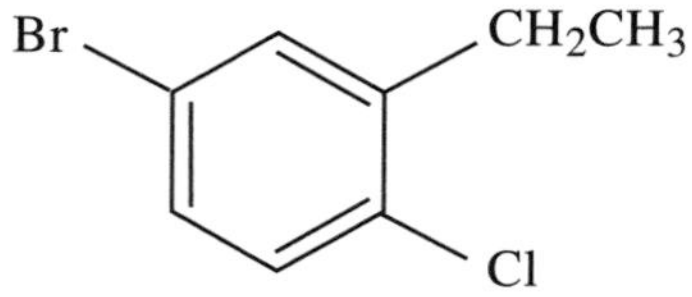 Br CH_2CH_3 Cl

l. 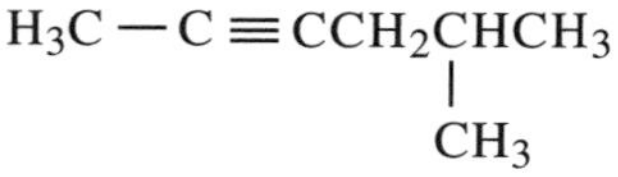 $H_3C-C\equiv CCH_2CHCH_3$ (with CH_3 on the CH)

$$\begin{array}{l} H_3C-C\equiv CCH_2\underset{\displaystyle CH_3}{\underset{|}{C}}HCH_3 \end{array}$$

m. 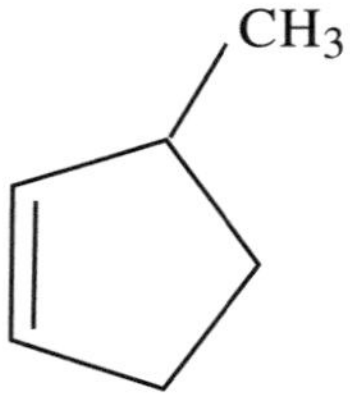 CH_3

n. 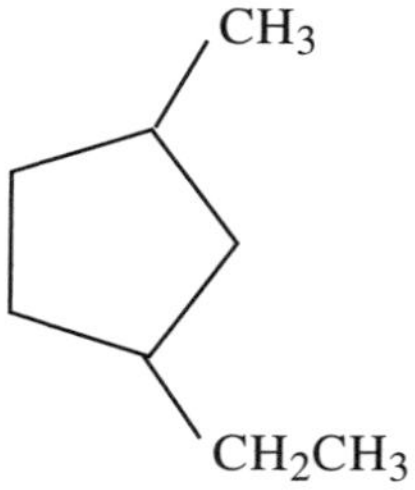 CH_3 CH_2CH_3

o. 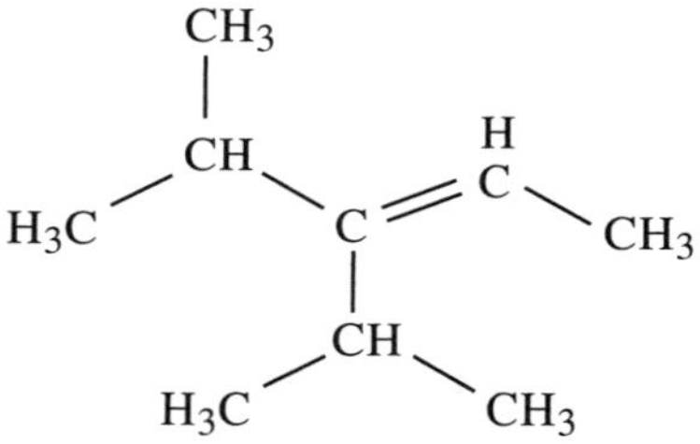 CH_3 CH H_3C C H C CH_3 CH H_3C CH_3

2. Draw structures for each of the following compounds.

a. 2,3,5-trimethyloctane

b. *o*-dibromobenzene

c. 3-ethyl-1-isopropyl-1-methylcyclohexane

d. *trans*-5,6,7-trimethyl-3-nonene

e. 2,2-dimethyl-4-propyldecane

f. 2,4,7-trichloro-1-heptene

g. 3,4,4-trimethylcyclohexene

h. 3-ethyl-1-hexyne

i. 1,2,4-trimethylbenzene

j. p-bromoisopropylbenzene

k. 4-chloro-1-butyne

l. *cis*-1-chloro-2,3-dimethyl-2-pentene

3. Which of the following is NOT a structural isomer of the others?

 ____________ Why? ________________________________

1. 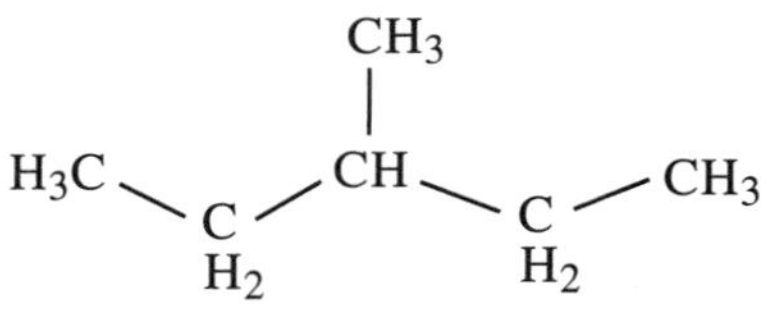 CH_3 | $H_3C \diagdown C(H_2) \diagup CH \diagdown C(H_2) \diagup CH_3$

2. CH_3 | $H_3C \diagup CH \diagdown C(H_2) \diagup C(H_2) \diagdown CH_3$

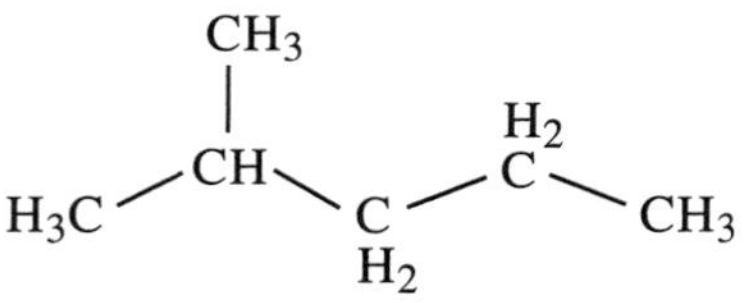

3. $H_3C \diagup C(H_2) \diagdown CH \diagup CH_3$ | CH_3

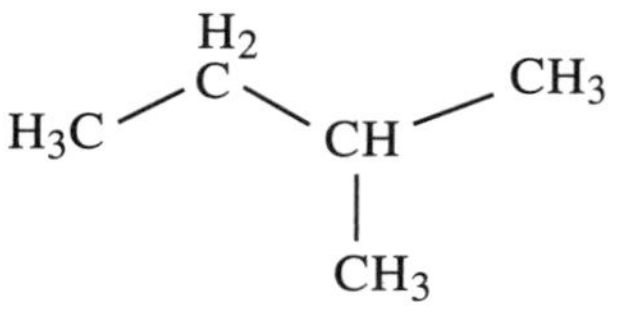

4. 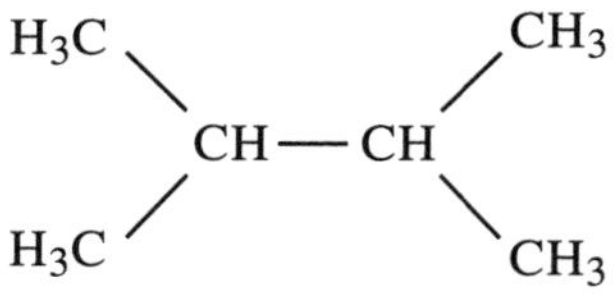 H_3C, H_3C \ / $CH — CH$ / \ CH_3, CH_3

5. 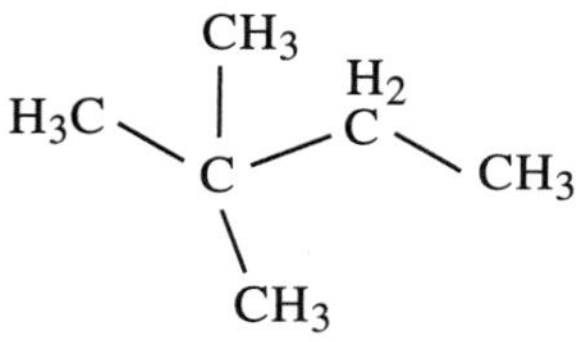 CH_3 | $H_3C \diagdown C \diagup C(H_2) \diagdown CH_3$ | CH_3

4. Draw the structures of and write names of 4 structural isomers with the molecular formula $C_5H_{11}Cl$.

5. Draw the structures and write the names of 4 isomers with the molecular formula C_4H_8.

6. One of the following compounds exhibits *cis-trans* isomerism. Which is it? Draw the structures for the *cis* and *trans* isomers.

2-methyl-1-pentene　　2-methyl-2-pentene　　3-methyl-2-pentene

7. The reaction of H_2O with $CH_3CH = CHCH_2CH_3$ is ________________ type of reaction.

8. Draw structures for the organic products of the following reactions.

a. (cyclohexane) $+ Br_2 \xrightarrow{\text{light}}$

b. $CH_3CH_3 + Cl_2 \xrightarrow{\text{light}}$

c. $CH_2{=}CHCH_2CH_3 + HI \longrightarrow$

d. (cyclopentene) $+ Br_2 \longrightarrow$

e. $CH_2{=}CHCH_2CH_2CH_3 + HBr \longrightarrow$

f.

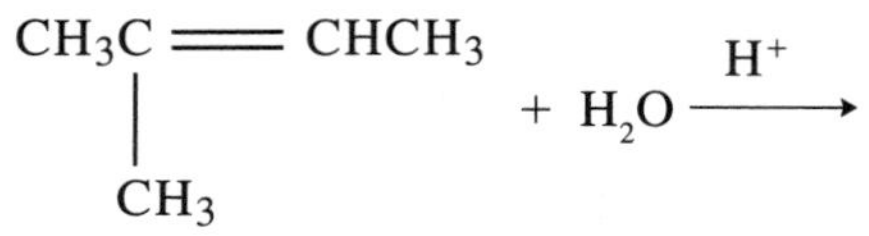

$$\begin{array}{l} CH_3C = CHCH_3 \\ \quad\;| \\ \quad CH_3 \end{array} + H_2O \xrightarrow{H^+}$$

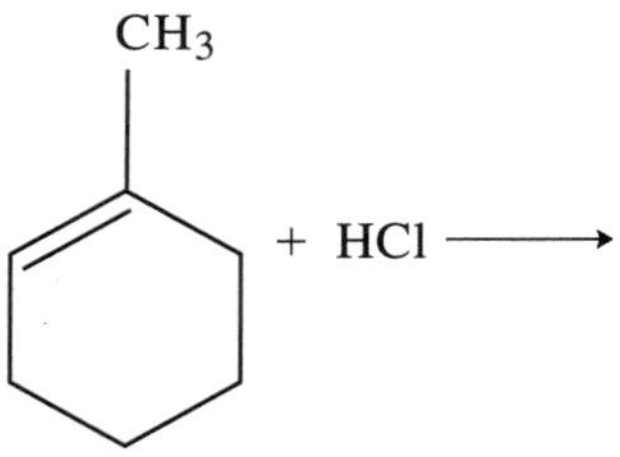

g.

$$\text{(1-methylcyclohexene: ring with } CH_3 \text{ on double-bonded carbon)} + HCl \longrightarrow$$

h.

$$\begin{array}{l} \qquad\quad CH_3 \\ \qquad\quad\;| \\ CH_2 = CCH_2CH_3 \end{array} + H_2 \xrightarrow{Pt}$$

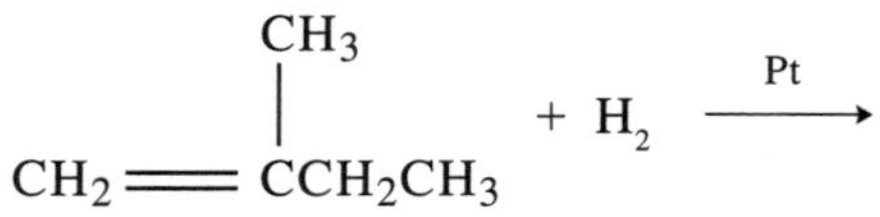

9. Draw reactants and products for the reaction between cyclobutane and chlorine. Also give the name of the product.

10. Draw reactants and products for the reaction between 1-methylcyclopentene and water. Also give the name of the product.

10

Alcohols, Aldehydes, and Ketones

There is a great variety of oxygen-containing organic compounds. Among the earliest known is the fermentation product of grapes and other fruit. The compound produced is one of the simplest alcohols, ethanol. Other oxygen-containing compounds include ethers—one of the earliest anesthetics—and aldehydes and ketones.

I. Alcohols

Alcohols are a family of organic compounds that have a hydroxyl (−OH) group attached to a carbon atom. Some examples of common alcohols are ethanol (drinking alcohol), isopropyl alcohol (rubbing alcohol), and glycerol (found in some fats and hand lotions).

$CH_3 - CH_2 - OH$ — ethanol

$CH_3 - \underset{\displaystyle OH}{\underset{|}{CH}} - CH_3$ — isopropyl alcohol

$\underset{\displaystyle OH}{\underset{|}{CH_2}} - \underset{\displaystyle OH}{\underset{|}{CH}} - \underset{\displaystyle OH}{\underset{|}{CH_2}}$ — glycerol

Alcohols are classified as primary (1°), secondary (2°), or tertiary (3°), depending on how many carbon atoms are *directly* attached to the carbon atom with the −OH group. For primary alcohols, the carbon with the OH group has only one other carbon bonded to it. When two carbons are directly attached to the carbon with the OH group, this is classified as a secondary alcohol. In the case of tertiary alcohols, the carbon attached to the OH group has three carbons bonded to it and no hydrogen atoms remain bonded to the carbon. The following are examples of these three types of alcohols:

Primary (1°)	**Secondary (2°)**	**Tertiary (3°)**
H above, H below: $-C-C-OH$	H above, OH below: $-C-C-C-$	$-C-$ above, $-C-$ below: $-C-C-OH$
CH_3-CH_2-OH	$CH_3-CH(OH)-CH_3$	$CH_3-C(CH_3)(OH)-CH_3$
1° Alcohol Carbon with OH has only 1 neighbor carbon	2° Alcohol Carbon with OH has 2 neighbor carbons	3° Alcohol Carbon with OH has 3 neighbor carbons

Alcohols are very different from inorganic bases. In alcohols, the hydroxyl group (–OH) is attached to a carbon atom by a **covalent** bond; this is different from the hydroxide ion (OH^-) which is a negatively charged particle found in bases. In bases, this hydroxide ion is held to a positive ion by an **ionic** bond.

Problem 1. Identify the following alcohols as primary, secondary, or tertiary alcohols:

a. $CH_3-CH_2-CH(OH)-CH_2-C(CH_3)_2-CH_3$

b. cyclohexane ring bearing CH_2-CH_3, OH, and CH_2-CH_3 on the same carbon

c. $CH_3-CH-CH_3$ attached to a cyclopropane ring bearing OH

d. $CH_3-CH_2-CH_2-C(CH_3)(CH_2-CH_2-CH_3)-CH_2-CH(CH_2-OH)-CH_2-CH_2-CH_3$

e. $CH_3-CH_2-CH_2-CH_2-C(CH_3)(CH_2-CH_3)-OH$

II. Nomenclature for Alcohols

1. Straight Chain Alcohols

To name the alcohol, first find the parent chain, the longest continuous chain that contains the –OH group. Second, number this parent chain so that the –OH group gets the lowest possible number and this number is part of the name. To name the parent chain, change the final "e" ending of the alkane to "ol."

As with other compounds: denote the location and name of each branch in alphabetical order, and if there are two or more of the same branch, use prefixes (di, tri, tetra).

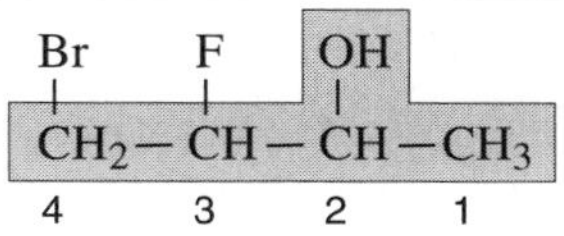 The chain is numbered so that the −OH gets priority (position #2 on a four carbon chain); the name of the parent chain is thus 2-butanol. Since bromo comes alphabetically before fluoro it is written first. The name is: **4-bromo-3-fluoro-2-butanol.**	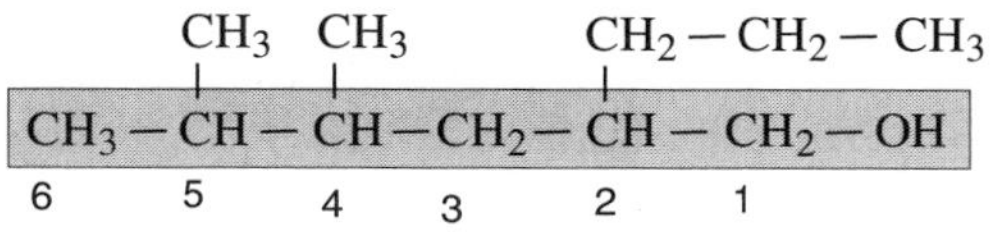 The longest chain which contains the −OH is shown (1-hexanol). There are two methyl branches at 4,5 (the prefix *di-* is used) and a propyl branch at 2. The name is: **4,5-dimethyl-2-propyl-1-hexanol.**

2. **Cyclic Alcohols**

   The parent chain will be the cyclic structure. The name will have the prefix "cyclo" and will end in "ol." The ring should be numbered so that the −OH gets position #1 and the branches have the lowest possible numbers. Since the −OH is in position #1, its location is not included in front of the parent name.

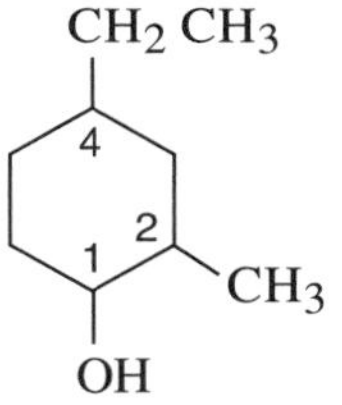 −OH is in position #1 and then the ring is numbered (counterclockwise) so that the branches get the lowest possible numbers. The name is: **4-ethyl-2-methylcyclohexanol.**	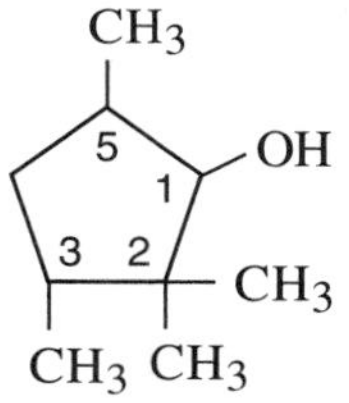 −OH must be position #1 and then the ring is numbered (clockwise) so that the branches have the lowest possible numbers. The name is: **2,2,3,5-tetramethylcyclopentanol.**

Problem 2. Name the following compounds:

a. 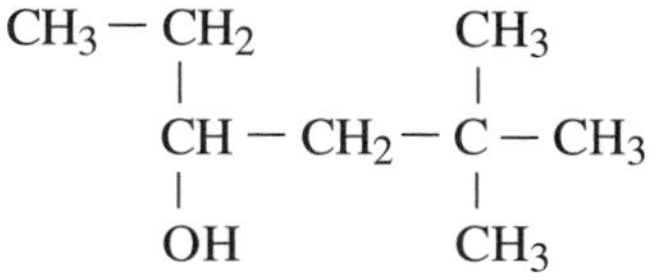

b. 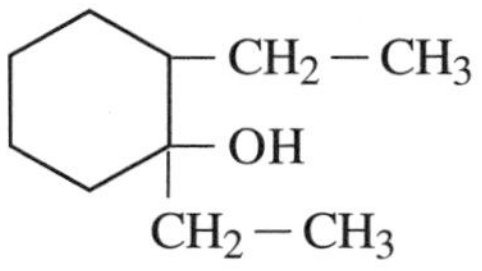

c. 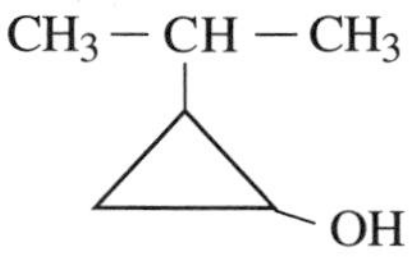

d. 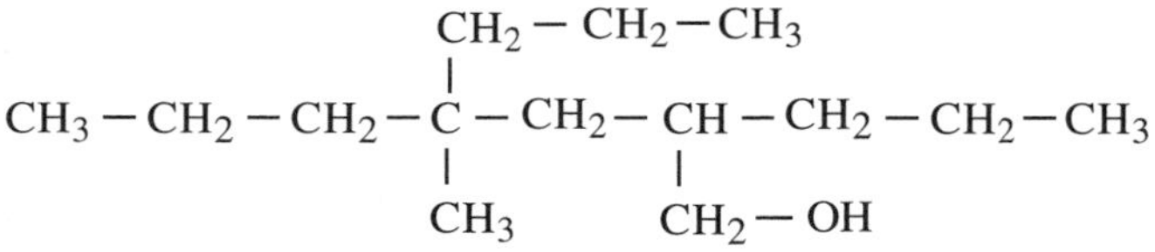

$$\text{e. } CH_3-CH_2-CH_2-CH_2-\overset{\displaystyle CH_3}{\underset{\displaystyle CH_2-CH_3}{\overset{|}{\underset{|}{C}}}}-OH$$

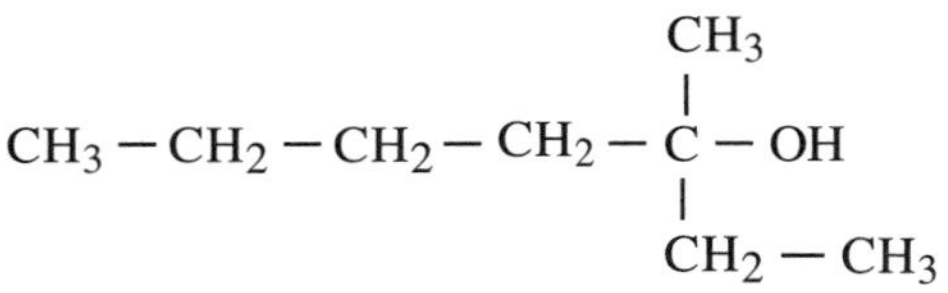

Problem 3. Draw structures for the following compounds:

a. 2,3-dibromocyclopentanol

b. 2-methyl-2-pentanol

c. 4-ethyl-3-hexanol

d. 4-ethyl-1-propylcyclohexanol

e. 3-bromo-2,2-dimethyl-1-butanol

f. 2-isopropylcyclopentanol

III. Reactions of Alcohols

A. High Temperature Dehydration

$$-\underset{H}{\overset{|}{\underset{|}{C}}}-\underset{OH}{\overset{|}{\underset{|}{C}}}- \xrightarrow[\text{high temp}]{H^+} -\overset{|}{C}=\overset{|}{C}- \quad + \quad H_2O$$

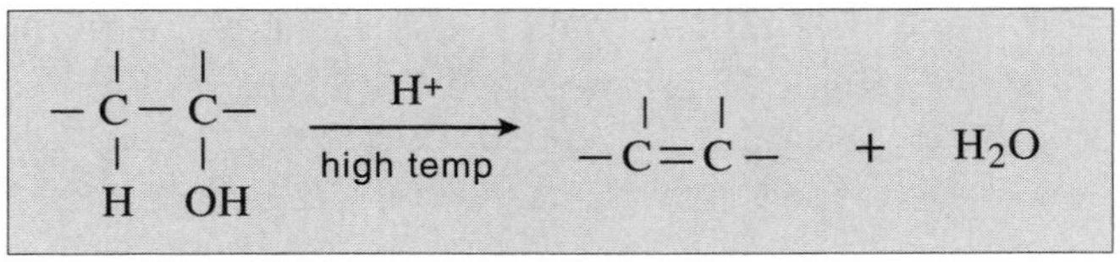

When an alcohol is heated in the presence of an acid (e.g., sulfuric or phosphoric acid) the products obtained are an alkene and water. This reaction is the reverse of an alkene reacting with water under acidic conditions to produce an alcohol. For example, ethylene is prepared by heating ethanol with concentrated sulfuric acid at 180°C.

Example A: High temperature dehydrations.

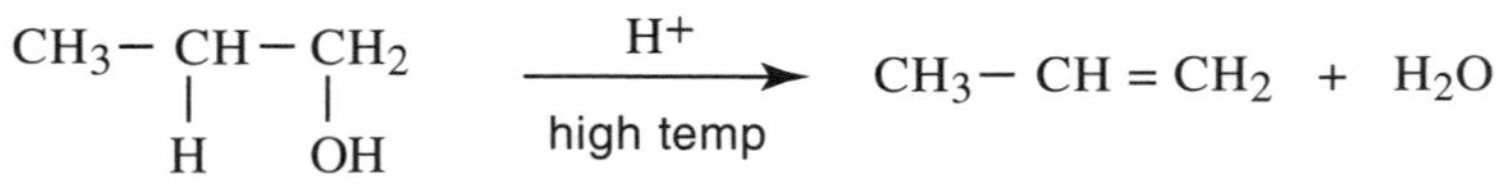

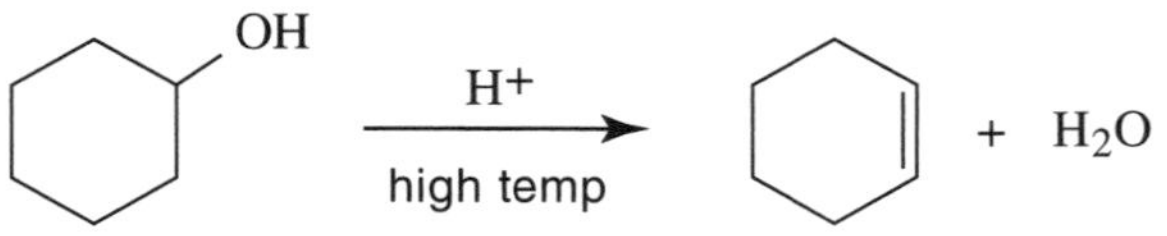

$$CH_3-\underset{H}{\underset{|}{CH}}-\underset{OH}{\underset{|}{CH_2}} \xrightarrow[\text{high temp}]{H^+} CH_3-CH=CH_2 \ + \ H_2O$$

$$\text{cyclohexanol (ring–OH)} \xrightarrow[\text{high temp}]{H^+} \text{cyclohexene} \ + \ H_2O$$

Problem 4. Give the products from the following high temperature dehydration reactions:

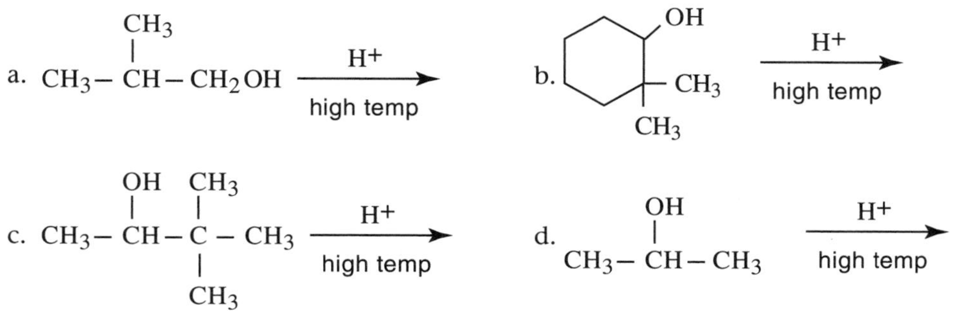

a. $CH_3-\underset{|}{\overset{CH_3}{CH}}-CH_2OH \xrightarrow[\text{high temp}]{H^+}$

b. 1-methylcyclohexanol ring bearing OH and CH_3 on one carbon and CH_3 on the adjacent carbon $\xrightarrow[\text{high temp}]{H^+}$

c. $CH_3-\overset{OH}{\overset{|}{CH}}-\underset{CH_3}{\underset{|}{\overset{CH_3}{\overset{|}{C}}}}-CH_3 \xrightarrow[\text{high temp}]{H^+}$

d. $CH_3-\overset{OH}{\overset{|}{CH}}-CH_3 \xrightarrow[\text{high temp}]{H^+}$

B. Low Temperature Dehydration (OPTIONAL)

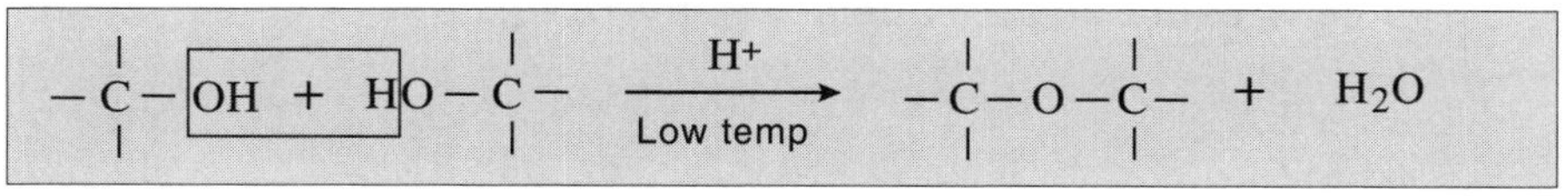

$$-\underset{|}{\overset{|}{C}}-\boxed{OH\ +\ H}O-\underset{|}{\overset{|}{C}}- \xrightarrow[\text{Low temp}]{H^+} -\underset{|}{\overset{|}{C}}-O-\underset{|}{\overset{|}{C}}- \ +\ H_2O$$

When a primary alcohol reacts (at low temperature) with an acid (e.g., sulfuric or phosphoric acid) the products obtained are an ether and water. The ether is obtained from the removal of an $-OH$ from one alcohol molecule and the H from the hydroxyl group of another alcohol molecule. For example, diethyl ether is prepared by heating a mixture of ethanol and sulfuric acid at 140 °C.

Example B: Low temperature dehydrations.

$$2CH_3-CH_2-OH \xrightarrow[\text{low temp}]{H^+} CH_3-CH_2-\boxed{OH\ \ H}O-CH_2-CH_3 \longrightarrow CH_3-CH_2-O-CH_2-CH_3+HOH$$

Problem 5. Give the organic product for the following low temperature dehydration reactions:

a. $2\ CH_3-OH \xrightarrow[\text{low temp}]{H^+}$

b. $2\ CH_3-CH_2-OH \xrightarrow[\text{low temp}]{H^+}$

C. Oxidation

The result of oxidation in organic compounds is the removal of two hydrogen atoms or the addition of one oxygen atom to the compound.

The product that is obtained when an alcohol is treated with an oxidizing agent (such as potassium permanganate, $KMnO_4$, or potassium dichromate, $K_2Cr_2O_7$) depends on whether the alcohol is 1°, 2°, or 3°. The symbol used for an oxidizing agent is [O].

1. Oxidation of 1° Alcohols

$$-\overset{|}{\underset{|}{C}}-\overset{OH}{\underset{H}{C}}-H \xrightarrow[\text{mild}]{[O]} -\overset{|}{\underset{|}{C}}-\overset{O}{\overset{\|}{C}}-H \xrightarrow{[O]} -\overset{|}{\underset{|}{C}}-\overset{O}{\overset{\|}{C}}-OH$$

aldehyde   carboxylic acid

Mild **oxidation of a primary alcohol yields an aldehyde.** An **aldehyde can then be further oxidized to yield a carboxylic acid**. Vigorous oxidation of a primary alcohol yields a carboxylic acid directly. The aldehyde product is obtained when the H from the −OH and an H from the carbon bearing the −OH are removed, consequently forming a double bond between the alcohol carbon and the oxygen.

Example C: Oxidation reaction of a 1° alcohol yielding both the aldehyde and carboxylic acid products.

$$CH_3-\overset{OH}{\underset{H}{C}}-H \xrightarrow[\text{mild}]{[O]} CH_3-\overset{O}{\overset{\|}{C}}-H \xrightarrow{[O]} CH_3-\overset{O}{\overset{\|}{C}}-OH$$

2. Oxidation of 2° Alcohols

$$-\overset{|}{\underset{|}{C}}-\overset{OH}{\underset{H}{C}}-\overset{|}{\underset{|}{C}}- \xrightarrow[\text{mild}]{[O]} -\overset{|}{\underset{|}{C}}-\overset{O}{\overset{\|}{C}}-\overset{|}{\underset{|}{C}}-$$

ketone

Oxidation of a 2° alcohol yields a ketone. The ketone is obtained when the H from the −OH and an H from the carbon bearing the −OH are removed, consequently forming a double bond between the alcohol carbon and the oxygen. Ketones cannot be further oxidized.

Example D: Oxidation reactions of 2° alcohols

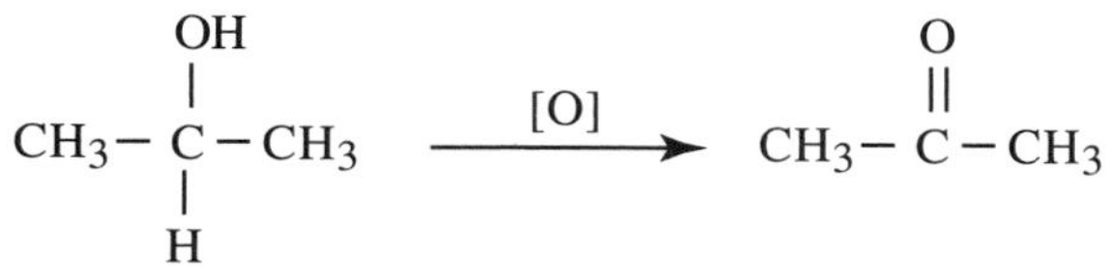

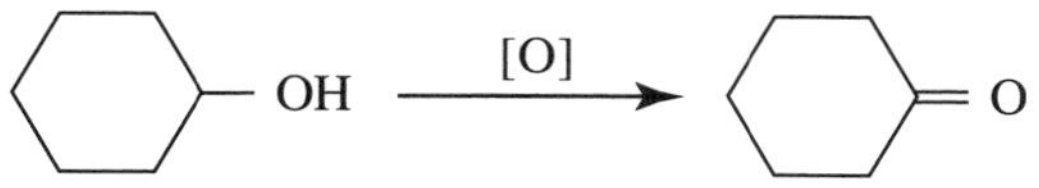

$$CH_3-\underset{\displaystyle H}{\overset{\displaystyle OH}{C}}-CH_3 \xrightarrow{[O]} CH_3-\overset{\displaystyle O}{\overset{\|}{C}}-CH_3$$

Cyclohexanol (cyclohexane ring–OH) $\xrightarrow{[O]}$ cyclohexanone (cyclohexane ring=O)

3. **Oxidation of 3° Alcohols**

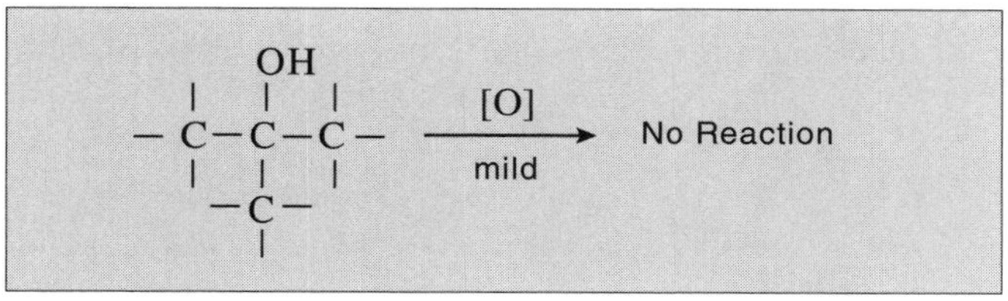

$$-\overset{|}{\underset{|}{C}}-\overset{OH}{\underset{-\underset{|}{C}-}{C}}-\overset{|}{\underset{|}{C}}- \xrightarrow[\text{mild}]{[O]} \text{No Reaction}$$

Tertiary alcohols cannot undergo oxidation because there is no hydrogen atom to remove from the carbon bonded to the –OH.

Problem 6. Complete the following oxidations:

a. 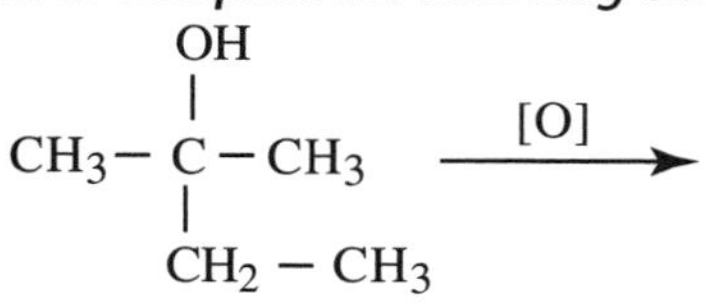 $CH_3-\underset{\displaystyle CH_2-CH_3}{\overset{\displaystyle OH}{C}}-CH_3 \xrightarrow{[O]}$

b. $CH_3-\overset{\displaystyle OH}{CH}-CH_2-CH_3 \xrightarrow{[O]}$

c. $CH_3-\underset{\displaystyle CH_3}{CH}-CH_2OH \xrightarrow{[O]}$

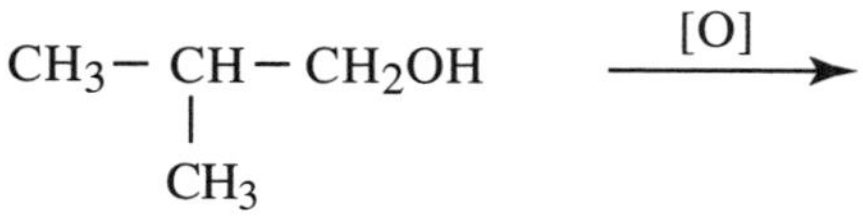

d. 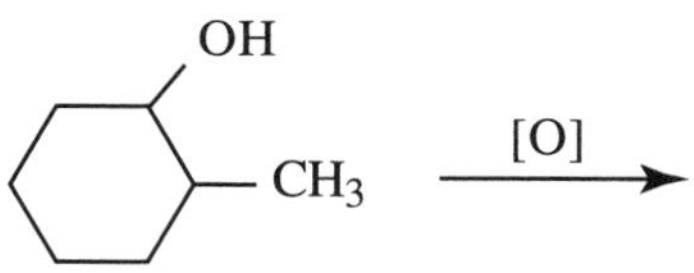 2-methylcyclohexanol (cyclohexane ring with OH and adjacent CH_3) $\xrightarrow{[O]}$

e. 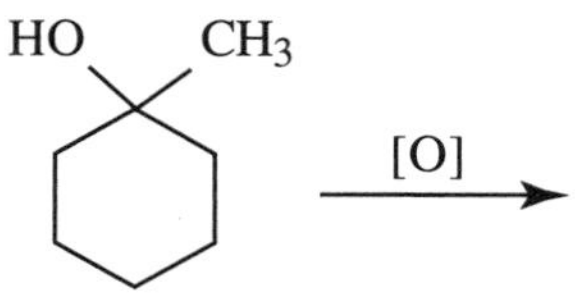 1-methylcyclohexanol (cyclohexane ring with HO and CH_3 on the same carbon) $\xrightarrow{[O]}$

f. 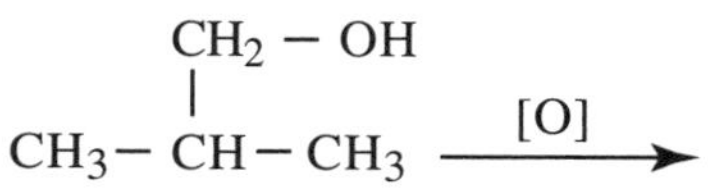 $CH_3-\overset{\displaystyle CH_2-OH}{CH}-CH_3 \xrightarrow{[O]}$

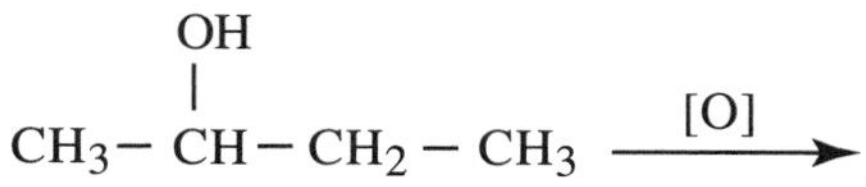

IV. Ethers

Ethers are organic compounds in which an oxygen atom bonds to two alkyl groups (i.e., methyl group, ethyl group, etc.). By far the most important ether is diethyl ether (often just called ether), which in the past was used as an anesthetic.

$$CH_3-CH_2-O-CH_2-CH_3$$

diethyl ether

V. Aldehydes and Ketones

Both aldehydes and ketones contain a carbon-oxygen double bond (C=O) known as a **carbonyl group**. The difference between an aldehyde and a ketone is that in an aldehyde the carbonyl group is at the end of the chain, and in a ketone the carbonyl group is in a secondary carbon (i.e., the carbonyl group of a ketone has no hydrogens).

H neighbor

$$CH_3-\overset{\overset{\large O}{\|}}{C}-H \qquad\qquad CH_3-\overset{\overset{\large O}{\|}}{C}-CH_3$$

Aldehyde Ketone

[NOTE: The carbonyl carbon of an aldehyde is many times abbreviated as −CHO. Do not confuse this symbol with that of an alcohol.]

A. Nomenclature for Aldehydes (OPTIONAL)

The longest continuous chain must contain the carbonyl group (C=O) and its name will end in "al."

The carbonyl carbon of an aldehyde is always given first position. Hence there is no need to specify its location in front of the parent name.

As with other compounds: denote the location and name of each branch in alphabetical order and if there are two or more of the same branch use prefixes (di, tri, tetra).

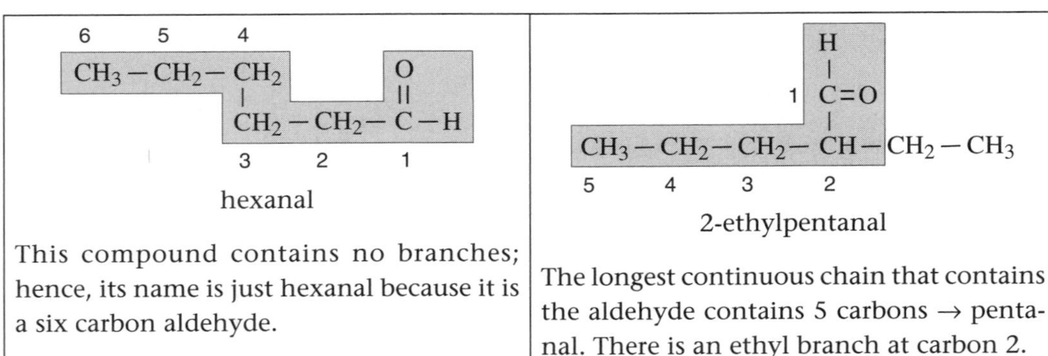

hexanal	2-ethylpentanal
This compound contains no branches; hence, its name is just hexanal because it is a six carbon aldehyde.	The longest continuous chain that contains the aldehyde contains 5 carbons → pentanal. There is an ethyl branch at carbon 2.

B. Nomenclature for Ketones (OPTIONAL)

1. **Straight Chain Ketones**

The longest carbon chain must contain the carbonyl (C=O) group. The parent name will end in "one."

Number the parent chain in the direction such that the carbonyl carbon gets the lowest possible number. Place the number for the location of the carbonyl carbon in front of the parent name.

As with other compounds: denote the location and name of each branch in alphabetical order, and if there are two or more of the same branch, use prefixes.

Br F O (C=O) $CH_2-CH-C-CH_3$ 4 3 2 1	CH_3 CH_3 O (C=O) $CH_3-CH-CH-CH_2-C-CH_3$ 6 5 4 3 2 1
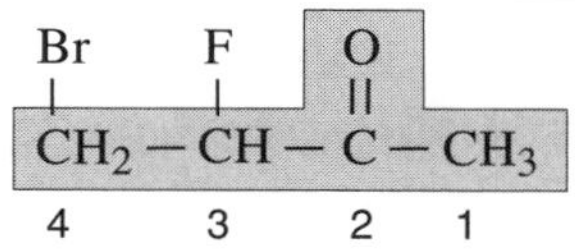 The way the chain is numbered, the carbonyl carbon gets the lowest number, position #2, on a four carbon chain; the name of the parent chain is 2-butanone. Since bromo comes alphabetically before fluoro it is written first. The name is:	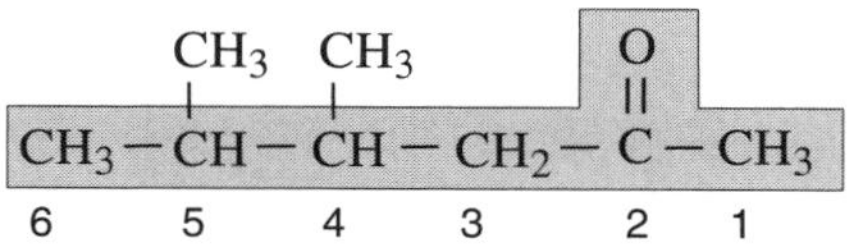 The way the chain is numbered, the carbonyl carbon gets the lowest number, position #2, on a six carbon chain; the name of the parent chain is 2-hexanone. There are two methyl branches at carbons 4 and 5; hence the use of the prefix *di-*. The name is:
4-bromo-3-fluorobutanone.	**4,5-dimethyl-2-hexanone.**

2. **Cyclic Ketones**

The parent chain will be the cyclic structure and its name will start with "cyclo" and will end in "one." Number the ring so that the carbonyl carbon gets first position and so that branches have the lowest possible number. Since the carbonyl carbon is in position #1, its location is not included in front of the parent name. Branch location and names are as previously discussed.

CH_2CH_3 (position 4), CH_3 (position 2), O (position 1)	CH_3 (position 5), O (position 1), I (position 2), CH_3 (position 3)
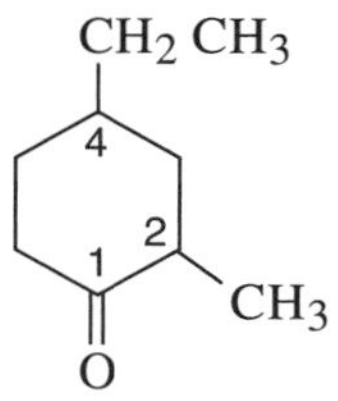 The carbonyl carbon gets position #1 and then the ring is numbered (counterclockwise) to give the branches the lowest possible number. Ethyl comes before methyl. The name is:	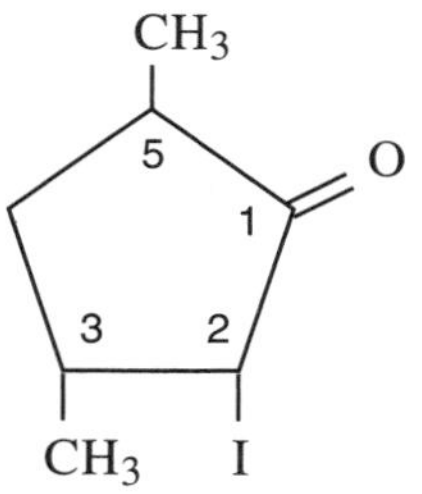 The carbonyl carbon gets position #1 and then the ring is numbered (clockwise) to give the branches the lowest possible number. Iodo comes before dimethyl (prefixes are not used when alphabetizing). The name is:
4-ethyl-2-methylcyclohexanone.	**2-iodo-3,5-dimethylcyclopentanone.**

Problem 7. Name the following compounds:

a. 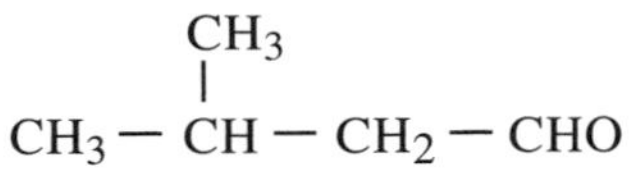 $CH_3-CH(CH_3)-CH_2-CHO$

b. 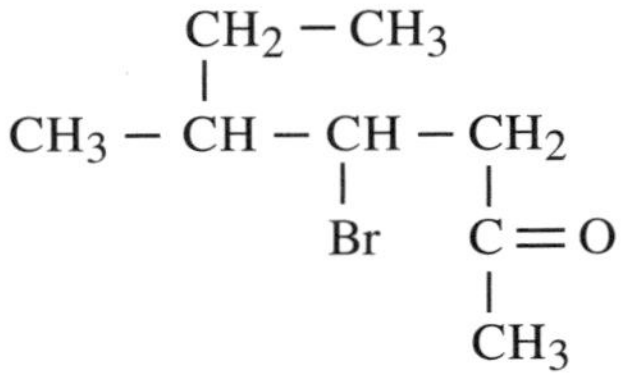 $CH_3-CH(CH_2-CH_3)-CH(Br)-CH_2-C(=O)-CH_3$

c. (cyclopentanone ring, C=O, with ring substituent) $CH_2-CH_2-CH_3$

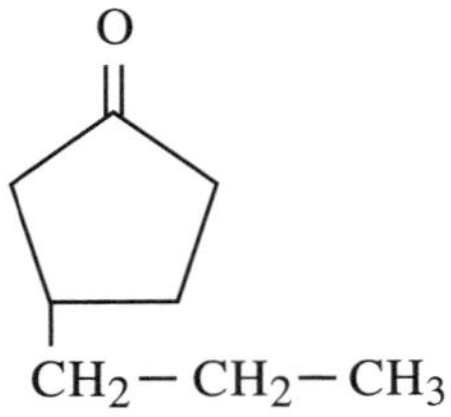

d. 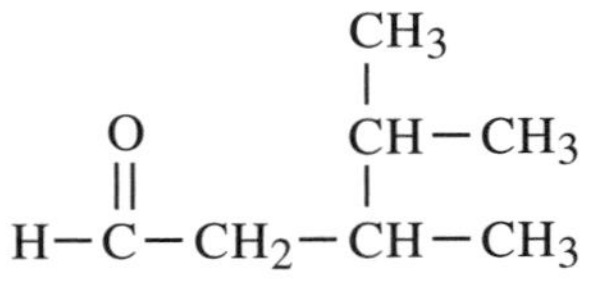 $H-C(=O)-CH_2-CH(CH_3)-CH(CH_3)-CH_3$

e. 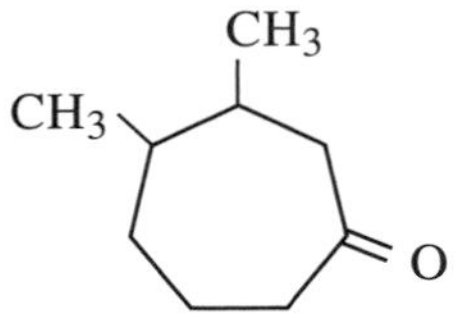 (cycloheptanone ring, =O, with two ring substituents) CH_3, CH_3

f. 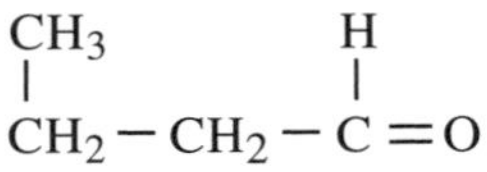 $CH_2(CH_3)-CH_2-C(H)=O$

Problem 8. Draw structures for the following compounds:

a. 3-methyl-2-pentanone

b. 3,3-dibromo-2-pentanone

c. cyclohexanone

d. 3,3-dimethylbutanal

e. 2,4-diethylcyclohexanone

f. 4-methylheptanal

VI. Reactions of Aldehydes and Ketones

A. Oxidation Reactions

1. **Oxidation of Aldehydes**

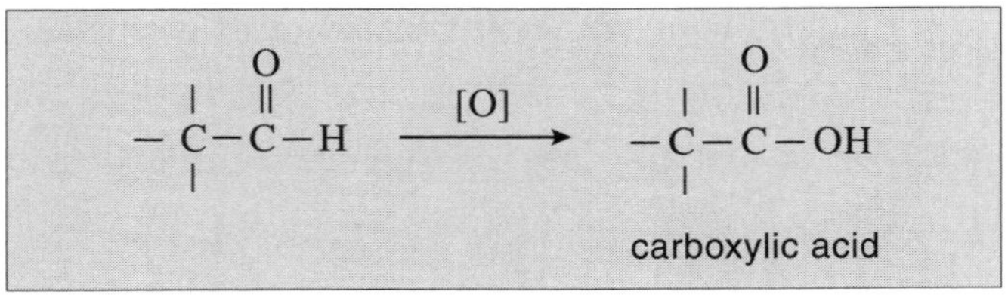

$$-\overset{|}{\underset{|}{C}}-\overset{O}{\overset{\|}{C}}-H \xrightarrow{[O]} -\overset{|}{\underset{|}{C}}-\overset{O}{\overset{\|}{C}}-OH$$

carboxylic acid

As previously mentioned, aldehydes can be oxidized to carboxylic acids. For example,

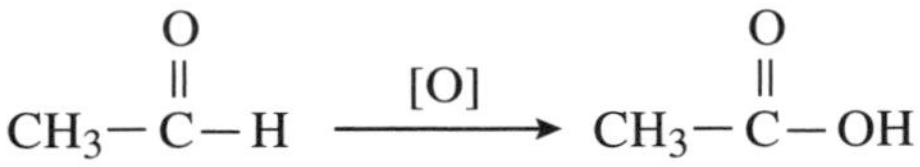

$$CH_3-\overset{O}{\overset{\|}{C}}-H \xrightarrow{[O]} CH_3-\overset{O}{\overset{\|}{C}}-OH$$

2. **Oxidation of Ketones**

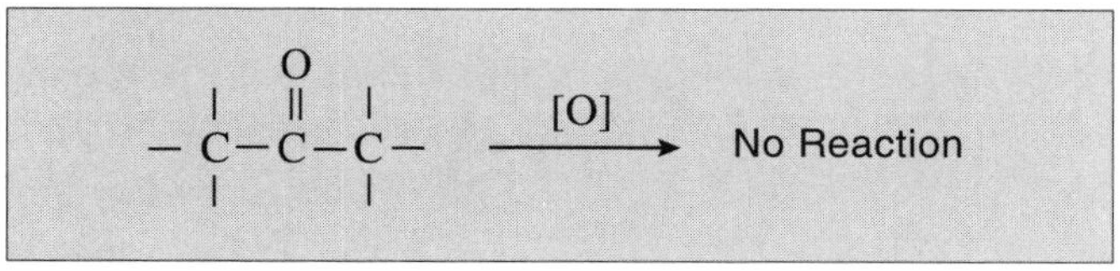

$$-\overset{|}{\underset{|}{C}}-\overset{\overset{O}{\|}}{C}-\overset{|}{\underset{|}{C}}- \xrightarrow{[O]} \text{No Reaction}$$

Ketones are resistant to oxidation.

Problem 9. Complete the following oxidation reactions:

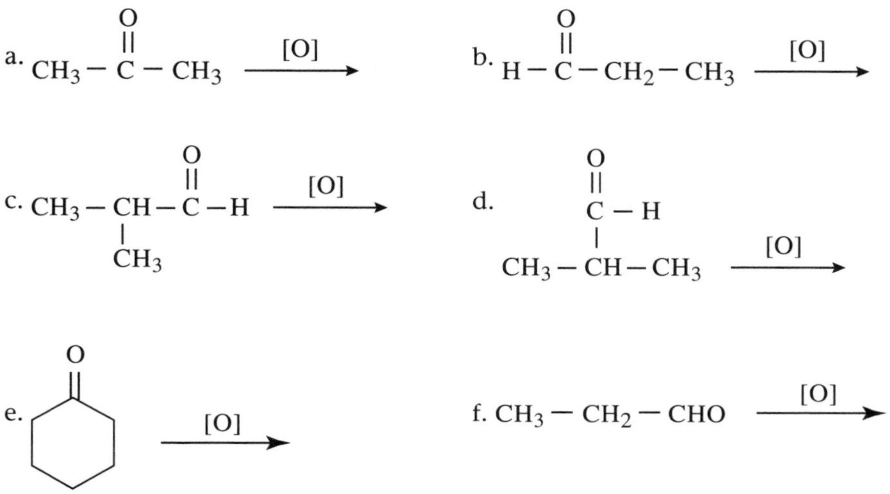

a. $CH_3-\overset{\overset{O}{\|}}{C}-CH_3 \xrightarrow{[O]}$

b. $H-\overset{\overset{O}{\|}}{C}-CH_2-CH_3 \xrightarrow{[O]}$

c. $CH_3-\underset{\underset{CH_3}{|}}{CH}-\overset{\overset{O}{\|}}{C}-H \xrightarrow{[O]}$

d. $CH_3-\overset{\overset{\overset{O}{\|}}{\overset{C-H}{|}}}{CH}-CH_3 \xrightarrow{[O]}$

e. cyclohexanone $\xrightarrow{[O]}$

f. $CH_3-CH_2-CHO \xrightarrow{[O]}$

B. Reduction Reactions

The symbol used for a reducing agent is [H]. A reducing agent such as H_2 in the presence of a catalyst such as Ni or Pt can be used. **A reduction reaction is the reverse of an oxidation.**

1. **Reduction of Aldehydes**

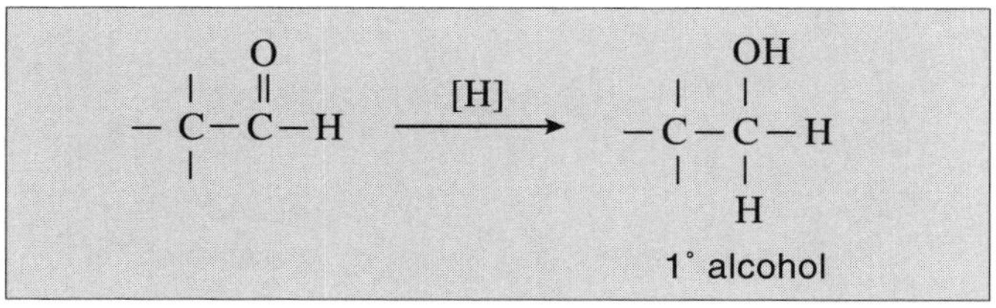

$$-\overset{|}{\underset{|}{C}}-\overset{\overset{O}{\|}}{C}-H \xrightarrow{[H]} -\overset{|}{\underset{|}{C}}-\overset{\overset{OH}{|}}{\underset{\underset{H}{|}}{C}}-H$$

1° alcohol

Since oxidation is the reverse of reduction, when a 1° alcohol is oxidized, two hydrogen atoms are removed to form an aldehyde; therefore, when an aldehyde is reduced, two hydrogen atoms are added to produce a 1° alcohol.

The following is an example of a reduction reaction of an aldehyde.

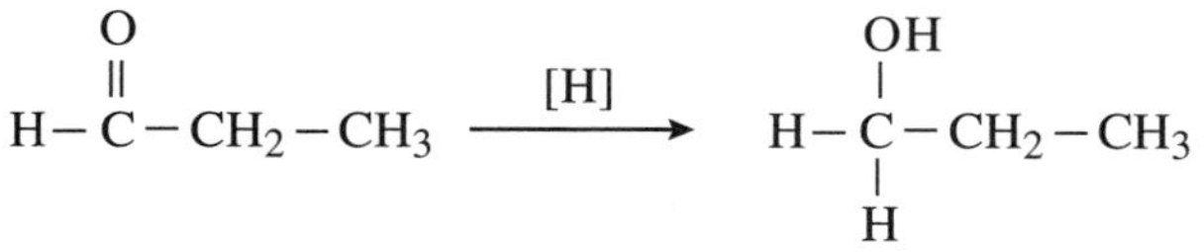

$$H-\overset{\overset{O}{\|}}{C}-CH_2-CH_3 \xrightarrow{[H]} H-\overset{\overset{OH}{|}}{\underset{\underset{H}{|}}{C}}-CH_2-CH_3$$

2. **Reduction of Ketones**

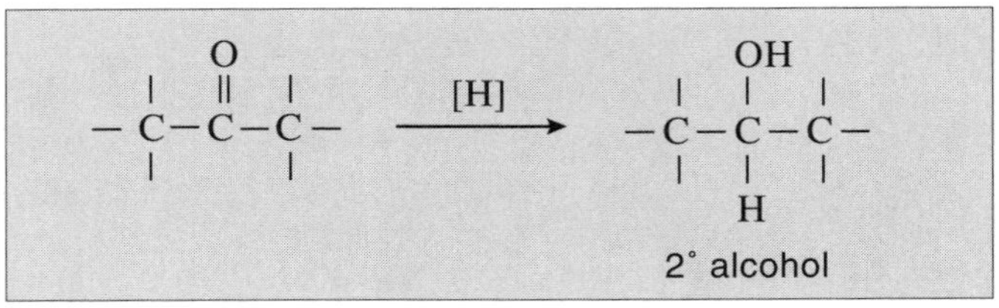

$$-\overset{|}{\underset{|}{C}}-\overset{\overset{O}{\|}}{C}-\overset{|}{\underset{|}{C}}- \xrightarrow{[H]} -\overset{|}{\underset{|}{C}}-\overset{\overset{OH}{|}}{\underset{\underset{H}{|}}{C}}-\overset{|}{\underset{|}{C}}-$$

2° alcohol

The same reaction occurs for a ketone. The product of this reaction, however, is a 2° alcohol.

The following is an example of a reduction reaction of a ketone.

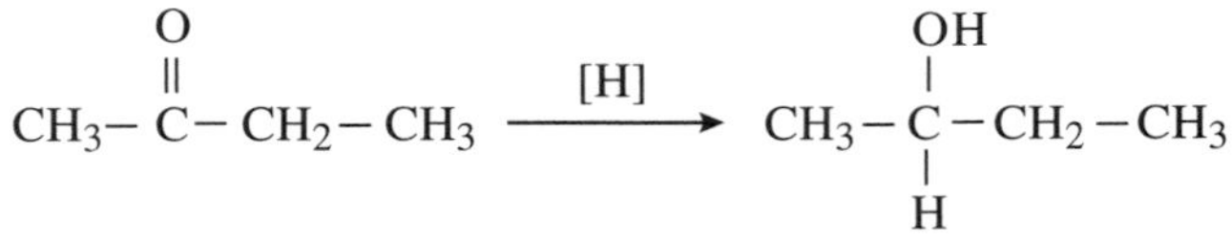

$$CH_3-\overset{\overset{O}{\|}}{C}-CH_2-CH_3 \xrightarrow{[H]} CH_3-\overset{\overset{OH}{|}}{\underset{\underset{H}{|}}{C}}-CH_2-CH_3$$

Problem 10. Complete the following reduction reactions:

a. 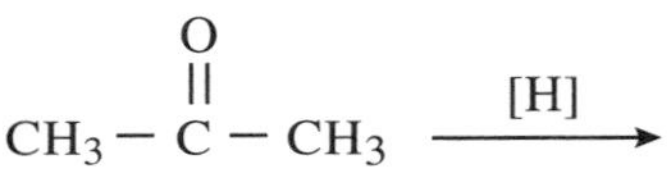 $CH_3-\overset{\overset{O}{\|}}{C}-CH_3 \xrightarrow{[H]}$

b. 2-methylcyclopentanone (cyclopentane ring with CH_3 and $=O$) $\xrightarrow{[H]}$

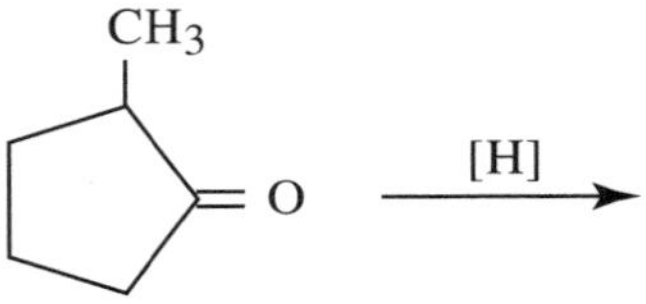

c. $CH_3-\underset{\underset{CH_3}{|}}{CH}-\overset{\overset{O}{\|}}{C}-H \xrightarrow{[H]}$

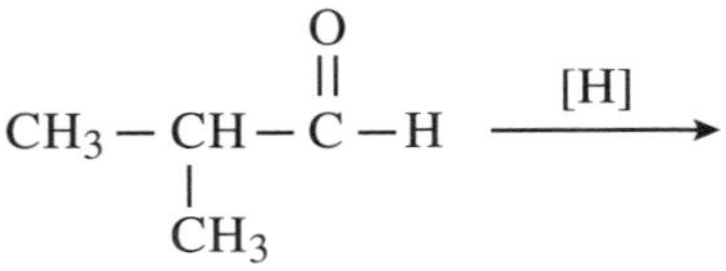

d. 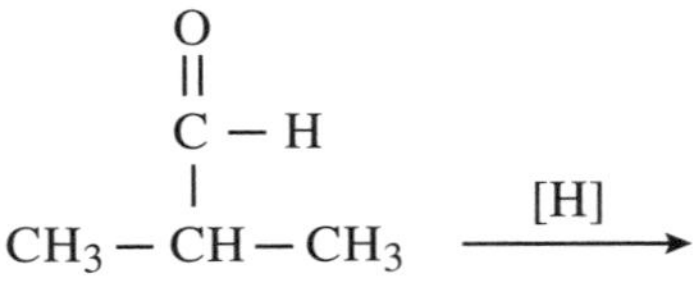 $CH_3-\underset{\overset{|}{\overset{C-H}{\overset{\|}{O}}}}{CH}-CH_3 \xrightarrow{[H]}$

e. 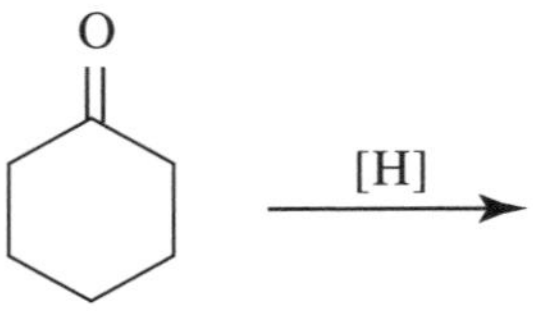 cyclohexanone (cyclohexane ring with $=O$) $\xrightarrow{[H]}$

f. $CH_3-CH_2-CHO \xrightarrow{[H]}$

VII. Summary

A. Bonding Around Oxygen

In organic compounds oxygen atoms have two bonds and two lone electron pairs. The two bonds around oxygen can be arranged in one of the following common patterns. [NOTE: Lone electron pairs are usually not shown.]

2 Single Bonds	1 Double Bond
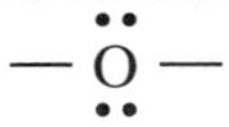 $-\ddot{\underset{\cdot\cdot}{O}}-$	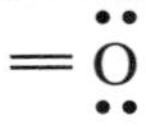 $=\ddot{\underset{\cdot\cdot}{O}}$

B. Types of Organic Compounds Containing One Oxygen Atom

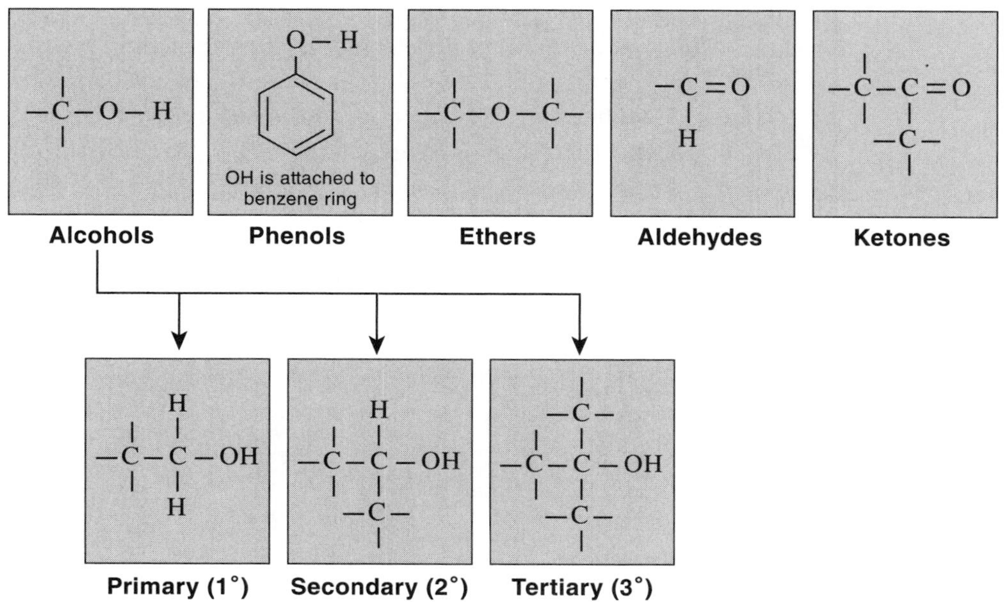

Suffixes will denote the specific functional group:

Alkane	Alcohol	Ether	Aldehyde	Ketone
____e	____ol	_____ ether	____al	____one

In naming these compounds, the ending is changed from "e" in the alkane to: "*ol,*" "*al,*" or "*one*" depending on the functional group present.

Problem 11. Classify each of the following compounds as either: alcohol (1°, 2°, or 3°), aldehyde, ketone, or ether:

a.

b. $CH_3 - CH_2 - \underset{}{C}(H) = O$

c.

d. OH

e. $HO - CH_3$

f. HO CH₃

C. Physical Properties and Hydrogen Bonds

Hydrogen bonds are intermolecular forces of attraction that may occur when the hydrogen of one molecule (like in H-O-H) bonds to an oxygen of another molecule (like in alcohols or aldehydes). Hydrogen bonds are strong forces of attraction and are responsible for the solubility of certain compounds in water. ***In general, oxygen containing hydrocarbons, which have 5 carbons or fewer, are water soluble;*** this is because they are capable of hydrogen bonding with water. A hydrogen bond is depicted by a dotted line below.

The following are examples of a hydrogen bond formed between:

a. alcohol and water

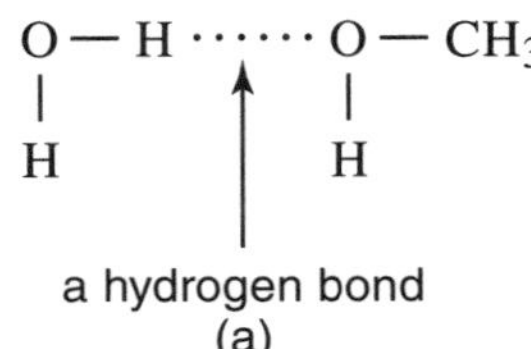

(a)

b. aldehyde and water

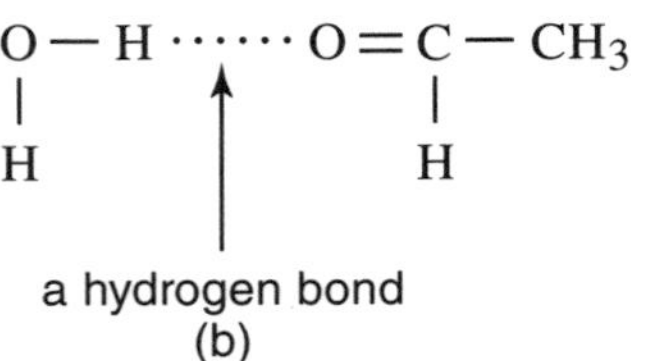

(b)

ANSWERS

1. a. secondary
   b. tertiary
   c. secondary
   d. primary
   e. tertiary

2. a. 5,5-dimethyl-3-hexanol
   b. 1,2-diethylcyclohexanol
   c. 2-isopropylcyclopropanol
   d. 4-methyl-2,4-dipropyl-1-heptanol
   e. 3-methyl-3-heptanol

3. a.

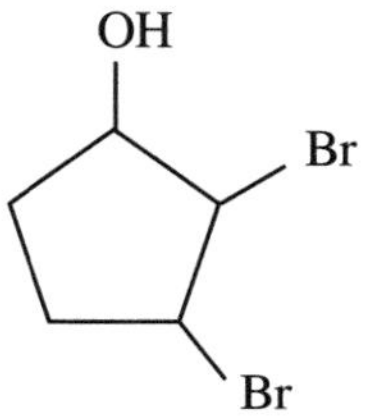

OH

Br

Br

b.

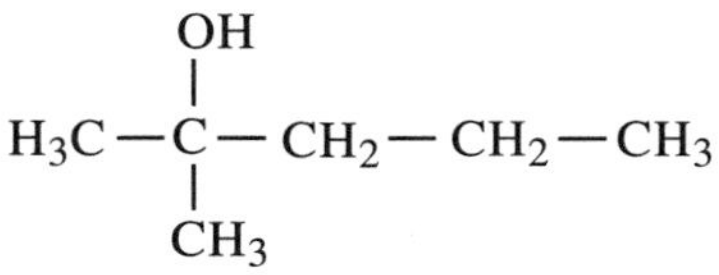

OH

$H_3C-C-CH_2-CH_2-CH_3$

CH_3

c.

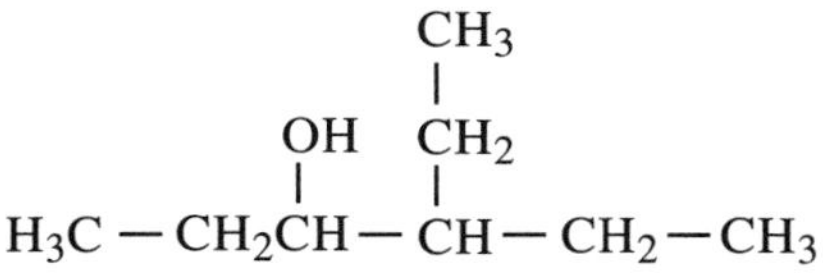

CH_3

OH CH_2

$H_3C-CH_2CH-CH-CH_2-CH_3$

d.

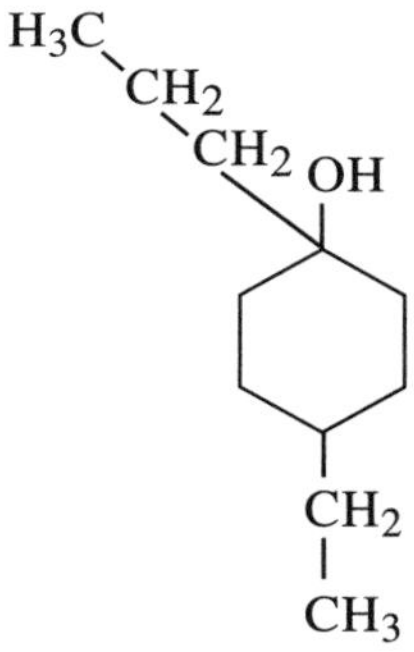

H_3C

CH_2

CH_2 OH

CH_2

CH_3

e.

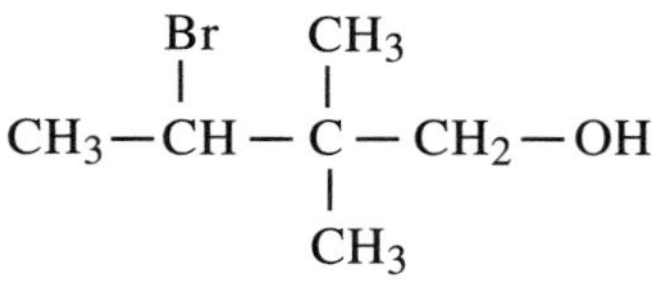

Br CH_3

$CH_3-CH-C-CH_2-OH$

CH_3

f.

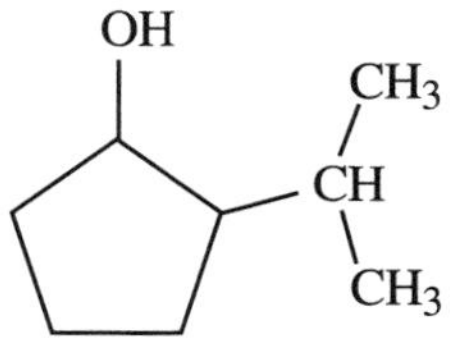

OH

CH_3

CH

CH_3

4. a. 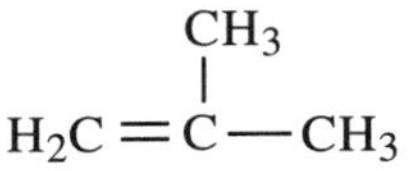 $H_2C{=}C(CH_3){-}CH_3 + H_2O$

   b. 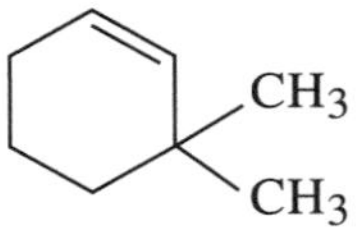 3,3-dimethylcyclohexene (ring with CH_3, CH_3) $+ H_2O$

   c. 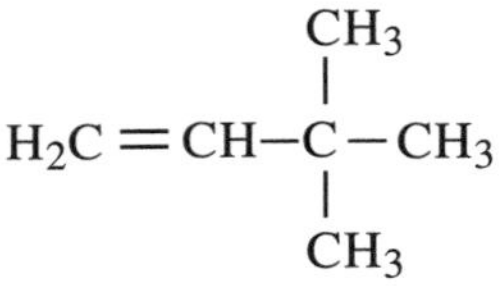 $H_2C{=}CH{-}C(CH_3)_2{-}CH_3 + H_2O$

   d. $H_2C{=}CH{-}CH_3 + H_2O$

5. a. $CH_3{-}O{-}CH_3$

   b. $CH_3{-}CH_2{-}O{-}CH_2{-}CH_3$

6. a. No reaction

   b. 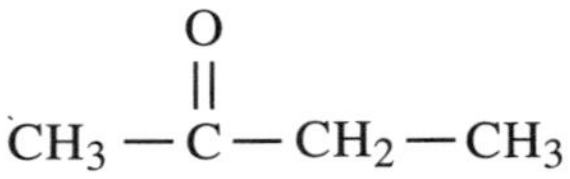 $CH_3{-}C({=}O){-}CH_2{-}CH_3$

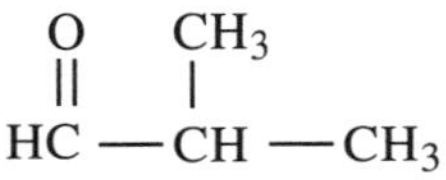

   c. $HC({=}O){-}CH(CH_3){-}CH_3$ or $HO{-}C({=}O){-}CH(CH_3){-}CH_3$

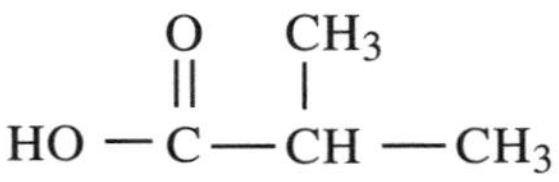

   d. 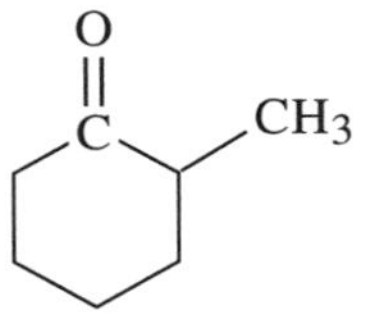 2-methylcyclohexanone (ring C=O with CH_3)

   e. No reaction

   f. 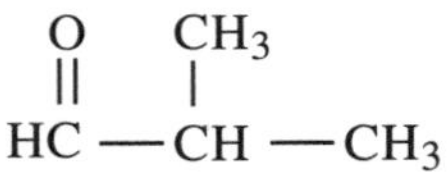 $HC({=}O){-}CH(CH_3){-}CH_3$ or $HO{-}C({=}O){-}CH(CH_3){-}CH_3$

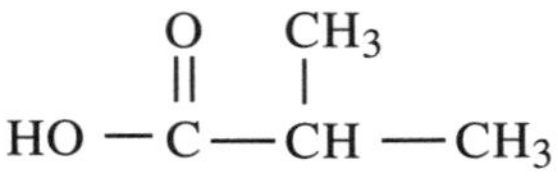

7. a. 3-methylbutanal

   b. 4-bromo-5-methyl-2-heptanone

   c. 3-propylcyclopentanone

   d. 3,4-dimethylpentanal

   e. 3,4-dimethylcycloheptanone

   f. butanal

8. a. 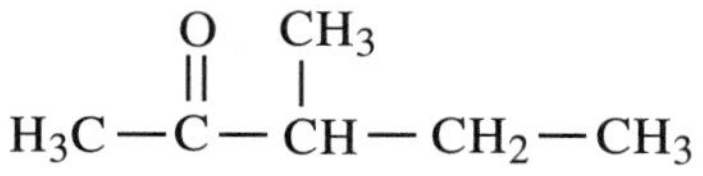 $H_3C-C(=O)-CH(CH_3)-CH_2-CH_3$

b. $H_3C-C(=O)-CBr_2-CH_2-CH_3$

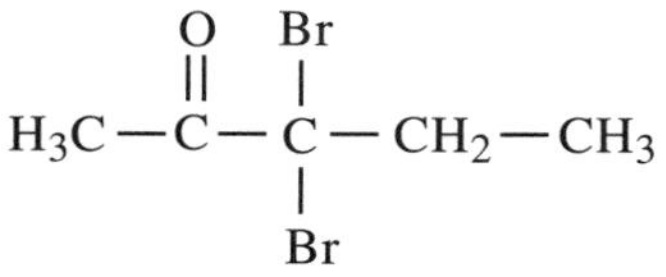

c. Cyclohexanone (ring with C=O)

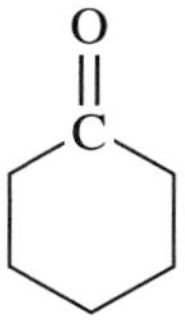

d. 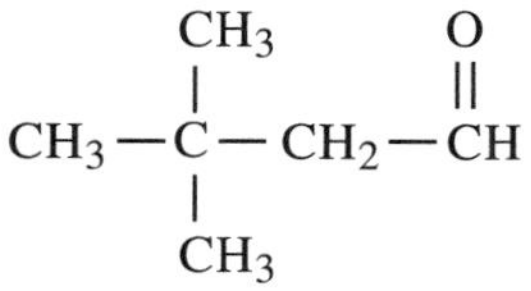 $CH_3-C(CH_3)_2-CH_2-CH(=O)$

e. 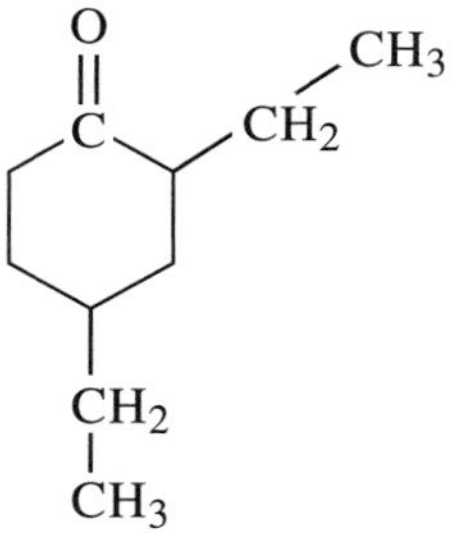 Ring with C=O, CH_2-CH_3 on the adjacent carbon, and CH_2-CH_3 at the 4-position

f. 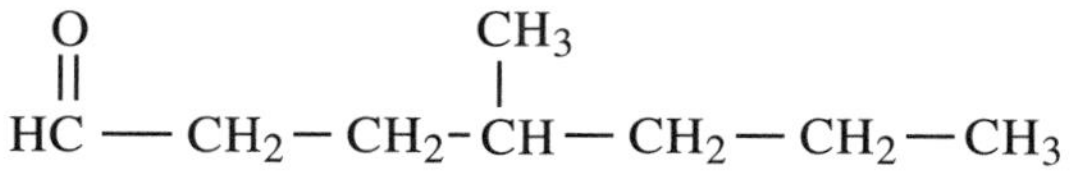 $HC(=O)-CH_2-CH_2-CH(CH_3)-CH_2-CH_2-CH_3$

9. a. No reaction

b. 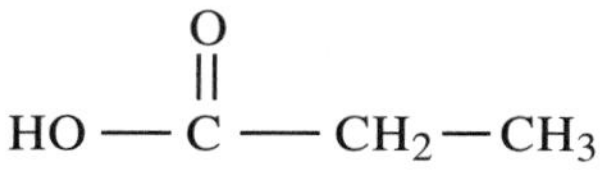 $HO-C(=O)-CH_2-CH_3$

c. $HO-C(=O)-CH(CH_3)-CH_3$

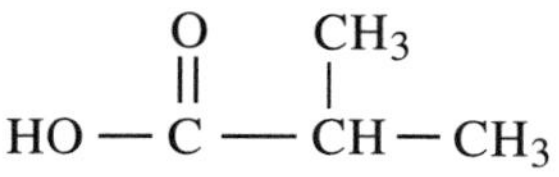

d. 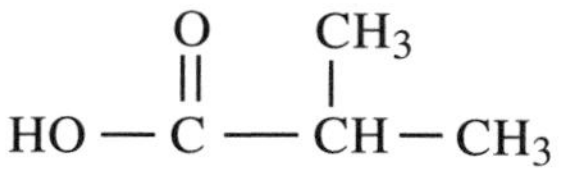 $HO-C(=O)-CH(CH_3)-CH_3$

e. No reaction

f. 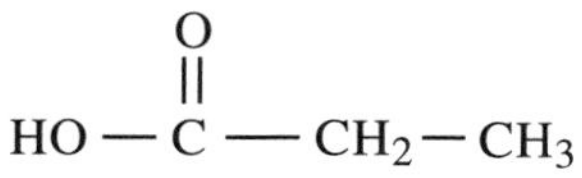 $HO-C(=O)-CH_2-CH_3$

10. a. 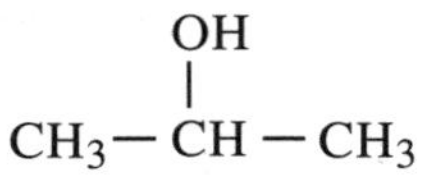 $CH_3-CH(OH)-CH_3$

b. 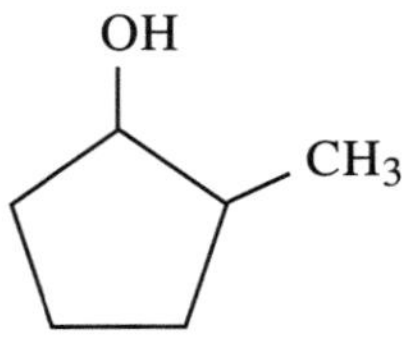 (cyclopentane ring with OH on one carbon and CH_3 on the adjacent carbon)

c. 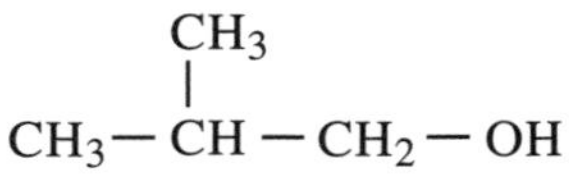 $CH_3-CH(CH_3)-CH_2-OH$

d. 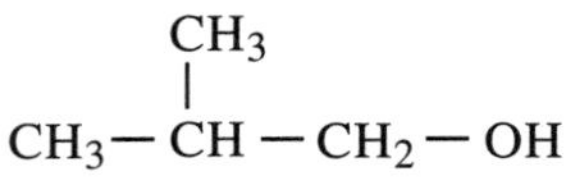 $CH_3-CH(CH_3)-CH_2-OH$

e. 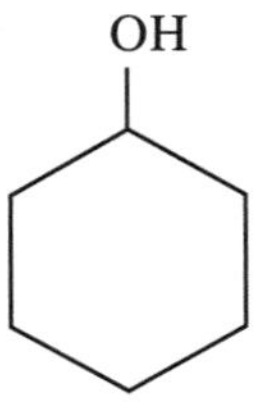 (cyclohexane ring with OH)

f. $CH_3-CH_2-CH_2-OH$

11. a. ketone
b. aldehyde
c. ether
d. secondary alcohol
e. primary alcohol
f. tertiary alcohol

Alcohols, Aldehydes, and Ketones

Assignment 10

Name

Student Number

Date Instructor

1. Identify the following structures as primary (1°), secondary (2°), or tertiary (3°) alcohols, aldehydes, or ketones.

a. 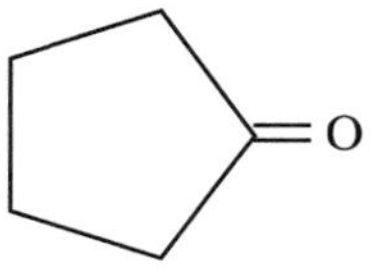 (cyclopentane ring)=O

b. 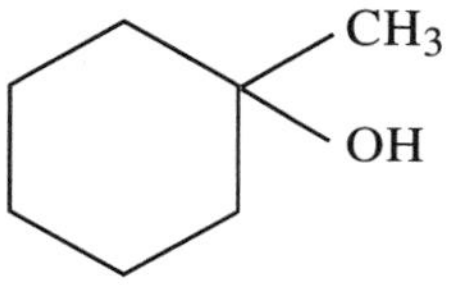 (cyclohexane ring bearing CH_3 and OH on the same carbon)

c. 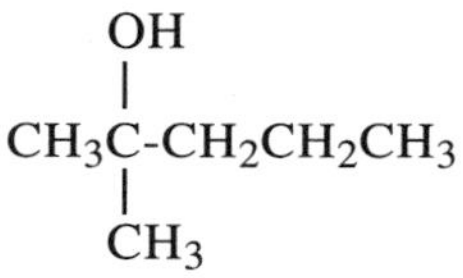 $CH_3C(OH)(CH_3)\text{-}CH_2CH_2CH_3$

d. 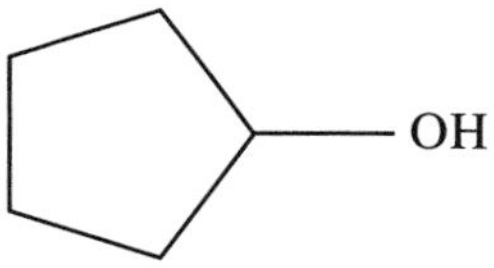 (cyclopentane ring)—OH

e. $CH_3CH_2CH_2CH_2CHO$

f. 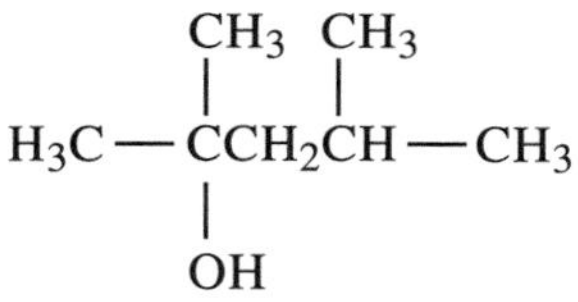 $H_3C—C(CH_3)(OH)CH_2CH(CH_3)—CH_3$

g. $CH_3CH_2\overset{O}{\overset{\|}{C}}H$

h. $CH_3\overset{OH}{\overset{|}{C}}HCH_3$

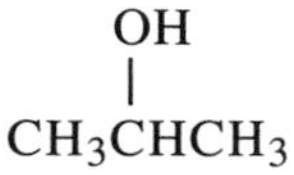

i. 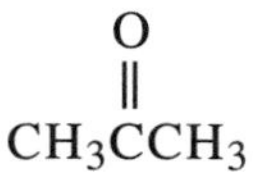 $CH_3\overset{O}{\overset{\|}{C}}CH_3$

j. $CH_3\text{–}CH_2\text{–}CH_2\text{–}OH$

k. 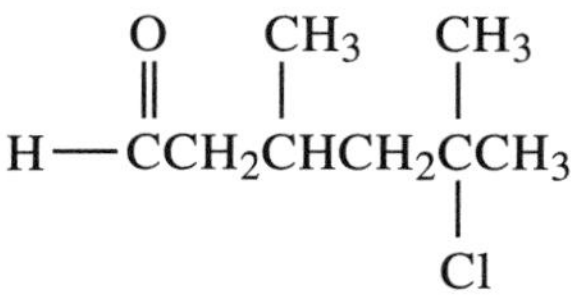 $H—\overset{O}{\overset{\|}{C}}CH_2\overset{CH_3}{\overset{|}{C}}HCH_2C(CH_3)(Cl)CH_3$

l. 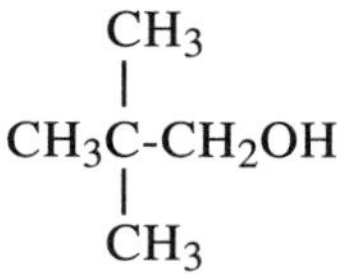 $CH_3C(CH_3)_2\text{-}CH_2OH$

m. 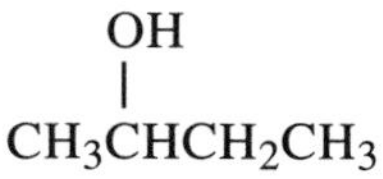 $CH_3\overset{OH}{\overset{|}{C}}HCH_2CH_3$

n. 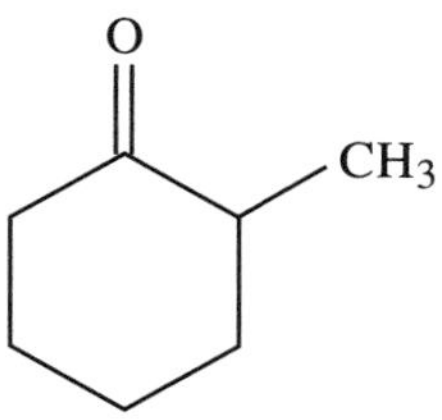 (cyclohexanone ring with CH_3 on the carbon adjacent to C=O)

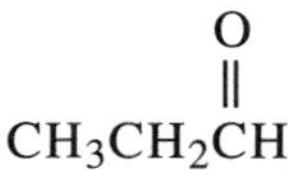

2. Write the correct name for each structure in Question 1.

a. ______________________ b. ______________________

c. ______________________ d. ______________________

e. ______________________ f. ______________________

g. ______________________ h. ______________________

i. ______________________ j. ______________________

k. ______________________ l. ______________________

m. ______________________ n. ______________________

3. When a secondary alcohol is oxidized, the product is ______________________.

4. When an aldehyde is oxidized, the product is ______________________.

5. When an aldehyde is reduced, the product is ______________________.

6. When ______________ is treated with an oxidizing agent, no reaction occurs.

7. Mild oxidation of 2-methyl-1-butanol produces (give both the structure and name).

8. Which of the following compounds would you expect to have chemical properties similar to $CH_3CH_2OCH_2CH_2CH_3$? Why?

$CH_3CH_2CH_2CH_2CH_3$ $\qquad$ $CH_3CH_2OCH_2CH_3$

$CH_3CH(OH)CH_2CH_3$ $\qquad$ $CH_3C(=O)CH_2CH_3$

9. Draw structures for the products for each of the following reactions. If no reaction occurs, write "no reaction."

a. $CH_3-CH(OH)-CH_3 \xrightarrow[\text{high temp.}]{H+}$

b. $CH_3CH_2CH_2OH \xrightarrow[\text{high temp.}]{H+}$

c. $CH_3CH_2OH \xrightarrow[\text{high temp.}]{H+}$

d. $CH_3CH(OH)CH_2CH_3 \xrightarrow[\text{high temp.}]{H+}$

e. $CH_3CH_2C(=O)\text{-}OH \xrightarrow{[H]}$

f. 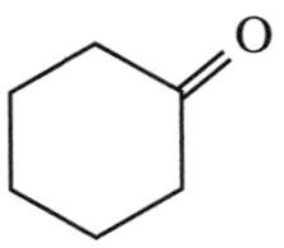 $\xrightarrow{[H]}$

g. $CH_3CH(OH)CH_2CH_3 \xrightarrow{[O]}$

h. 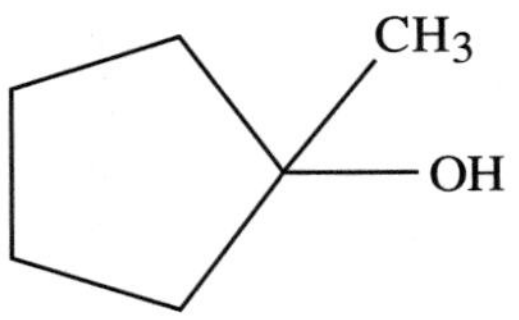 (1-methylcyclopentanol: cyclopentane ring with CH_3 and OH on the same carbon) $\xrightarrow{[O]}$

i. $CH_3CH_2C(CH_3)_2\text{-}OH$ $\xrightarrow{[O]}$

$$\begin{array}{c} CH_3 \\ | \\ CH_3CH_2C\text{-}OH \\ | \\ CH_3 \end{array} \xrightarrow{[O]}$$

j. 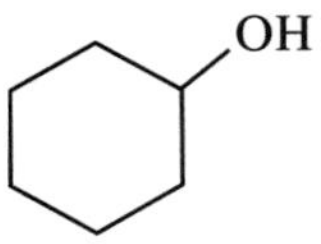 (cyclohexanol: cyclohexane ring with OH) $\xrightarrow{[O]}$

k. $CH_3CH_2CH_2OH$ $\xrightarrow{[O]}$

11

Carbohydrates

Simple carbohydrate molecules are produced in the leaves of green plants by a process called *photosynthesis*. The green plant takes carbon dioxide (CO_2) from the air, combines it with water (H_2O) from the soil and produces carbohydrates (mainly glucose), releasing the excess oxygen formed during the process. The catalyst for this particular reaction is called *chlorophyll* and the energy needed for this reaction to proceed is obtained from the sun.

Carbohydrates are one of the three major dietary components; the other two are fats and proteins. Our bodies use carbohydrates primarily to provide energy. Originally carbohydrates were considered hydrates of carbon with the general formula: $C_n(H_2O)_n$. Another term for carbohydrates is saccharides, which comes from the Latin word *saccharum* for sugar.

Analysis of carbohydrate molecules indicates that, although there are two hydrogen atoms for each oxygen atom, carbohydrates are not hydrates but are polyhydroxy aldehydes or polyhydroxy ketones.

I. Classification of Saccharides by Functional Group

All carbohydrates are composed of simple units called *monosaccharide* units. These monosaccharide units contain either an aldehyde or a ketone functional group on one carbon atom and hydroxyl (alcohol) groups on all the other carbons. The monosaccharide units can have as few as three carbon atoms and as many as seven. Monosaccharides may be classified by size (number of carbon atoms) and functional group content. For example, if the monosaccharide contains 3 carbon atoms and has a ketone functional group, it may be described as a keto*tri*ose. If the saccharide unit contains 6 carbon atoms and an aldehyde functional group, it may be classified as an aldo*hex*ose.

# of Carbons	General Name	Aldose	Ketose
3	triose	aldotriose	ketotriose
4	tetrose	aldotetrose	ketotetrose
5	pentose	aldopentose	ketopentose
6	hexose	aldohexose	ketohexose
7	heptose	aldoheptose	ketoheptose

Example A: Classification of Saccharides.

To classify a saccharide, one must count the number of carbon atoms in the molecule and identify the functional group as either an aldehyde or a ketone.

```
        O     aldehyde
        ||
      1 C—H
        |
   H—2C—OH
        |
   H—3C—OH
        |
      4 CH2OH
```

aldotetrose

Since the structure contains 4 carbon atoms and an aldehyde group, it is classified as an **aldotetrose**.

```
ketone      1 CH2OH
               |
            2  C=O
               |
       HO—3 C—H
               |
        H—4 C—OH
               |
        H—5 C—OH
               |
            6 CH2OH
```

ketohexose

Since the structure contains 6 carbon atoms and a ketone group, it is classified as a **ketohexose**.

Problem 1. Classify the following as aldo- or keto- trioses, tetroses, pentoses, hexoses, or heptoses:

```
a.      CHO
         |
     H—C—OH
         |
    HO—C—H
         |
    HO—C—H
         |
        CH2OH
```

```
b.      CHO
         |
     H—C—OH
         |
    HO—C—H
         |
    HO—C—H
         |
     H—C—OH
         |
        CH2OH
```

```
c.      CHO
         |
     H—C—OH
         |
        CH2OH
```

```
d.      CH2OH
         |
         C=O
         |
    HO—C—H
         |
    HO—C—H
         |
        CH2OH
```

II. Haworth Structures and Fischer Projections

Pentose, hexose, and heptose chains are large enough to close upon themselves to form cyclic structures, called Haworth structures. The carbonyl group (aldehyde or ketone functional group) reacts with the hydroxyl group in the next to the last carbon atom to form a hemiacetal or a hemiketal.

A. Reaction of an Alcohol with an Aldehyde

hemiacetal

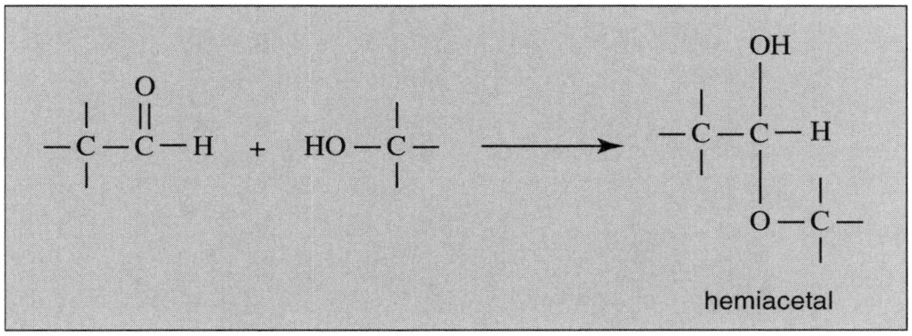

When an alcohol reacts with an aldehyde, the product is called a hemiacetal. The reaction is represented below.

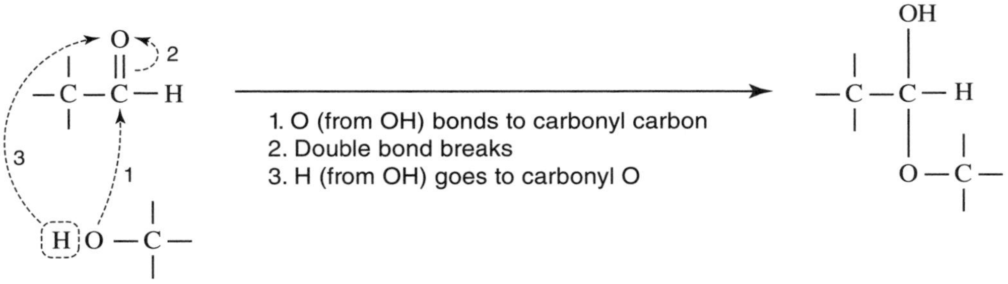

1. O (from OH) bonds to carbonyl carbon
2. Double bond breaks
3. H (from OH) goes to carbonyl O

The following is a specific example of a reaction of an alcohol with an aldehyde.

$$CH_3-\overset{\overset{\displaystyle O}{\|}}{C}-H \quad + \quad HO-CH_2-CH_3 \longrightarrow CH_3-\underset{\underset{\displaystyle O-CH_2-CH_3}{|}}{\overset{\overset{\displaystyle OH}{|}}{C}}-H$$

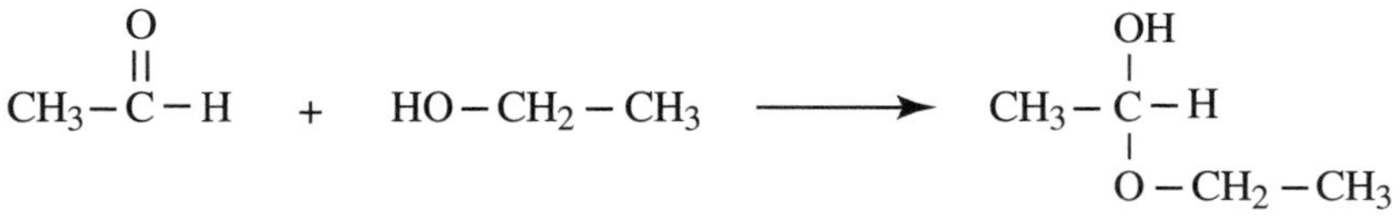

B. Reaction of an Alcohol with a Ketone

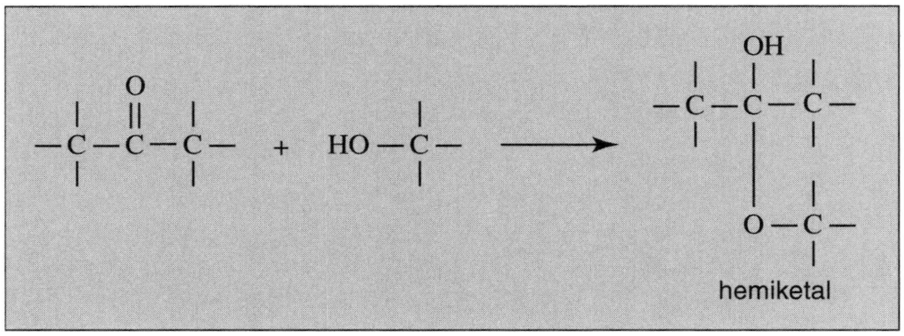

hemiketal

The carbonyl carbon of a ketone reacts in the same fashion with an alcohol; however, the product is called a hemiketal.

The following is an example of a ketone reacting with an alcohol.

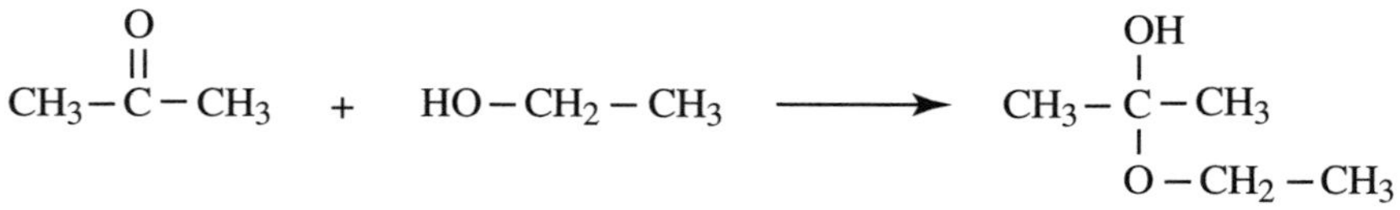

$$CH_3-\overset{\overset{\displaystyle O}{\|}}{C}-CH_3 \quad + \quad HO-CH_2-CH_3 \longrightarrow CH_3-\underset{\underset{\displaystyle O-CH_2-CH_3}{|}}{\overset{\overset{\displaystyle OH}{|}}{C}}-CH_3$$

Problem 2.

a. 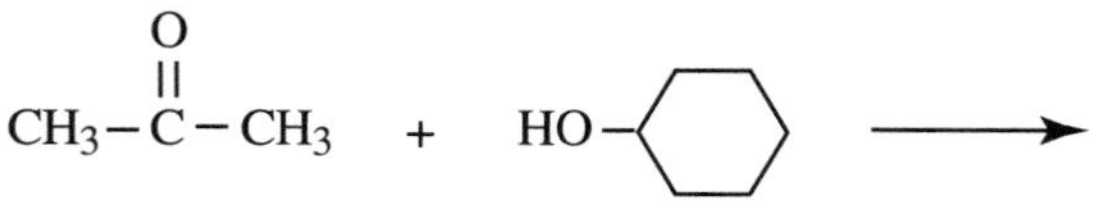 $$CH_3-\overset{\overset{\displaystyle O}{\|}}{C}-CH_3 \quad + \quad HO-C_6H_{11} \text{ (cyclohexyl)} \longrightarrow$$

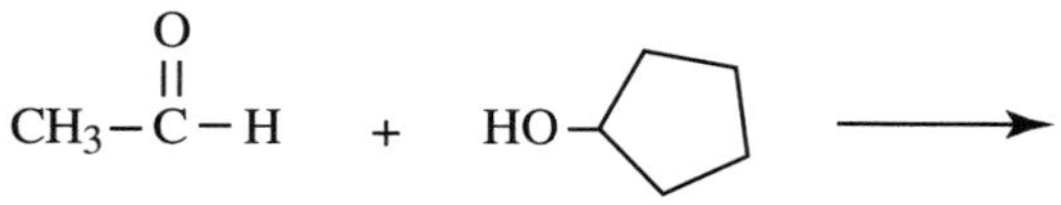

b. $$CH_3-\overset{\overset{\displaystyle O}{\|}}{C}-H \quad + \quad HO-C_5H_9 \text{ (cyclopentyl)} \longrightarrow$$

c. $$C_6H_{10}{=}O \text{ (cyclohexanone)} \quad + \quad HO-CH_3 \longrightarrow$$

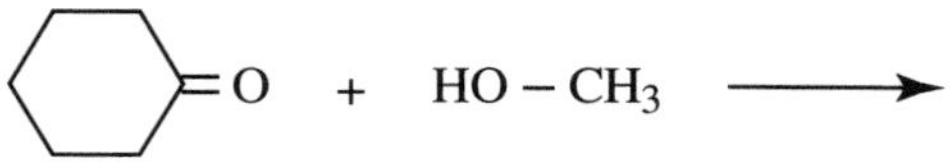

d. 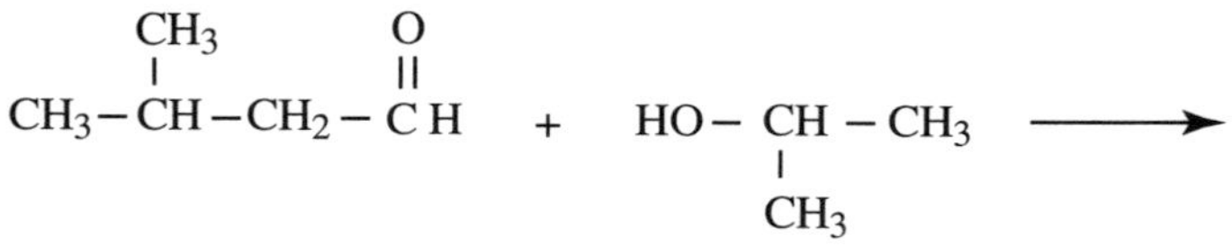 $$CH_3-\overset{\overset{\displaystyle CH_3}{|}}{CH}-CH_2-\overset{\overset{\displaystyle O}{\|}}{C}H \quad + \quad HO-\underset{\underset{\displaystyle CH_3}{|}}{CH}-CH_3 \longrightarrow$$

C. Alpha and Beta Anomers—Mutarotation

When a structure is drawn as the open-chain formula, it is called the Fischer projection. In the formation of the closed-ring (Haworth) structure a new alcohol group is formed on the carbon which was formerly the carbonyl carbon. This newly formed –OH group may be placed downward or upward. When the –OH group is drawn downward, the molecule is designated as the alpha (α) form, while having the –OH group positioned upward is referred to as the beta (β) structure.

Example B: Mutarotation.

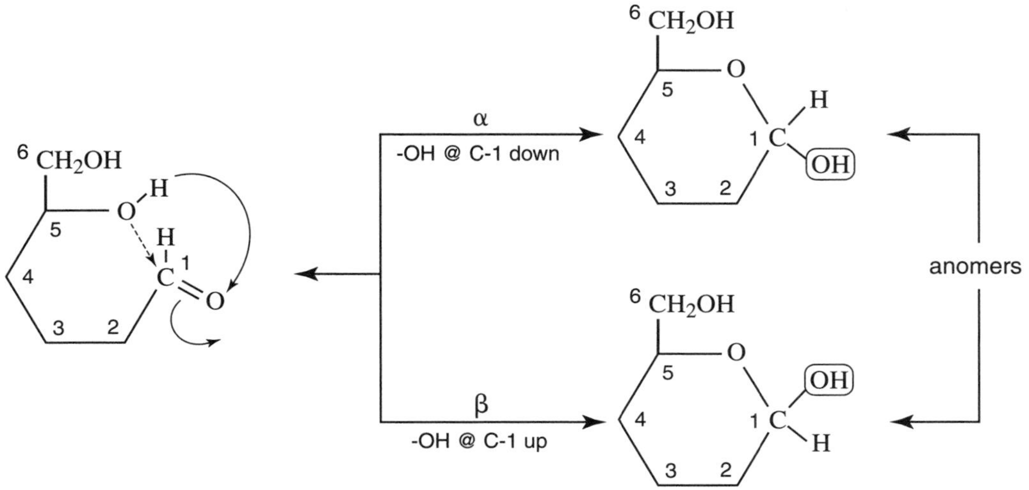

Because the alpha and beta isomers differ only at C-1, they are called anomers, and C-1 is called the anomeric carbon.

To convert from a Fischer projection to a Haworth structure, the following may be used as a guide. On C-2, C-3, and C-4, if the –OH is on the right in the Fischer projection, it is drawn downward in the Haworth structure. On the other hand, if the –OH is on the left in the Fischer projection, it will be drawn upward in the Haworth structure.

Example C: Conversion of an Aldohexose.

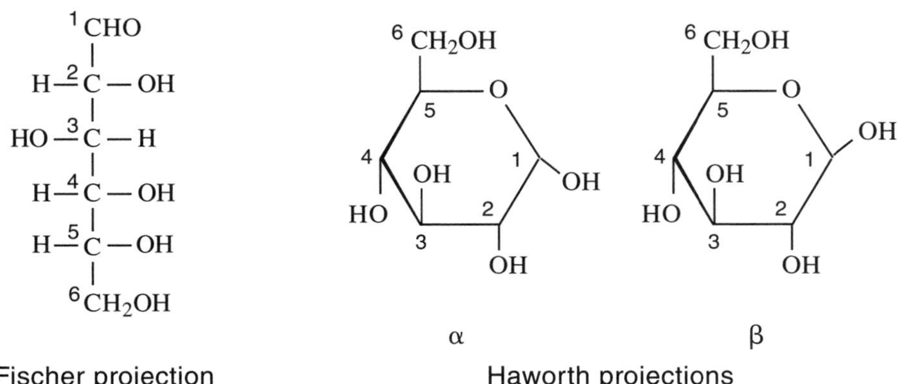

Fischer projection

Haworth projections

Example D: Conversion of a ketohexose.

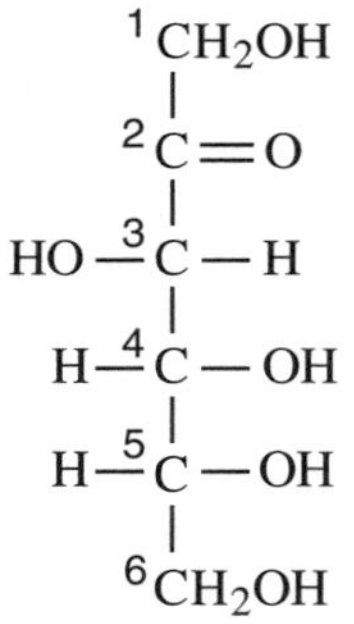

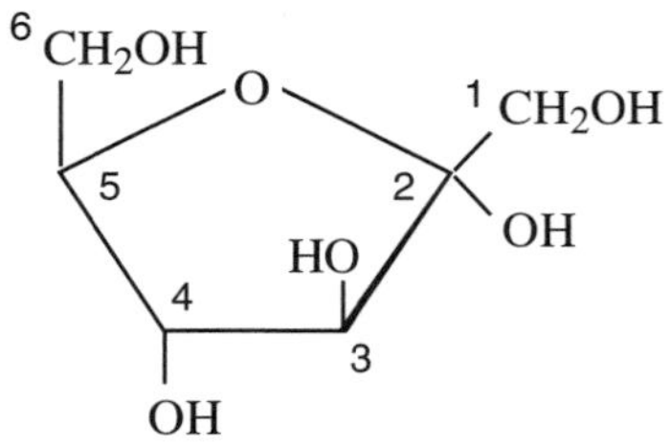

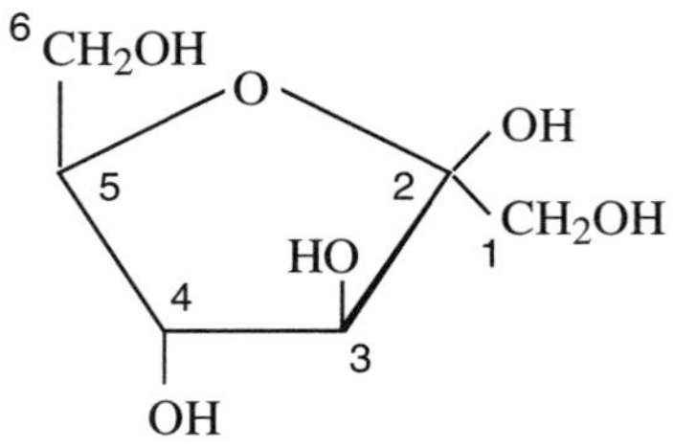

$^{1}CH_2OH$
$^{2}C{=}O$
$HO-^{3}C-H$
$H-^{4}C-OH$
$H-^{5}C-OH$
$^{6}CH_2OH$

$^{6}CH_2OH$, O, $^{1}CH_2OH$, 5, 2, OH, HO, 4, 3, OH

$^{6}CH_2OH$, O, OH, 5, 2, CH_2OH, 1, HO, 4, 3, OH

α β

Fischer projection Haworth projections

Problem 3. Identify the following structures as hemiacetals or hemiketals and give the alpha (α) or beta (β) designation:

a. 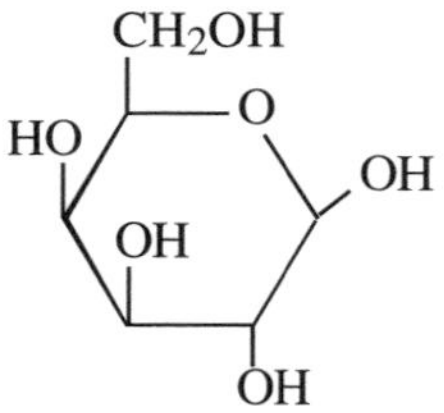 CH_2OH, O, HO, OH, OH, OH

b. 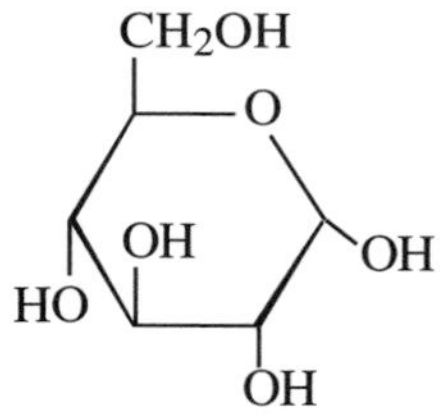 CH_2OH, O, OH, OH, HO, OH

c. 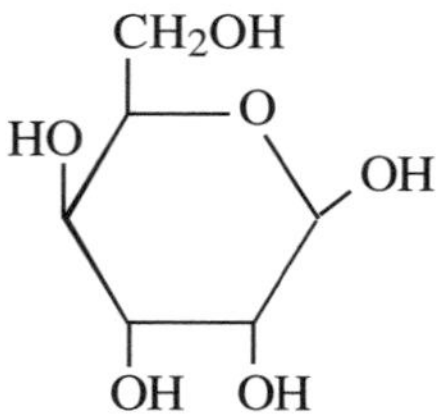 CH_2OH, O, HO, OH, OH, OH

d. 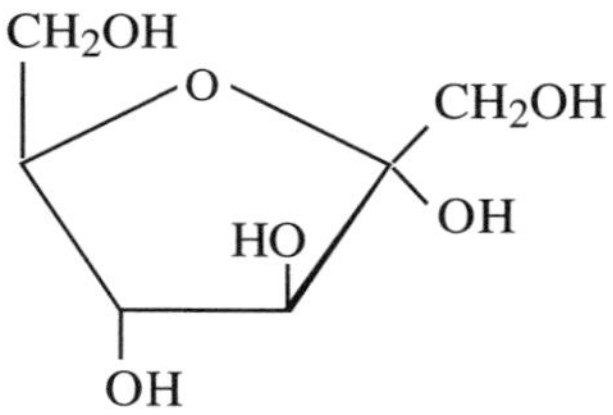 CH_2OH, O, CH_2OH, OH, HO, OH

Problem 4. For each of the following hexoses draw and label both its α and β Haworth structures:

a. 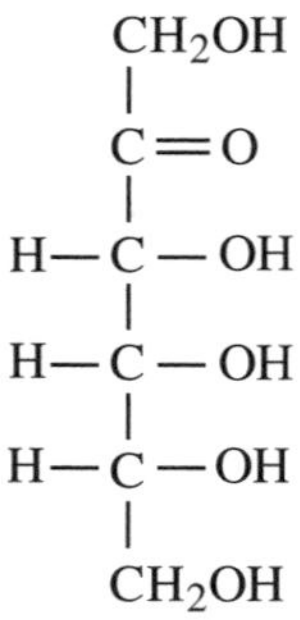
CH_2OH
$C{=}O$
$H-C-OH$
$H-C-OH$
$H-C-OH$
CH_2OH

b.
CHO
$H-C-OH$
$HO-C-H$
$HO-C-H$
$H-C-OH$
CH_2OH

c.
CHO
$H-C-OH$
$H-C-OH$
$HO-C-H$
$H-C-OH$
CH_2OH

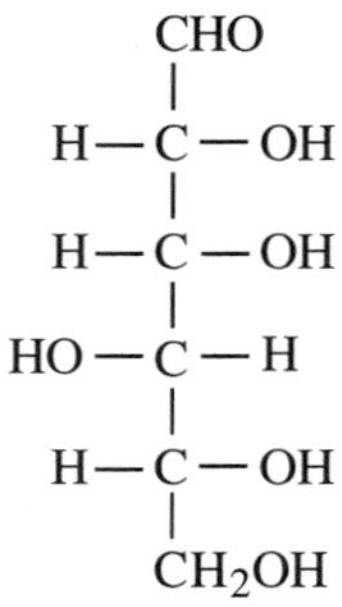

d. 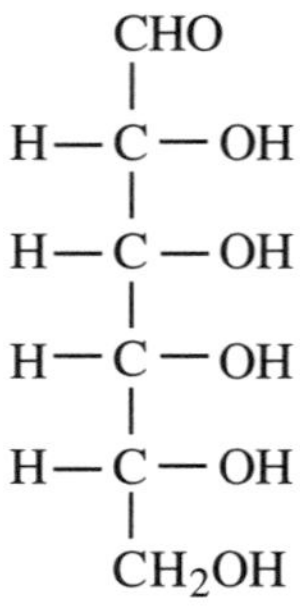
CHO
$H-C-OH$
$H-C-OH$
$H-C-OH$
$H-C-OH$
CH_2OH

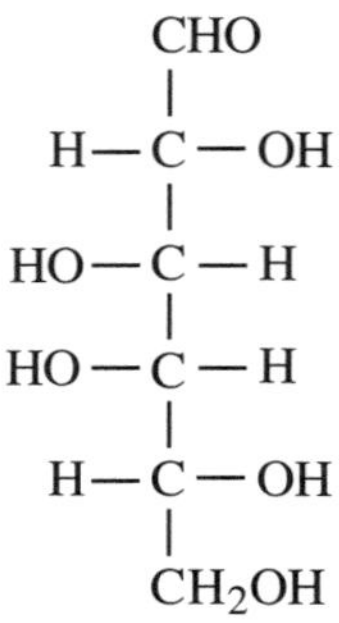

III. Stereochemistry

A. Chiral Carbons

When a carbon atom is bonded to four different groups it is called a chiral carbon. Chiral carbons are asymmetrical. Chiral compounds, such as sugars, contain chiral carbons and have special isomeric structures. The mirror image of a chiral compound is a different compound, just like your left and right hands are mirror images of each other, yet are different. Have you noticed that you cannot switch a baseball glove from one hand to the other one? Every carbohydrate molecule contains at least one chiral carbon.

Problem 5. Identify the number of chiral carbons in each of the following compounds:

a.

CHO
|
H—C—OH
|
HO—C—H
|
HO—C—H
|
CH_2OH

b.

CHO
|
H—C—OH
|
HO—C—H
|
HO—C—H
|
H—C—OH
|
CH_2OH

c.

CHO
|
H—C—OH
|
CH_2OH

d.

CH_2OH
|
C=O
|
HO—C—H
|
HO—C—H
|
CH_2OH

B. Classification As D- Or L- Sugars

Since sugars are chiral compounds, they may also be classified according to the position of the hydroxyl group (–OH) in the next to the last carbon on the end opposite the carbonyl group. If the hydroxyl group points to the right, then the sugar is labeled a D-sugar. If the hydroxyl group points to the left, then the sugar is labeled an L-sugar. The rotation of light is based on the position of the hydroxyl groups in glyceraldehyde, a triose. In nature only D-sugars are found.

CHO
|
H—C—[OH]
|
CH_2OH

D-sugar
-OH on next to last carbon
is pointing to the right

CH_2OH
|
C=O
|
HO—C—H
|
[HO]—C—H
|
CH_2OH

L-sugar
-OH on next to last carbon
is pointing to the left

Problem 6. Classify the compounds given in Problem 5 as D or L monosaccharides.

IV. Classification by Number of Units

All carbohydrates are composed of simple units called saccharides. If the carbohydrate molecule contains only one saccharide unit, it is called a *mono*saccharide. If the carbohydrate molecule contains two saccharide units bonded to each other by an ether functional group, then it is called a *di*saccharide. When many saccharide units are joined by ether linkages, it is called a *poly*saccharide.

Mono- and disaccharides are considered simple carbohydrates, while polysaccharides are complex carbohydrates.

A. Monosaccharides

Glucose is also known as dextrose or blood sugar. Glucose is the building block for complex carbohydrates such as starch and cellulose. The normal concentration of glucose in the blood is 70–90 mg/dL. However, this concentration of glucose varies according to the type of food ingested as well as the time elapsed.

To evaluate blood glucose levels, a glucose tolerance test is employed. The patient fasts for 12 hours and then drinks a solution containing 100 g of glucose. Samples of blood are then removed periodically. If the blood glucose exceeds 130 mg/dL and remains high, hyperglycemia may be indicated. Diabetes mellitus, which occurs when the pancreas is unable to produce sufficient quantities of insulin, can result in hyperglycemia. Symptoms of diabetes include thirst, excessive urination, increased appetite, and weight loss. When a person is hypoglycemic, the blood glucose level can fall to as low as 40 mg/dL. In some cases, hypoglycemia is produced by overproduction of insulin. Low blood glucose may result in dizziness, general weakness, and muscle tremors.

Glucose may be stored as glycogen (a glucose-based polysaccharide) in the liver or muscles, or metabolized and used as an energy source.

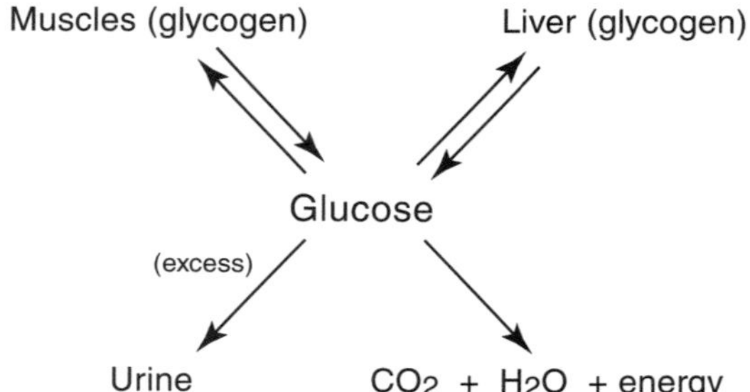

Three common monosaccharides are glucose, fructose, and galactose. Glucose is produced by plants during photosynthesis, fructose is found in fruit juices and honey, while galactose is commonly found in milk as part of a disaccharide.

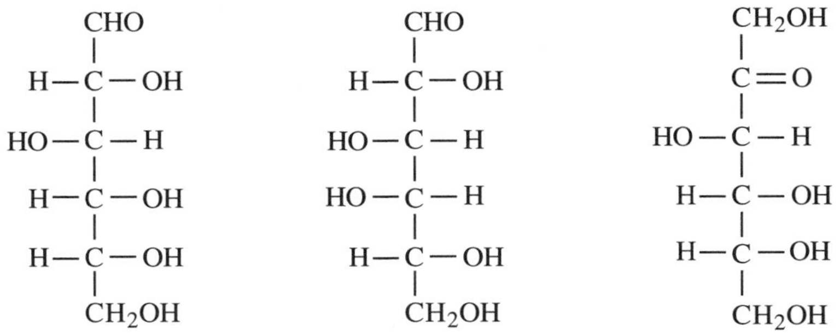

D-glucose D-galactose D-fructose

B. Disaccharides

Disaccharides can be formed by combining two monosaccharide units. These two sugar molecules are joined together by what is known as a glycosidic bond. The three most common disaccharides are sucrose and maltose, found in plants, and lactose (milk sugar) found in milk.

1. **Maltose**

   Maltose, or malt sugar, is a disaccharide obtained from the hydrolysis of starch. The following shows how maltose is formed from two molecules of α-D-glucose. The structure shown is specifically called α-maltose because the circled –OH on the anomeric carbon is down.

α - 1,4-glycosidic linkage

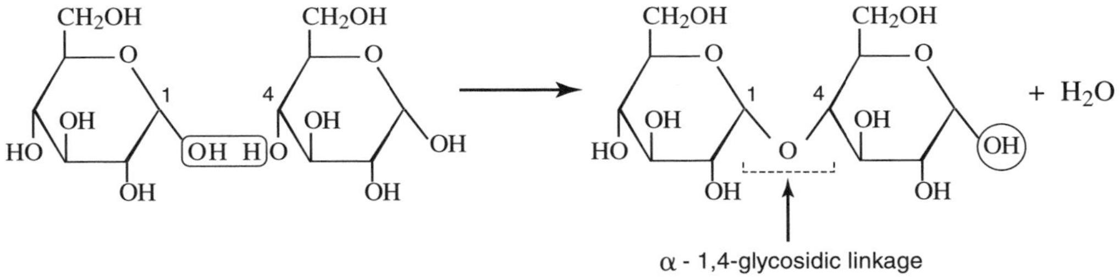

α - D-glucose α - D-glucose α - maltose

   The two sugars are joined by what is called an α-1,4-glycosidic bond. Hydrolysis of **maltose** yields two molecules of D-glucose.

2. **Lactose**

   Lactose, or milk sugar, is a disaccharide found in milk and milk products. Approximately 8% of human milk and about 5% of cow's milk is lactose. Insufficient production of an enzyme needed to break down lactose causes it to remain undigested in the stomach and intestinal tract, producing abdominal cramps and diarrhea.

   The following structure shows how lactose is formed from β-D-galactose and α-D-glucose. The structure shown is specifically called α-lactose because the circled –OH on the anomeric carbon is down.

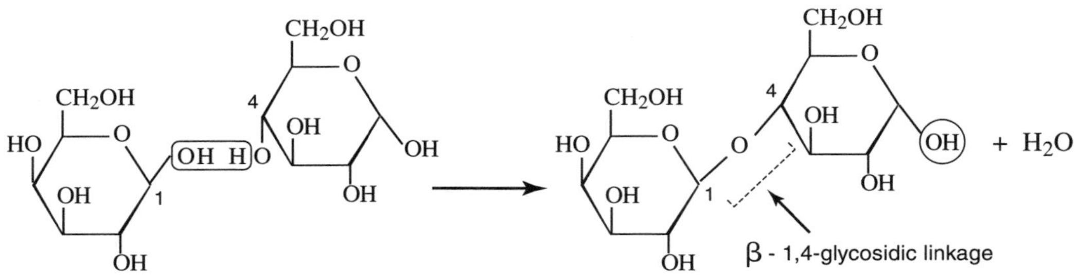

β - 1,4-glycosidic linkage

β - D-galactose α - D-glucose α - lactose

The two sugars are joined by what is called a β-1,4-glycosidic bond. Hydrolysis of lactose yields one molecule of D-galactose and one molecule D-glucose.

3. **Sucrose**

Sucrose, or table sugar, is obtained from sugar cane and sugar beets.

The following example shows how sucrose is formed from α-D-glucose and β-D-fructose. In sucrose, there is no free –OH group on either anomeric carbon; therefore, sucrose does not produce α or β structures.

α - D-glucose

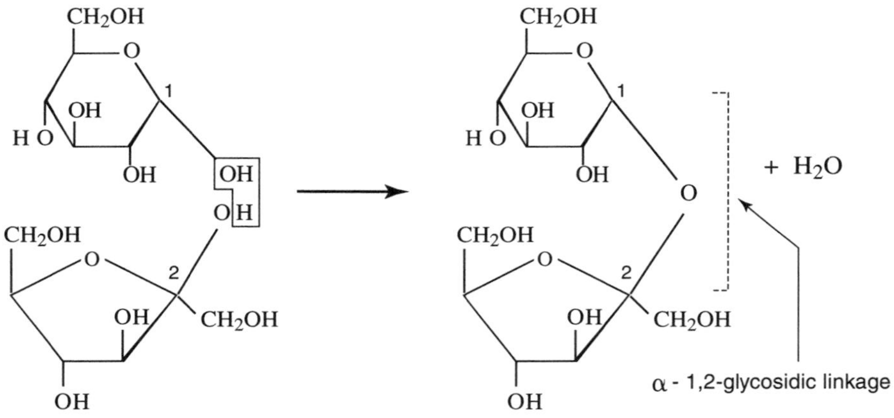

β - D-fructose

α - 1,2-glycosidic linkage

sucrose

The two sugars are joined by what is called an α 1,2-glycosidic bond. Hydrolysis of **sucrose** yields one molecule of D-glucose and one molecule of D-fructose.

C. Polysaccharides

Polysaccharides are high molecular weight polymers of monosaccharides (many saccharide units joined by ether linkages). Starch and glycogen are molecules used to store energy in plants and animals, respectively. Cellulose is the structural material found in plant cell walls.

1. **Starch**

Starch is a storage form of glucose in plants and is found in rice, wheat, potatoes, grains, and cereals. Starch is composed of two polysaccharides: amylose and amylopectin.

In amylose, the D-glucose molecules are connected by ∝-1,4-glycosidic bonds. A typical polymer of amylose contains from 250 to 4000 glucose units. The following figure shows a small portion of amylose's general structure.

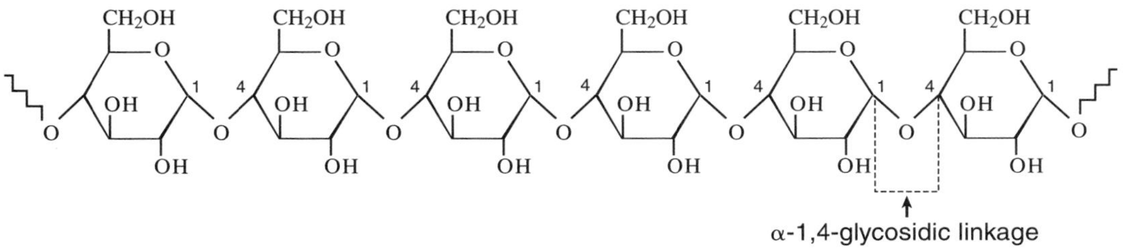

α-1,4-glycosidic linkage

Starch is as much as 80% amylopectin. Amylopectin is similar to amylose except that there are branches of glucose chains. At every 20–25 glucose units along the chain, there is a branch of glucose molecules attached by an ∝-1,6-glycosidic bond. The following figure shows a small portion of amylopectin's general structure.

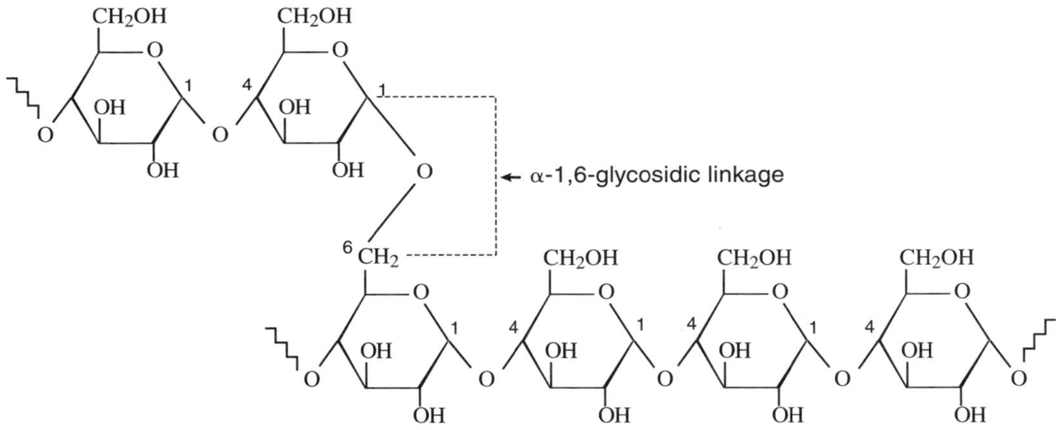

α-1,6-glycosidic linkage

Amylopectin

2. **Glycogen**

Glycogen, or animal starch, is the storage form of glucose found in the muscles and liver of animals. The structure of glycogen is very similar to that of the amylopectin found in plants (it contains both α-1,4 and α-1,6-glycosidic bonds). Glycogen, however, contains many more glucose units and is more highly branched, with branches occurring about every 10 glucose units.

3. **Cellulose**

Cellulose is the major structural component of plants. Cotton is almost pure cellulose. In cellulose, the glucose molecules are joined by a β-1,4-glycosidic bond. The following is a small portion of the structure of cellulose.

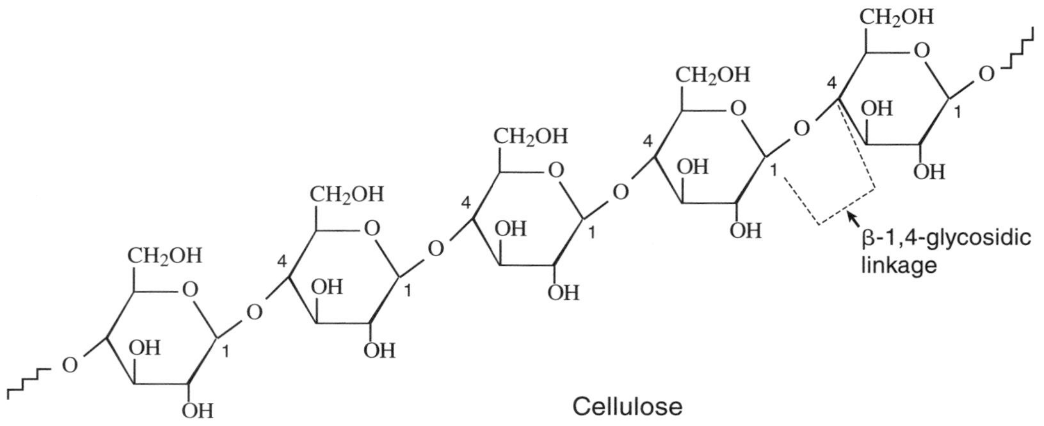

Cellulose

V. Digestion of Polysaccharides

The two forms of starch, amylose and amylopectin, contain α-1,4-glycosidic linkages while cellulose contains β-1,4-glycosidic linkages. Humans have enzymes that are able to hydrolyze the α-1,4-glycosidic linkages in starch and glycogen, but not the β-1,4-glycosidic linkages in cellulose. Therefore, cellulose is not digestible by humans; instead it provides the roughage or fiber in our diet.

VI. Testing for Carbohydrates

There are two common tests that are used in the laboratory to determine the presence or absence of carbohydrates. These two tests are Benedict's test and the iodine test.

A. Benedict's Test

In Benedict's test, a solution containing copper +2 ions, is added to a sugar solution and this mixture is heated. The blue copper ion solution, Cu^{2+}, is converted to a brick-red solid, Cu_2O, in the presence of certain sugars called *reducing sugars. All monosaccharides and most disaccharides (with the exception of sucrose) are reducing sugars,* resulting in a positive Benedict's test (blue solution → brick-red solid). Any nonreducing disaccharide (e.g., sucrose) or polysaccharide will give a positive Benedict's test only if the saccharide is first hydrolyzed to maltose or glucose. When a di- or polysaccharide is completely hydrolyzed, monosaccharides are produced, resulting in a positive Benedict's test.

B. Iodine Test

Iodine reacts with the polysaccharide amylose, which is found in starch, to form a characteristic deep blue-black complex. Cellulose, glycogen, and amylopectin produce a reddish-purple or brown color. Monosaccharides and disaccharides do not react with iodine.

Problem 7. Complete the following table:

Sugar	Hydrolysis Product(s)	Type of Glycosidic Linkage	Reducing Sugar (Y or N)
maltose			
lactose			
sucrose			
amylose			
amylopectin			
glycogen			
cellulose			

ANSWERS

1. a. aldopentose b. aldohexose

   c. aldotriose d. ketopentose

2. a.

$$\begin{array}{c} OH \\ | \\ CH_3-C-CH_3 \\ | \\ O- \end{array}$$

   b.

$$\begin{array}{c} OH \\ | \\ CH_3-C-H \\ | \\ O- \end{array}$$

   c.

$$\begin{array}{l} OH \\ O-CH_3 \end{array}$$

   d.

$$\begin{array}{c} CH_3 \quad\quad\quad\quad OH \\ | \quad\quad\quad\quad\quad | \\ CH_3-CH-CH_2-C-H \\ | \\ O-CH-CH_3 \\ | \\ CH_3 \end{array}$$

3. a. hemiacetal, beta b. hemiacetal, alpha

   c. hemiacetal, beta d. hemiketal, alpha

4.

a. 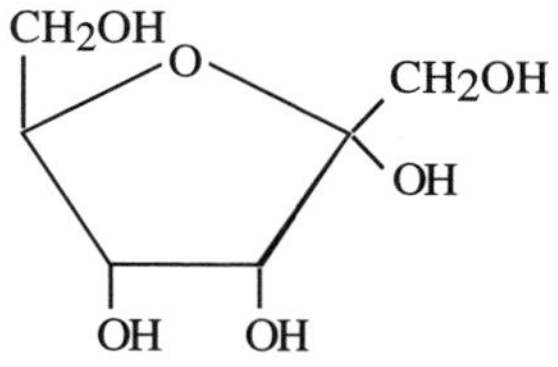 CH_2OH, O, CH_2OH, OH, OH, OH

α

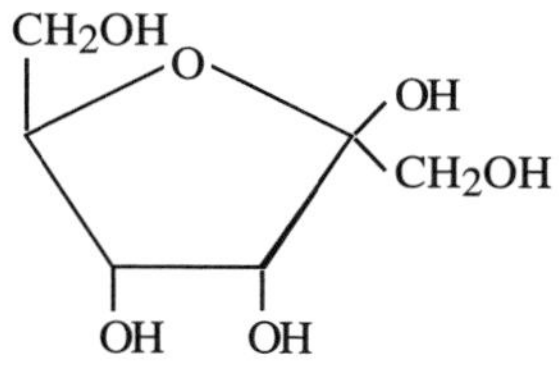

CH_2OH, O, OH, CH_2OH, OH, OH

β

b. 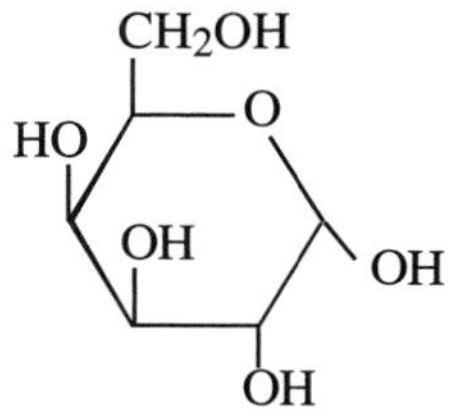 CH_2OH, O, HO, OH, OH, OH

α

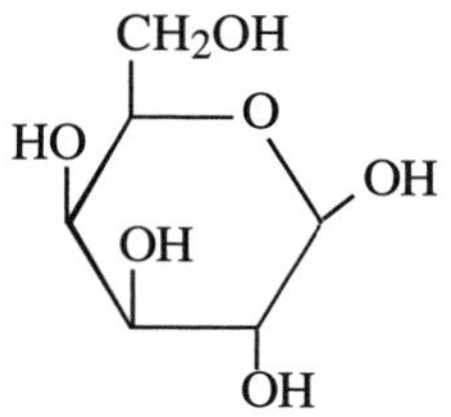

CH_2OH, O, HO, OH, OH, OH

β

c. 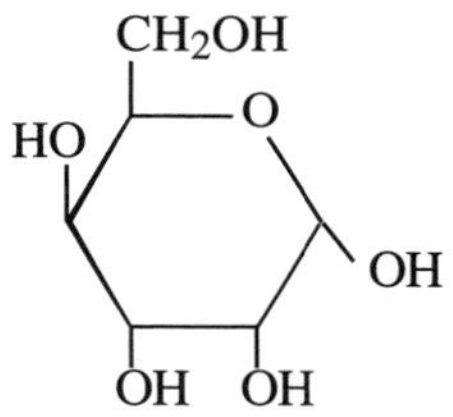 CH_2OH, O, HO, OH, OH, OH

α

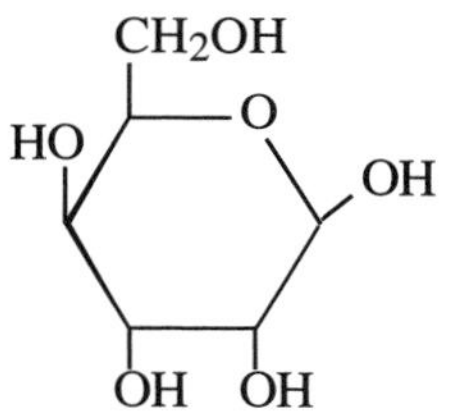

CH_2OH, O, HO, OH, OH, OH

β

d. 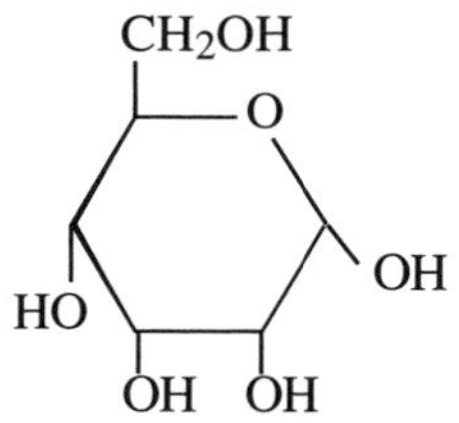 CH_2OH, O, OH, HO, OH, OH

α

CH_2OH, O, OH, HO, OH, OH

β

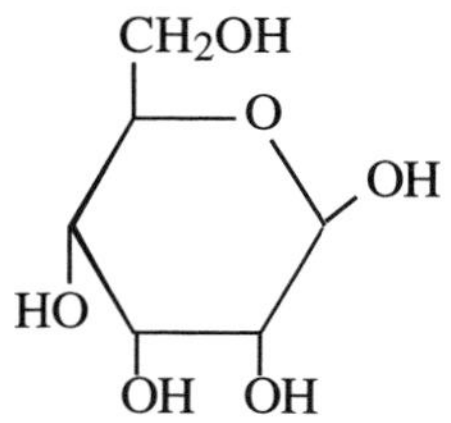

5. a. 3

b. 4

c. 1

d. 2

6. a. L-sugar b. D-sugar

   c. D-sugar d. L-sugar

7.

Sugar	Hydrolysis Product(s)	Type of Glycosidic Linkage	Reducing Sugar (Y Or N)
maltose	2 D-glucose molecules	α-1,4-	Y
lactose	D-galactose + D-glucose	β-1,4-	Y
sucrose	D-glucose + D-fructose	α-1,2-	N
amylose	many D-glucose molecules	α-1,4-	N
amylopectin	many D-glucose molecules	α-1,4- and α-1,6-	N
glycogen	many D-glucose molecules	α-1,4- and α-1,6-	N
cellulose	many D-glucose molecules	β-1,4-	N

Carbohydrates

11 Assignment

Name

Student Number

Date Instructor

1. A simple sugar with the molecular formula $C_4H_8O_4$ is a ______________.

   a. triose b. tetrose c. pentose d. hexose e. heptose

2. Give the Fisher projection formula of a simple sugar which is

   a. a ketopentose b. an aldotriose

3. The following carbohydrate is a(n):

   ________________________.

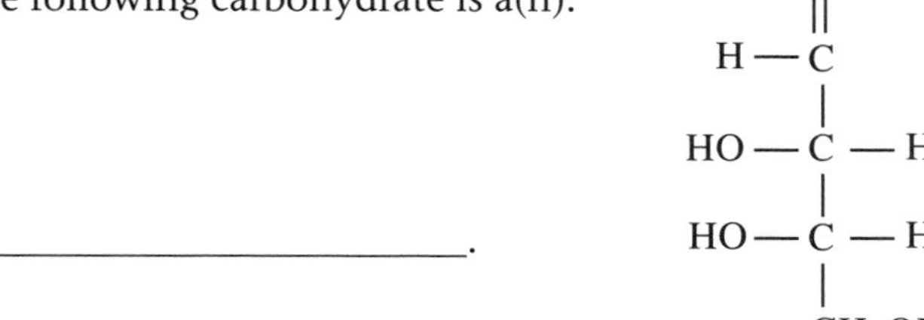

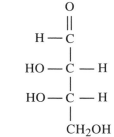

4. When a carbohydrate is drawn in its closed-ring structure, it is called a

   ________________________________ projection.

5. Draw the structure of the hemiacetal or hemiketal which results when the following are mixed.

   a. 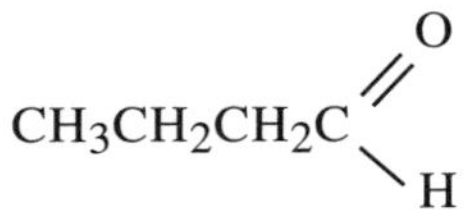 $CH_3CH_2CH_2C(=O)H$ and $CH_3CH_2—OH$

   b. 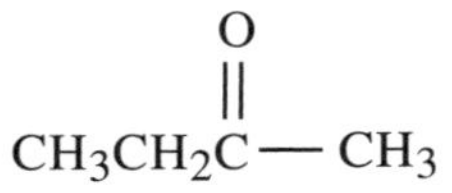 $CH_3CH_2C(=O)—CH_3$ and $CH_3—OH$

6. What is the name of the following carbohydrate?

$$\begin{array}{c} O \\ \| \\ C—H \\ | \\ H—C—OH \\ | \\ HO—C—H \\ | \\ H—C—OH \\ | \\ H—C—OH \\ | \\ CH_2OH \end{array}$$

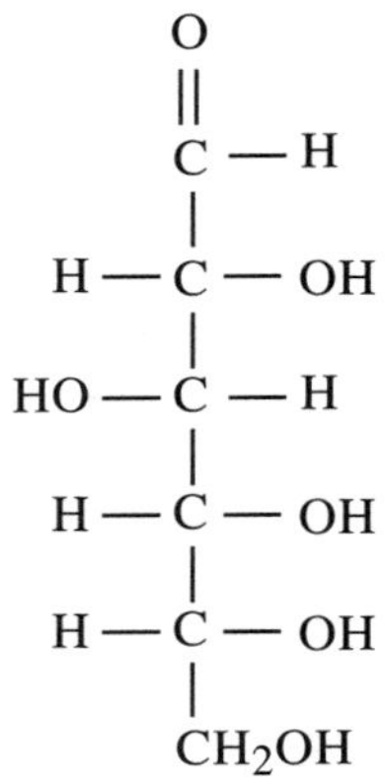

7. Is the following carbohydrate an example of a "D" or "L" isomer?

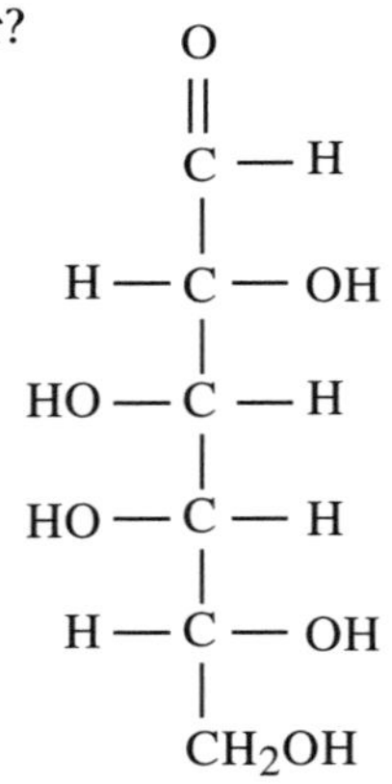

$$\begin{array}{c} O \\ \| \\ C—H \\ | \\ H—C—OH \\ | \\ HO—C—H \\ | \\ HO—C—H \\ | \\ H—C—OH \\ | \\ CH_2OH \end{array}$$

8. Draw the Fisher projection formulas of each of the following.

   a. D-glucose b. D-galactose c. D-fructose

9. Draw the structures of each of the following.

   a. α-D-glucose

   b. β-D-galactose

   c. α-D-fructose

   d. β-maltose

   e. α-lactose

   f. sucrose

10. Maltose can be hydrolyzed to: ______________ and ________________.

11. What is the name of the process by which glucose and other monosaccharides can switch between the alpha configuration and the beta configuration?

12. ______________________________ is a highly branched storage polysaccharide stored in the liver and muscle of animals.

13. How are the following pairs of carbohydrates similar, and how are they different?

    a. amylose and cellulose

    b. amylose and amylopectin

    c. amylopectin and glycogen

14. a. What does a positive Benedict's test look like? __________________________

    b. What does a positive iodine test look like? __________________________

    c. For each of the following carbohydrates, indicate whether the Benedict's test is positive or negative and whether the iodine test is positive or negative.

Sugar	Benedict's Test	Iodine Test
sucrose		
glucose		
fructose		
lactose		
starch		
glycogen		

12

Carboxylic Acids and Esters

Carboxylic acids, also known as organic acids, are compounds with a carboxyl group (–COOH) at the terminal end of a carbon chain. These compounds are weak acids. The most common carboxylic acid is ethanoic acid, known for centuries as acetic acid (*acetum* in Latin). It is found in vinegar. Esters are derivatives of carboxylic acids, prepared by reacting the organic acid with an alcohol. Flowers and fruit contain esters, giving them a pleasant aroma and flavor.

I. Carboxylic Acids

A. Structure and Function

The carboxyl group is $-\overset{O}{\overset{\|}{C}}-OH$. Carboxylic acids are organic compounds that contain the carboxyl group. The carboxyl group is always on a terminal carbon atom. Carboxylic acids are weak acids, since only a small fraction of acid molecules exist as ions when dissolved in water. The dissociation of acetic acid is:

$$H-\underset{\underset{H}{|}}{\overset{\overset{H}{|}}{C}}-\overset{\overset{O}{\|}}{C}-O-H \quad + \quad H_2O \quad \rightleftharpoons \quad H-\underset{\underset{H}{|}}{\overset{\overset{H}{|}}{C}}-\overset{\overset{O}{\|}}{C}-O^- \quad + \quad H_3O^+$$

Acetic acid + Water ⇌ Acetate ion + Hydronium ion

Some other examples of common carboxylic acids are:

$$H-\underset{\underset{H}{|}}{\overset{\overset{H}{|}}{C}}-\underset{\underset{H}{|}}{\overset{\overset{\overset{H}{|}}{O}}{|}}{C}-\overset{\overset{O}{\|}}{C}-O-H$$

Lactic acid

$$\begin{array}{c} OH \\ | \\ C=O \\ | \\ C_6H_5 \end{array}$$

Benzoic acid

$$CH_3-CH_2-CH_2-\overset{\overset{O}{\|}}{C}-OH$$

Butanoic acid

B. Nomenclature of Carboxylic Acids (Optional)

To name carboxylic acids, the "e" ending of the alkane is changed to "oic acid." The parent chain is the longest possible chain that contains the carboxyl group. The carboxyl carbon atom is always considered carbon-1.

Example A: Name the following compounds:

a.

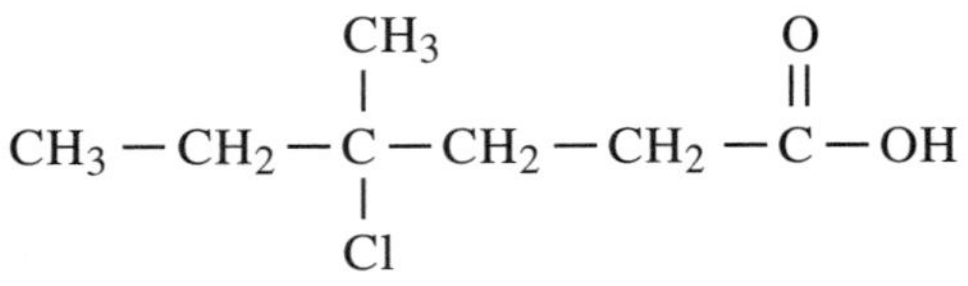

$$CH_3-CH_2-\underset{\underset{Cl}{|}}{\overset{\overset{CH_3}{|}}{C}}-CH_2-CH_2-\overset{\overset{O}{\|}}{C}-OH$$

The parent chain contains 6 carbon atoms, therefore called hexanoic acid. A methyl group ($-CH_3$) and a chloro group (–Cl) are present, both on carbon-4, since the chain is numbered from the carboxyl carbon.

The name of this compound is **4-chloro-4-methylhexanoic acid.**

b.

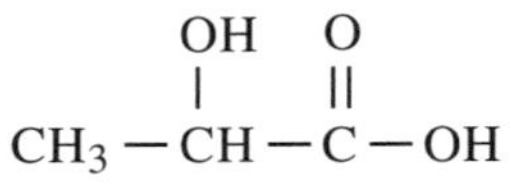

$$CH_3-\overset{\overset{OH}{|}}{CH}-\overset{\overset{O}{\|}}{C}-OH$$

This molecule is commonly known as lactic acid. The carboxyl group takes precedence over the hydroxyl group so this compound is a carboxylic acid with a hydroxyl group attached to it.

The name of this compound is **2-hydroxypropanoic acid.**

Problem 1. Name the following carboxylic acids:

a. 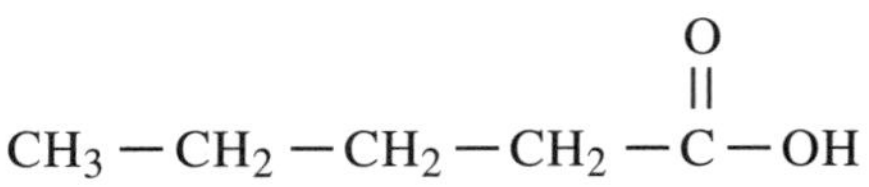 $CH_3-CH_2-CH_2-CH_2-\overset{\overset{O}{\|}}{C}-OH$

b. $Cl-CH_2-CH_2-\overset{\overset{O}{\|}}{C}-OH$

c. $CH_3-CH_2-CH_2-\overset{\overset{O}{\|}}{C}-OH$

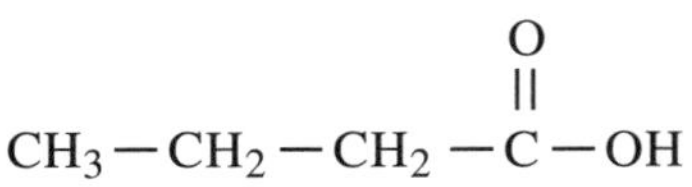

d. 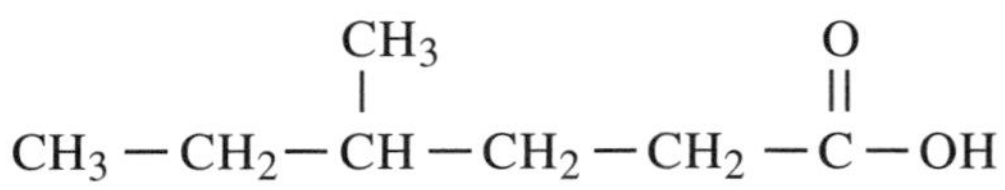 $CH_3-CH_2-\overset{\overset{CH_3}{|}}{CH}-CH_2-CH_2-\overset{\overset{O}{\|}}{C}-OH$

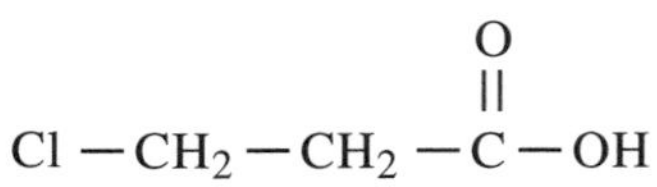

Problem 2. Draw structures for the following compounds:

a. 2,3-dimethylpentanoic acid

b. 3-bromopentanoic acid

c. 4-ethyl-5-methylheptanoic acid

d. 8-hydroxyoctanoic acid

C. Preparation of Carboxylic Acids

Carboxylic acids are usually prepared by oxidizing aldehydes. It is also possible to start with a primary alcohol, which is first oxidized to the aldehyde, then this newly-formed aldehyde can be further oxidized to form the carboxylic acid.

Example B:

1° alcohol $\xrightarrow{[O]}$ aldehyde $\xrightarrow{[O]}$ carboxylic acid

$$\mathrm{H{-}CH_2{-}CH_2{-}O{-}H} \xrightarrow{[O]} \mathrm{H{-}CH_2{-}CH{=}O} \xrightarrow{[O]} \mathrm{H{-}CH_2{-}C({=}O){-}O{-}H}$$

ethanol ethanal ethanoic acid

Problem 3. Complete the following oxidation reactions:

a. $\mathrm{H{-}CH_2{-}CH_2{-}CH_2{-}CH{=}O} \xrightarrow{[O]}$

b. $\mathrm{CH_3{-}CH_2{-}CH(CH_3){-}CH(CH_2CH_3){-}CH_2{-}CH_2{-}C({=}O)H} \xrightarrow{[O]}$

c. $\mathrm{CH_3{-}CH(CH_3){-}CH(CH_3){-}C({=}O)H} \xrightarrow{[O]}$

d. $\mathrm{CH_3{-}CH_2{-}CH(CH_3){-}CH_2{-}C({=}O)H} \xrightarrow{[O]}$

D. Reactions of Carboxylic Acids

1. **Neutralization Reactions**

   Carboxylic acids are weak acids capable of reacting with bases to form carboxylate salts and water. This is a neutralization reaction.

Example C:

carboxylic acid + base ⟶ carboxylate salt + water

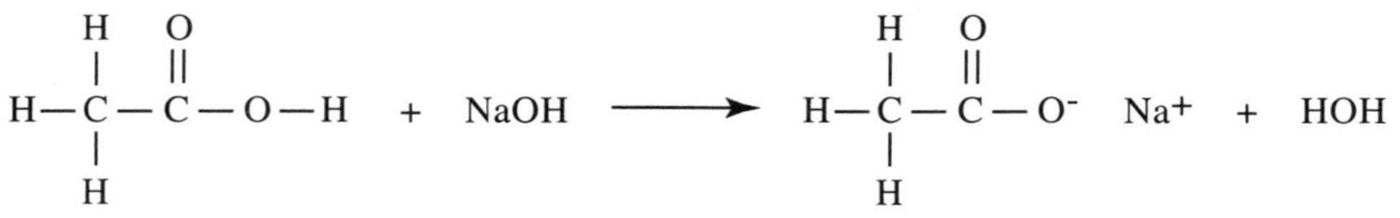

$$H{-}\underset{\underset{H}{|}}{\overset{\overset{H}{|}}{C}}{-}\overset{\overset{O}{||}}{C}{-}O{-}H \;+\; NaOH \longrightarrow H{-}\underset{\underset{H}{|}}{\overset{\overset{H}{|}}{C}}{-}\overset{\overset{O}{||}}{C}{-}O^{-}\;Na^{+} \;+\; HOH$$

Ethanoic acid + NaOH ⟶ Sodium ethanoate + Water

Problem 4. Complete the following neutralization reactions:

a. $CH_3{-}CH_2{-}CH_2{-}CH_2{-}\overset{\overset{O}{||}}{C}{-}OH \;+\; NaOH \longrightarrow$

b. $Cl{-}CH_2{-}CH_2{-}\overset{\overset{O}{||}}{C}{-}OH \;+\; KOH \longrightarrow$

c. $CH_3{-}CH_2{-}CH_2{-}\overset{\overset{O}{||}}{C}{-}OH \;+\; NaOH \longrightarrow$

d. $CH_3{-}CH_2{-}\overset{\overset{CH_3}{|}}{CH}{-}CH_2{-}CH_2{-}\overset{\overset{O}{||}}{C}{-}OH \;+\; KOH \longrightarrow$

2. **Formation of an Ester**

   The reaction of a carboxylic acid with an alcohol produces an ester molecule and water. In the reaction, the –OH group of the carboxylic acid combines with the –H from the alcohol group to produce the water molecule. The organic portions combine to produce the ester molecule.

Example D:

carboxylic acid	+	alcohol	⟶	ester	+	water

$$\mathrm{H{-}\overset{H}{\underset{H}{C}}{-}\overset{O}{\overset{\|}{C}}{-}O{-}H} + \mathbf{H{-}O{-}\overset{H}{\underset{H}{C}}{-}H} \xrightarrow{H^+} \mathrm{H{-}\overset{H}{\underset{H}{C}}{-}\overset{O}{\overset{\|}{C}}{-}}\mathbf{O{-}\overset{H}{\underset{H}{C}}{-}H} + \mathbf{H{-}O{-}H}$$

Ethanoic acid + Methanol ⟶ Methyl ethanoate + Water

Problem 5. Complete the following esterification reactions:

a. $CH_3{-}CH(CH_3){-}CH(CH_3){-}CH_2{-}C(=O){-}OH + H{-}O{-}CH_2{-}CH_2{-}CH_2{-}H \xrightarrow{H^+}$

b. $CH_3{-}CH(CH_3){-}C(=O){-}OH + HO{-}C_6H_{11}$ (cyclohexyl) $\xrightarrow{H^+}$

c. $CH_3{-}CH_2{-}CH_2{-}C(=O){-}OH + HO{-}CH(CH_3){-}CH_3 \xrightarrow{H^+}$

d. $CH_3{-}CH_2{-}CH(CH_3){-}C(=O){-}OH + HO{-}CH(CH_3){-}CH_2{-}CH_2{-}CH_3 \xrightarrow{H^+}$

II. Esters

A. Introduction

Esters can be considered derivatives of carboxylic acids in which an organic group replaces the acidic hydrogen of the carboxyl group. Perhaps the most familiar physical property of esters is their pleasant odor. The aromas of many flowers, fruits, and perfumes are due to mixtures of esters. Esters are widely used as food additives to impart specific flavors and aromas to processed foods.

Methyl Butyrate
(apple)

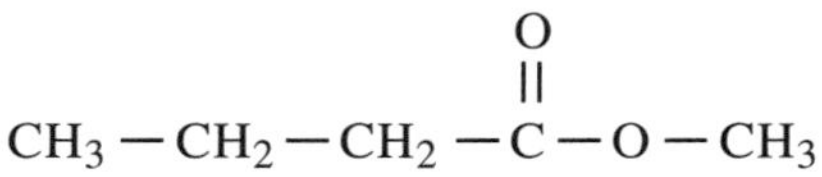

$$CH_3-CH_2-CH_2-\overset{\overset{\displaystyle O}{\|}}{C}-O-CH_3$$

Ethyl Butyrate
(pineapple)

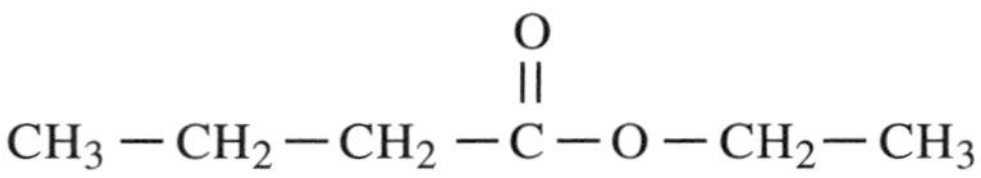

$$CH_3-CH_2-CH_2-\overset{\overset{\displaystyle O}{\|}}{C}-O-CH_2-CH_3$$

B. Preparation of Esters

The preparation of esters from carboxylic acids and alcohols has been previously described (see **Formation of an Ester**).

C. Reactions of Esters

1. **Acid Hydrolysis**

   The most important chemical reaction of esters is their hydrolysis to a carboxylic acid and an alcohol. Hydrolysis is the reverse of an esterification reaction. These reactions are catalyzed by strong acids.

Example E:

ester + water ⟶ carboxylic acid + alcohol

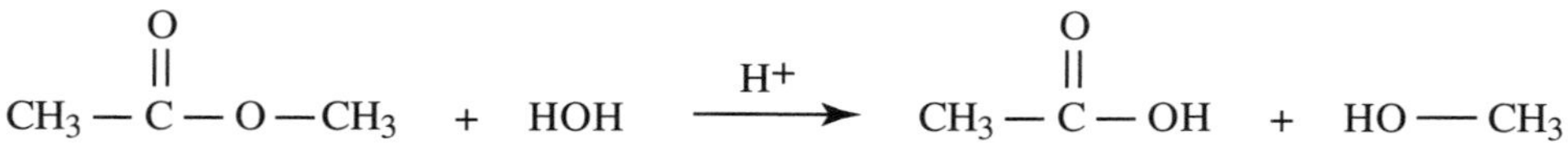

$$CH_3-\overset{\overset{\displaystyle O}{\|}}{C}-O-CH_3 + HOH \xrightarrow{H^+} CH_3-\overset{\overset{\displaystyle O}{\|}}{C}-OH + HO-CH_3$$

Methyl ethanoate + Water ⟶ Ethanoic acid + Methanol

Problem 6: Complete the following hydrolysis reactions:

a. 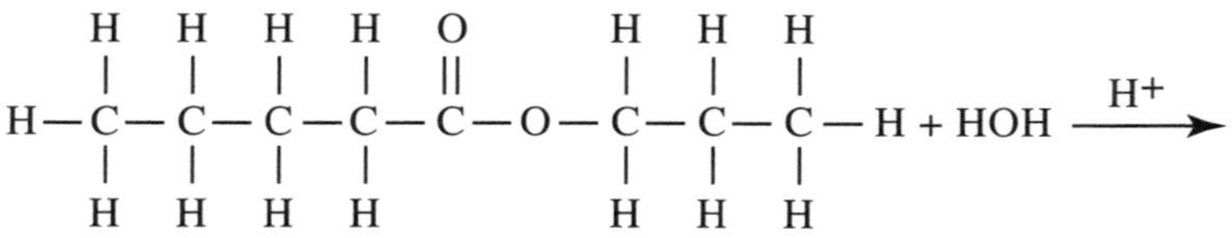 $$H-\underset{\underset{\displaystyle H}{|}}{\overset{\overset{\displaystyle H}{|}}{C}}-\underset{\underset{\displaystyle H}{|}}{\overset{\overset{\displaystyle H}{|}}{C}}-\underset{\underset{\displaystyle H}{|}}{\overset{\overset{\displaystyle H}{|}}{C}}-\underset{\underset{\displaystyle H}{|}}{\overset{\overset{\displaystyle H}{|}}{C}}-\overset{\overset{\displaystyle O}{\|}}{C}-O-\underset{\underset{\displaystyle H}{|}}{\overset{\overset{\displaystyle H}{|}}{C}}-\underset{\underset{\displaystyle H}{|}}{\overset{\overset{\displaystyle H}{|}}{C}}-\underset{\underset{\displaystyle H}{|}}{\overset{\overset{\displaystyle H}{|}}{C}}-H + HOH \xrightarrow{H^+}$$

b. $$CH_3-CH_2-\overset{\overset{\displaystyle O}{\|}}{C}-O-C_6H_{11} + HOH \xrightarrow{H^+}$$ (cyclohexyl ring)

c. $$CH_3-CH_2-CH_2-\overset{\overset{\displaystyle O}{\|}}{C}-O-\underset{\underset{\displaystyle CH_3}{|}}{\overset{\overset{\displaystyle CH_3}{|}}{CH}} + HOH \xrightarrow{H^+}$$

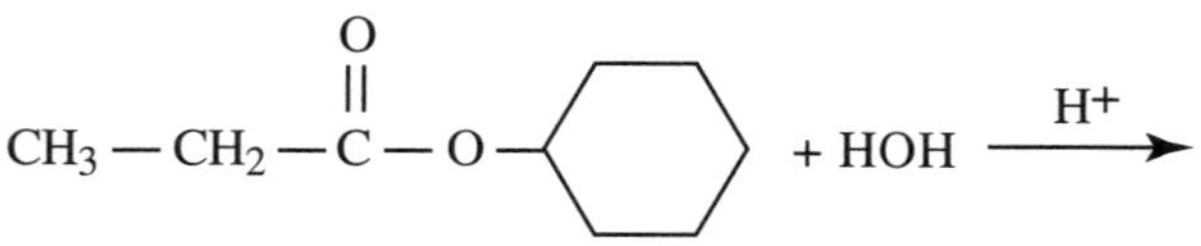

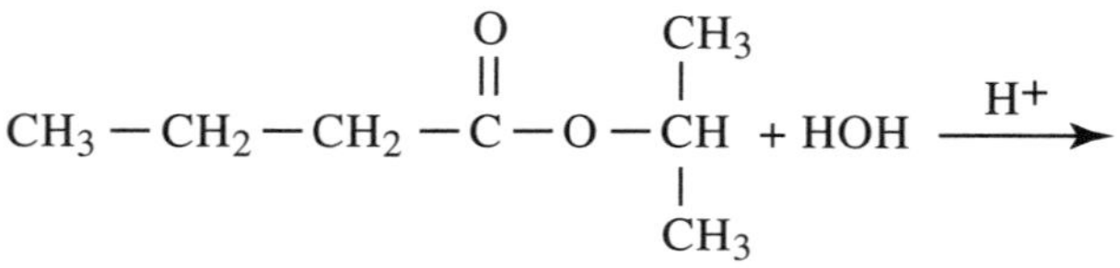

d. $CH_3-\overset{\overset{\displaystyle O}{\|}}{C}-O-CH_2-\underset{\underset{\displaystyle CH_3}{|}}{CH}-CH_3 + HOH \xrightarrow{H^+}$

2. **Base Hydrolysis (Saponification)**

   Saponification is the base-catalyzed hydrolysis of an ester. Usually, enough base is present so that the salt of the carboxylic acid is produced along with the alcohol.

Example F:

ester + strong base ⟶ carboxylate salt + alcohol

$$CH_3-\overset{\overset{\displaystyle O}{\|}}{C}-O-CH_3 + NaOH \longrightarrow CH_3-\overset{\overset{\displaystyle O}{\|}}{C}-O^- Na^+ + HO-CH_3$$

Methyl ethanoate + NaOH ⟶ Sodium ethanoate + Methanol

Problem 7. Complete the following saponification reactions:

a. $H-\underset{\underset{\displaystyle H}{|}}{\overset{\overset{\displaystyle H}{|}}{C}}-\underset{\underset{\displaystyle H}{|}}{\overset{\overset{\displaystyle H}{|}}{C}}-\underset{\underset{\displaystyle H}{|}}{\overset{\overset{\displaystyle H}{|}}{C}}-\underset{\underset{\displaystyle H}{|}}{\overset{\overset{\displaystyle H}{|}}{C}}-\overset{\overset{\displaystyle O}{\|}}{C}-O-\underset{\underset{\displaystyle H}{|}}{\overset{\overset{\displaystyle H}{|}}{C}}-\underset{\underset{\displaystyle H}{|}}{\overset{\overset{\displaystyle H}{|}}{C}}-\underset{\underset{\displaystyle H}{|}}{\overset{\overset{\displaystyle H}{|}}{C}}-H + NaOH \longrightarrow$

b. $CH_3-CH_2-\overset{\overset{\displaystyle O}{\|}}{C}-O-C_6H_{11}$ (cyclohexyl) $+ NaOH \longrightarrow$

c. $CH_3-CH_2-CH_2-\overset{\overset{\displaystyle O}{\|}}{C}-O-\underset{\underset{\displaystyle CH_3}{|}}{\overset{\overset{\displaystyle CH_3}{|}}{CH}} + NaOH \longrightarrow$

d. $CH_3-\overset{\overset{\displaystyle O}{\|}}{C}-O-CH_2-\underset{\underset{\displaystyle CH_3}{|}}{CH}-CH_3 + NaOH \longrightarrow$

ANSWERS

1. a. pentanoic acid
   b. 3-chloropropanoic acid
   c. butanoic acid
   d. 4-methylhexanoic acid

2. a.

$$\begin{array}{ccccccccccc} & & & & CH_3 & & CH_3 & & O & & \\ & & & & | & & | & & \| & & \\ CH_3 & - & CH_2 & - & CH & - & CH & - & C & - & OH \end{array}$$

b.

$$\begin{array}{ccccccccccc} & & & & Br & & & & O & & \\ & & & & | & & & & \| & & \\ CH_3 & - & CH_2 & - & CH & - & CH_2 & - & C & - & OH \end{array}$$

c.

$$\begin{array}{ccccccccccccccc} & & & & & & CH_3 & & & & & & & & \\ & & & & & & | & & & & & & & & \\ & & & & CH_3 & & CH_2 & & & & & & O & & \\ & & & & | & & | & & & & & & \| & & \\ CH_3 & - & CH_2 & - & CH & - & CH & - & CH_2 & - & CH_2 & - & C & - & OH \end{array}$$

d.

$$\begin{array}{ccccccccc} & & & & & & O & & \\ & & & & & & \| & & \\ HO & — & CH_2 & - & (CH_2)_6 & - & C & - & OH \end{array}$$

3. a.

$$\begin{array}{ccccccccc} & & & & & & O & & \\ & & & & & & \| & & \\ CH_3 & - & CH_2 & - & CH_2 & - & C & - & OH \end{array}$$

b.

$$\begin{array}{ccccccccccccccc} & & & & & & CH_3 & & & & & & & & \\ & & & & & & | & & & & & & & & \\ & & & & CH_3 & & CH_2 & & & & & & O & & \\ & & & & | & & | & & & & & & \| & & \\ CH_3 & - & CH_2 & - & CH & - & CH & - & CH_2 & - & CH_2 & - & C & - & OH \end{array}$$

c.

$$\begin{array}{ccccccccc} & & CH_3 & & CH_3 & & O & & \\ & & | & & | & & \| & & \\ CH_3 & - & CH & - & CH & - & C & - & OH \end{array}$$

d.

$$\begin{array}{ccccccccccc} & & & & CH_3 & & & & O & & \\ & & & & | & & & & \| & & \\ CH_3 & - & CH_2 & - & CH & - & CH_2 & - & C & - & OH \end{array}$$

4. a. $CH_3-CH_2-CH_2-CH_2-\overset{\overset{O}{\|}}{C}-O^-\ Na^+ + HOH$

   b. $\overset{\overset{Cl}{|}}{CH_2}-CH_2-\overset{\overset{O}{\|}}{C}-O^-\ K^+ + HOH$

   c. $CH_3-CH_2-CH_2-\overset{\overset{O}{\|}}{C}-O^-\ Na^+ + HOH$

   d. $CH_3-CH_2-\overset{\overset{CH_3}{|}}{CH}-CH_2-CH_2-\overset{\overset{O}{\|}}{C}-O^-\ K^+ + HOH$

5. a. $CH_3-\overset{\overset{CH_3}{|}}{CH}-\overset{\overset{CH_3}{|}}{CH}-CH_2-\overset{\overset{O}{\|}}{C}-O-\underset{\underset{H}{|}}{\overset{\overset{H}{|}}{C}}-\underset{\underset{H}{|}}{\overset{\overset{H}{|}}{C}}-\underset{\underset{H}{|}}{\overset{\overset{H}{|}}{C}}-H + HOH$

   b. $CH_3\overset{\overset{CH_3}{|}}{CH}-\overset{\overset{O}{\|}}{C}-O-C_6H_{11}$ (cyclohexyl) $+ HOH$

   c. $CH_3-CH_2-CH_2-\overset{\overset{O}{\|}}{C}-O-\underset{\underset{CH_3}{|}}{\overset{\overset{CH_3}{|}}{CH}} + HOH$

   d. $CH_3-CH_2-\overset{\overset{CH_3}{|}}{CH}-\overset{\overset{O}{\|}}{C}-O-\overset{\overset{CH_3}{|}}{CH}(-CH_2-CH_2-CH_3) + HOH$

6\. a. $H-\overset{H}{\underset{H}{C}}-\overset{H}{\underset{H}{C}}-\overset{H}{\underset{H}{C}}-\overset{H}{\underset{H}{C}}-\overset{O}{\overset{\|}{C}}-OH \quad + \quad H-O-\overset{H}{\underset{H}{C}}-\overset{H}{\underset{H}{C}}-\overset{H}{\underset{H}{C}}-H$

b. $CH_3-CH_2-\overset{O}{\overset{\|}{C}}-OH \quad + \quad HO-$ (cyclohexane ring)

c. $CH_3-CH_2-CH_2-\overset{O}{\overset{\|}{C}}-OH \quad + \quad HO-\overset{CH_3}{\underset{CH_3}{CH}}$

d. $CH_3-\overset{O}{\overset{\|}{C}}-OH \quad + \quad HO-CH_2-\underset{CH_3}{CH}-CH_3$

7\. a. $H-\overset{H}{\underset{H}{C}}-\overset{H}{\underset{H}{C}}-\overset{H}{\underset{H}{C}}-\overset{H}{\underset{H}{C}}-\overset{O}{\overset{\|}{C}}-O^- \ Na^+ \quad + \quad H-O-\overset{H}{\underset{H}{C}}-\overset{H}{\underset{H}{C}}-\overset{H}{\underset{H}{C}}-H$

b. $CH_3-CH_2-\overset{O}{\overset{\|}{C}}-O^- \ Na^+ \quad + \quad HO-$ (cyclohexane ring)

c. $CH_3-CH_2-CH_2-\overset{O}{\overset{\|}{C}}-O^- \ Na^+ \quad + \quad HO-\overset{CH_3}{\underset{CH_3}{CH}}$

d. $CH_3-\overset{O}{\overset{\|}{C}}-O^- \ Na^+ \quad + \quad HO-CH_2-\underset{CH_3}{CH}-CH_3$

Carboxylic Acids and Esters

Assignment 12

Name ______________________

Student Number ______________________

Date ______________ Instructor ______________

1. Classify each of the following as a/an aldehyde, alcohol, carboxylic acid, ester, ether, or ketone.

a. 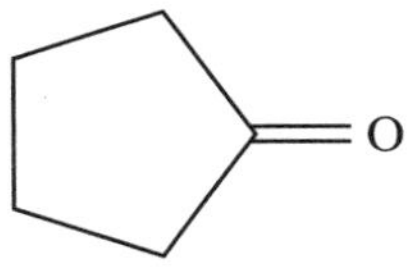 (cyclopentanone: five-membered ring with =O)

b. 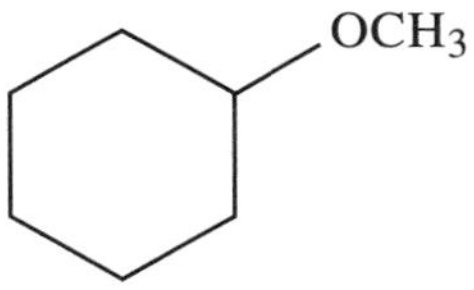 (cyclohexane ring bearing OCH_3)

c. $CH_3\overset{O}{\overset{||}{C}}\text{-O-}CH_3$

d. $CH_3CH_2\overset{O}{\overset{||}{C}}H$

e. $CH_3CH_2\overset{O}{\overset{||}{C}}\text{-OH}$

f. $CH_3CH_2\text{-O-}CH_3$

g. $CH_3\overset{O}{\overset{||}{C}}\text{-}OCH_3$

h. $CH_3\overset{OH}{\overset{|}{C}}HCH_3$

2. Complete oxidation of 2-methyl-1-butanol results in (draw structures):

3. The product of the reaction between a carboxylic acid and an alcohol is:

4. When an ester is saponified (base hydrolysis), the organic product is:

5. Give structures of the products for the following reactions. (Hint: Classify the reactions first as esterification, neutralization, acid hydrolysis, or basic hydrolysis.)

a. 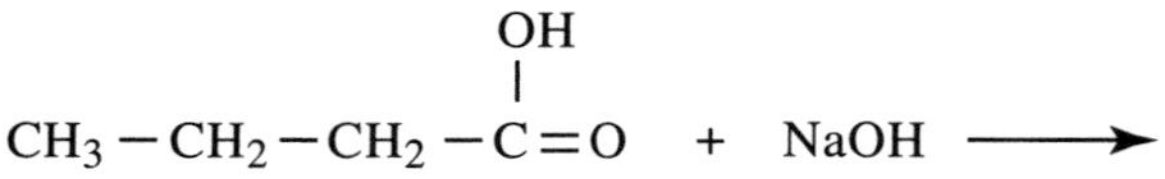 $$CH_3-CH_2-CH_2-\overset{\displaystyle OH}{\overset{|}{C}}=O \quad + \quad NaOH \longrightarrow$$

b. $$CH_3-CH_2-CH_2-\overset{\displaystyle OH}{\overset{|}{C}}=O \quad + \quad CH_3-\overset{\displaystyle OH}{\overset{|}{CH}}-CH_2-CH_3 \xrightarrow{H+}$$

c. $$CH_3-CH_2-\underset{\displaystyle CH_3}{\underset{|}{CH}}-\overset{\displaystyle OH}{\overset{|}{C}}=O \quad + \quad CH_3-CH_2-OH \xrightarrow{H+}$$

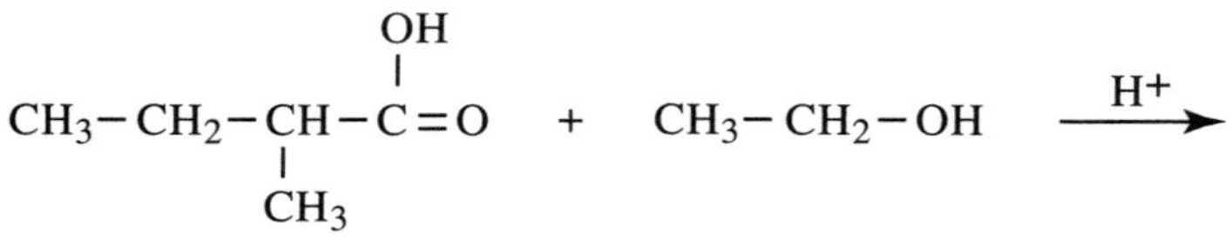

d. 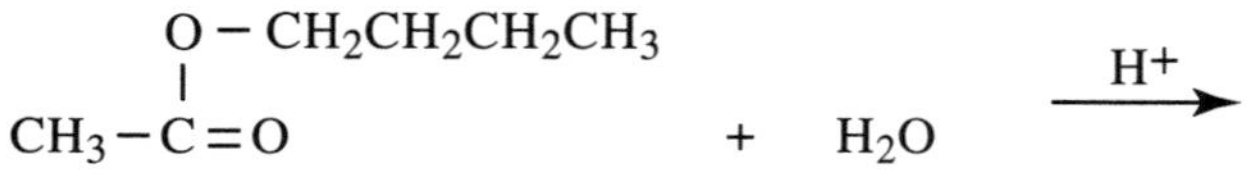 $$CH_3-\overset{\displaystyle O-CH_2CH_2CH_2CH_3}{\overset{|}{C}}=O \quad + \quad H_2O \xrightarrow{H+}$$

e. 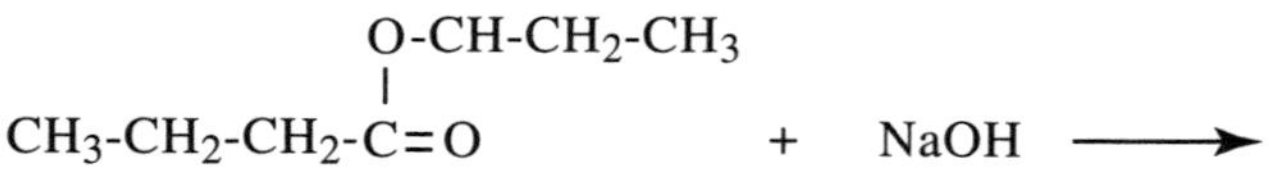 $$CH_3\text{-}CH_2\text{-}CH_2\text{-}\overset{\displaystyle O\text{-}CH\text{-}CH_2\text{-}CH_3}{\overset{|}{C}}=O \quad + \quad NaOH \longrightarrow$$

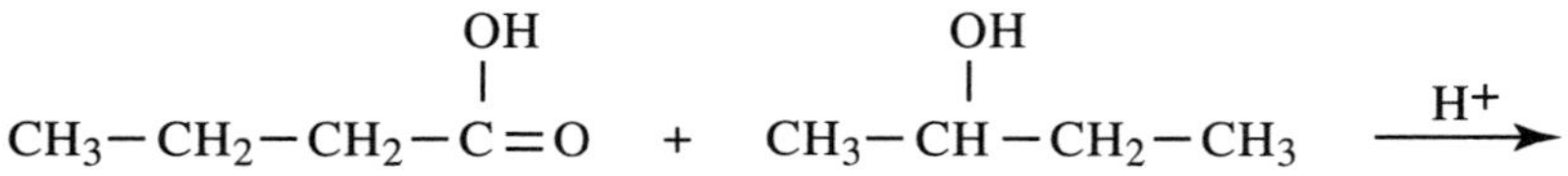

f. $$CH_3-CH_2-COOH \quad + \quad CH_3-CH_2-OH \xrightarrow{H+}$$

g. $C_6H_{11}-O-\overset{O}{\overset{\|}{C}}-CH_2CH_2CH_2CH_3 + NaOH \longrightarrow$

h. $CH_3-CH_2-COOH + KOH \longrightarrow$

i. $H_3C-\overset{O}{\overset{\|}{C}}-O-\overset{H_2}{C}-CH_3 + NaOH \longrightarrow$

6. The following compound is produced from the reaction of (draw structures).

$$C_6H_{11}-\overset{O}{\overset{\|}{C}}-O-\overset{CH_3}{\overset{|}{CH}}-CH_3$$

NOTES

13

Amines and Amides

Amines and amides contain carbon, hydrogen, oxygen, *and* nitrogen atoms. These compounds are very important for life. They are found in amino acids, proteins, and the nucleic acids DNA and RNA. Amines are considered weak bases. Alkaloids are amines found in plants. Nicotine, caffeine, quinine, cocaine, morphine and codeine are examples of alkaloids used as stimulants, anesthetics and antidepressants. Some of these are habit forming. When an amine reacts with a carboxylic acid, the resulting compound is an amide, a neutral compound.

I. Amines

A. Structure

Amines are organic molecules that are derivatives of ammonia (NH_3). Ammonia has three hydrogen atoms bonded to nitrogen. In amines, one or more of the hydrogen atoms have been replaced by an alkyl or aromatic group. Depending on the number of hydrogen atoms which have been replaced, amines are classified as primary (1°), secondary (2°), or tertiary (3°).

Some examples of amines are as follows:

$H_3C—NH_2$	$CH_3—N(CH_3)—CH_3$	$CH_3—CH_2—NH—CH_3$	$C_6H_5—NH_2$
methylamine primary (1°)	trimethylamine tertiary (3°)	ethylmethylamine secondary (2°)	aniline primary (1°)

B. Amines as Bases

Amines are weak bases, just like ammonia. The Lewis structures for ammonia and amines demonstrate that the nitrogen atom has a lone electron pair, which is capable of acting as a proton acceptor. The following equations show how ammonia and amines can accept a proton (a hydrogen ion) from water, thereby releasing hydroxide ions (OH^-).

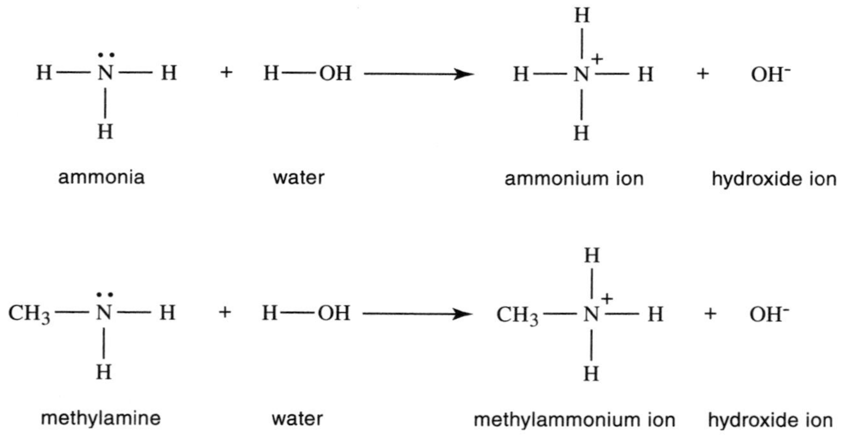

$$H-\ddot{N}(H)-H + H-OH \longrightarrow H-N^{+}(H)(H)-H + OH^-$$

ammonia water ammonium ion hydroxide ion

$$CH_3-\ddot{N}(H)-H + H-OH \longrightarrow CH_3-N^{+}(H)(H)-H + OH^-$$

methylamine water methylammonium ion hydroxide ion

C. Nomenclature of Amines (OPTIONAL)

To name amines, the carbon-containing groups attached to the nitrogen atom are listed in alphabetical order followed by the word amine.

Example A:

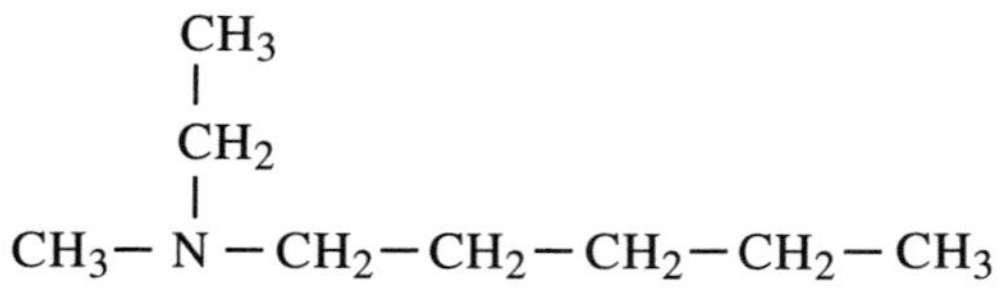

$$CH_3-N(CH_2CH_3)-CH_2-CH_2-CH_2-CH_2-CH_3$$

The nitrogen atom has three groups attached to it, making it a tertiary amine. This compound contains a methyl, ethyl, and pentyl groups, which must be listed alphabetically.

The name of this compound is **ethylmethylpentylamine**.

Example B:

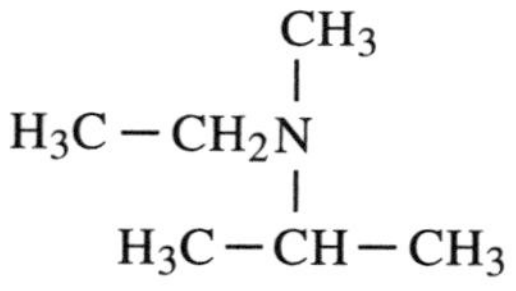

$$H_3C-CH_2N(CH_3)-CH(CH_3)-CH_3$$

The nitrogen atom has three groups attached to it, making it a tertiary amine. The three groups are named in alphabetical order. This compound contains the methyl, ethyl, and isopropyl groups.

The name for this compound is **ethylisopropylmethylamine**.

Problem 1. Name and classify the following amines as primary (1°), secondary (2°), or tertiary (3°):

a. CH_3–CH_2–NH–CH_2–CH_3

b. CH_3–NH–CH_2–CH_2–CH_2–CH_3

c. 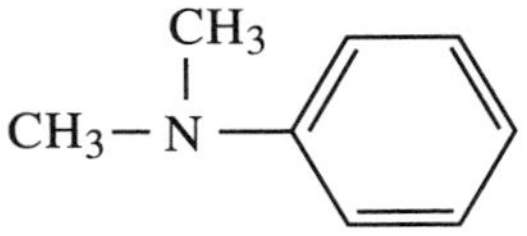 CH_3–N(CH_3)–(benzene ring)

d. H_2N—CH_2–CH_2–CH_2–CH_2–CH_3

e. CH_3–CH_2–NH–CH_2–CH_2–CH_3

Problem 2. Draw structures for the following amines:

a. diphenylamine

b. butyldimethylamine

c. propylamine

d. ethylpentylamine

e. ethylisopropylamine

f. ethylmethylamine

D. Reactions of Amines

Amines react as bases, therefore, they will react with any proton-donating substance. Water can donate a proton to the amine, producing an ammonium ion and a hydroxide ion.

Example C:

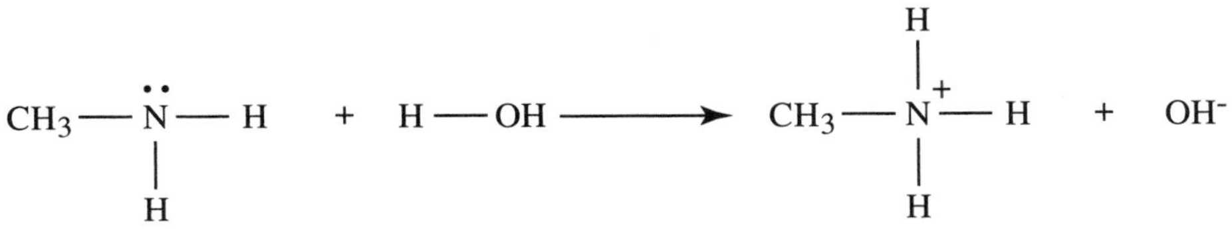

$$CH_3—\ddot{N}H_2 + H—OH \longrightarrow CH_3—\overset{+}{N}H_3 + OH^-$$

methylamine | water | methylammonium ion | hydroxide ion

Amine salts are formed by neutralizing amines with acids. Amine salts are ionic compounds, therefore, they are **soluble in water** and in body fluids. For this reason many amines used as drugs are converted into amine salts. Examples are: amine salts of ephedrine, used in Sudafed, and of diphenhydramine, used in Benadryl.

Example D:

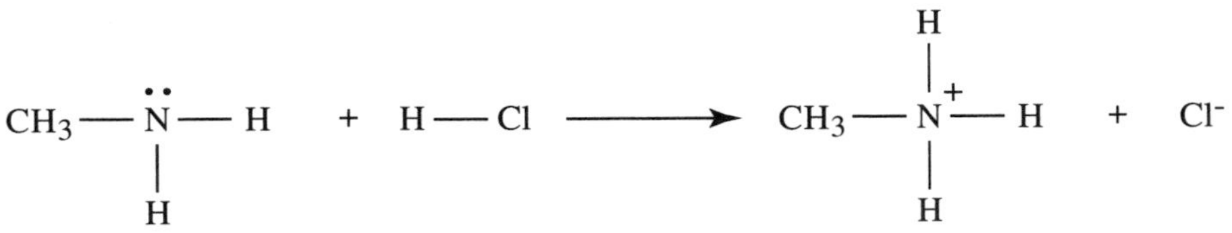

$$CH_3—\ddot{N}H_2 + H—Cl \longrightarrow CH_3—\overset{+}{N}H_3 + Cl^-$$

methylamine | hydrochloric acid | methylammonium ion | chloride ion

Problem 3. Complete the following reactions:

a. $H_2N—CH_2–CH_2–CH_2–CH_2–CH_3$ + HOH ⟶

b. $CH_3–CH_2–NH–CH_2–CH_3$ + HOH ⟶

c. $CH_3–NH–CH_2–CH_2–CH_2–CH_3$ + HOH ⟶

d. $CH_3–CH_2–NH–CH_2–CH_2–CH_3$ + HOH ⟶

Problem 4. Research the chemical structure for: a. nicotine (a stimulant) and b. ephedrine hydrochloride (a bronchodilator and decongestant). Classify these as either amine or amine salt.

II. Amides

A. Structure and Function

Amides are neutral compounds. Amides are considered a separate functional group from amines, and unlike amines they **are not proton-acceptors**. They are **not** proton-donors, either. In other words, the amide group does not affect the pH of an aqueous system.

Amides may be considered to be amine derivatives of carboxylic acids. The amide bond is very important in biochemistry since it is the essential link for amino acids in protein molecules. In protein molecules, the amide functional group is usually called a peptide linkage. An example of a common amide is ethanamide.

$$CH_3-\overset{\overset{\displaystyle O}{\|}}{C}-NH_2$$

Ethanamide

B. Reaction of Amides

The most important reaction of an amide is its hydrolysis (cleaving with water) to produce a carboxylic acid and an amine. The reaction can be catalyzed by either an acid or a base and with the addition of heat. Since humans must maintain a constant body temperature and a pH that is close to neutral, the hydrolysis process must occur with the use of enzymes rather than strong acid or base.

Example E: **Enzyme-catalyzed** hydrolysis reaction of an amide:

$$\text{Amide} + \text{Water} \xrightarrow{\text{enzyme}} \text{Carboxylic acid} + \text{Amine}$$

$$CH_3-\overset{\overset{\displaystyle O}{\|}}{C}-\overset{\overset{\displaystyle H}{|}}{N}-CH_3 + HOH \xrightarrow{\text{enzyme}} CH_3-\overset{\overset{\displaystyle O}{\|}}{C}-OH + H-\overset{\overset{\displaystyle H}{|}}{N}-CH_3$$

Problem 5. Give products for the following enzyme-catalyzed hydrolysis reactions:

a. $CH_3-\overset{\overset{O}{\|}}{C}-NH-CH_2-CH_3 \; + \; HOH \xrightarrow{\text{enzyme}}$

b. $CH_3-\overset{\overset{O}{\|}}{C}-NH-CH_2-CH_2-CH_2-CH_3 \; + \; HOH \xrightarrow{\text{enzyme}}$

c. $CH_3-CH_2-\overset{\overset{O}{\|}}{C}-N(CH_3)-C_6H_5 \; + \; HOH \xrightarrow{\text{enzyme}}$

d. $C_6H_5-\overset{\overset{O}{\|}}{C}-N(CH_3)-CH_3 \; + \; HOH \xrightarrow{\text{enzyme}}$

e. $C_6H_5-\overset{\overset{O}{\|}}{C}-NH-CH_2-CH_2-CH_2-CH_3 \; + \; HOH \xrightarrow{\text{enzyme}}$

Problem 6. By now, many different functional groups have been studied. The following 3 molecules are aspirin, acetaminophen, and caffeine. Identify the groups present in these 3 molecules distinguishing among the following:

1. alcohol
2. aldehyde
3. ketone
4. carboxylic acid
5. benzene ring
6. ester
7. amine
8. amide

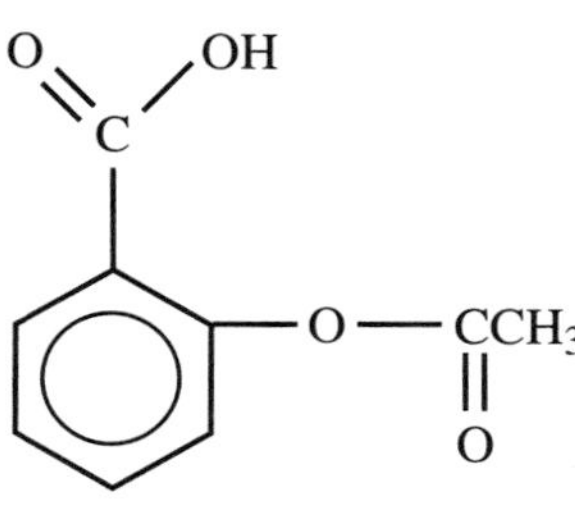

ASA
Acetylsalicylic Acid
(Aspirin)

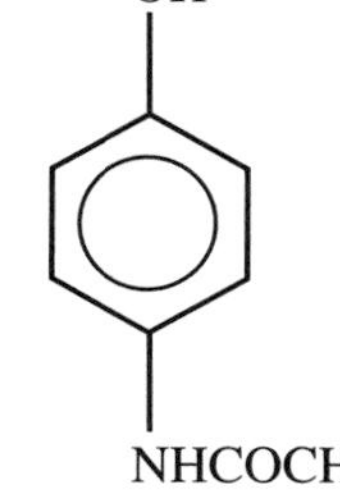

APHEN
Acetaminophen

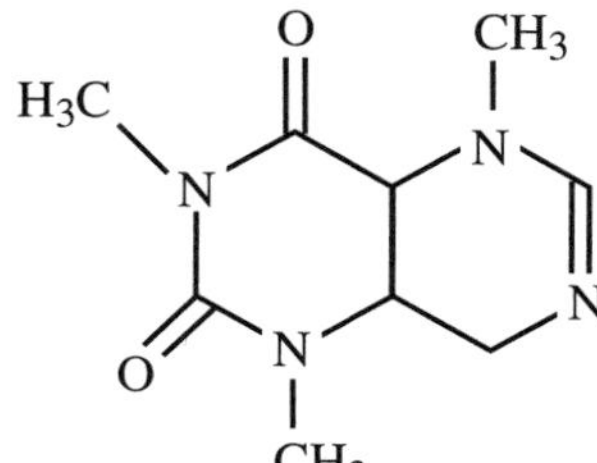

CAFF
Caffeine

ANSWERS

1. a. diethylamine, 2°

   b. butylmethylamine, 2°

   c. N,N-dimethylaniline (or dimethylphenylamine), 3°

   d. pentylamine, 1°

   e. ethylpropylamine, 2°

2. a. 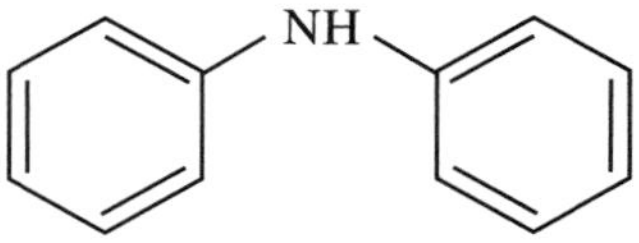 NH

   b. $N(CH_3)_2-CH_2-CH_2-CH_2-CH_3$

   c. $H_2N-CH_2-CH_2-CH_3$

   d. $CH_3-CH_2-NH-CH_2-CH_2-CH_2-CH_2-CH_3$

   e. $CH_3-CH_2-NH-CH(CH_3)_2$

   f. $CH_3-CH_2-NH-CH_3$

3. a. $H_2\overset{H}{\overset{|}{N}}{}^{+}\!\!-CH_2-CH_2-CH_2-CH_2-CH_3 \;+\; OH^-$

   b. $CH_3-CH_2-\overset{H}{\overset{|}{N}}{}^{+}H-CH_2-CH_3 \;+\; OH^-$

   c. $CH_3-\overset{H}{\overset{|}{N}}{}^{+}H-CH_2-CH_2-CH_2-CH_3 \;+\; OH^-$

   d. $CH_3-CH_2-\overset{H}{\overset{|}{N}}{}^{+}H-CH_2-CH_2-CH_3 \;+\; OH^-$

4. a. Nicotine is an amine.

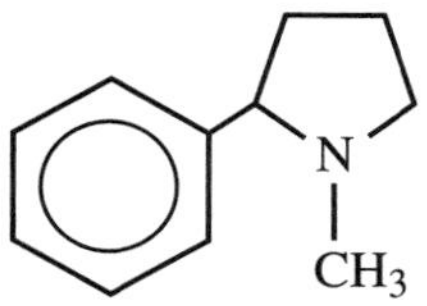

   N

   CH_3

   Nicotine

   b. Ephedrine hydrochloride is an amine salt, it is water soluble.

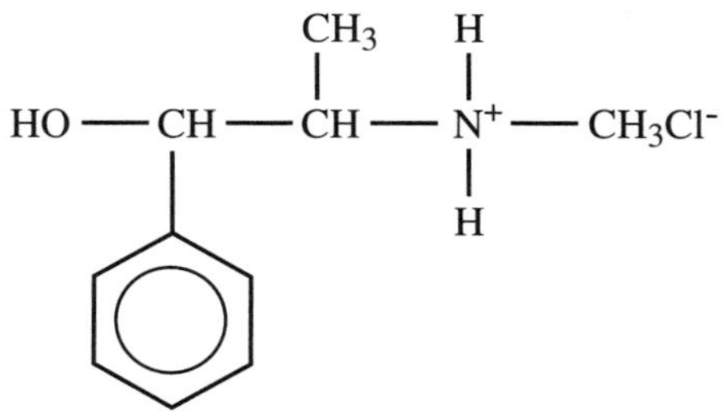

   $$HO-\underset{\displaystyle C_6H_5}{\underset{|}{CH}}-\overset{CH_3}{\overset{|}{CH}}-\overset{H}{\underset{H}{\overset{|}{\underset{|}{N^+}}}}-CH_3Cl^-$$

   Ephedrine hydrochloride
   Ephedrine HCl
   (Sudafed)

5. a. $CH_3-\overset{\overset{\large O}{\|}}{C}-OH \quad + \quad H-NH-CH_2-CH_3$

b. $CH_3-\overset{\overset{\large O}{\|}}{C}-OH \quad + \quad \overset{\overset{\large H}{|}}{HN}-CH_2-CH_2-CH_2-CH_3$

c. $CH_3-CH_2-\overset{\overset{\large O}{\|}}{C}-OH \quad + \quad H-\overset{\overset{\large CH_3}{|}}{N}-C_6H_5$

d. $C_6H_5-\overset{\overset{\large O}{\|}}{C}-OH \quad + \quad H-\overset{\overset{\large CH_3}{|}}{N}-CH_3$

e. $C_6H_5-\overset{\overset{\large O}{\|}}{C}-OH \quad + \quad H_2N-CH_2-CH_2-CH_2-CH_3$

6. a. ASA: carboxylic acid, ester, benzene ring

b. APHEN: alcohol, amide, benzene ring

c. CAFF: amide, amine

Amines and Amides
13
Assignment
Name
Student Number
Date
Instructor

1. Classify the following structures as primary amine, secondary amine, tertiary amine, or amide:

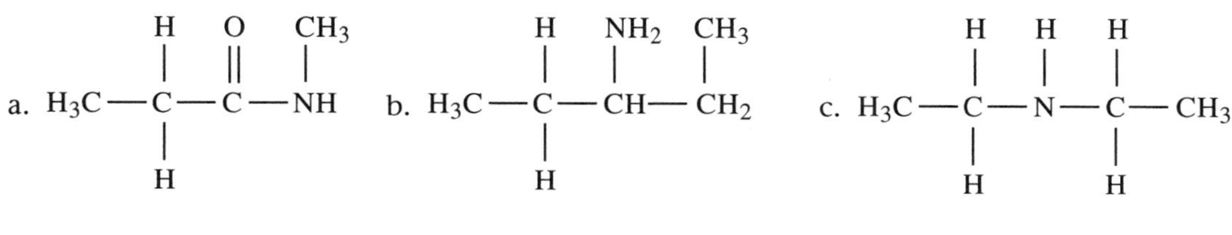

d. CH_3CHCH_3 with NH_2 on the central carbon

e. CH_3NCH_3 with CH_3 on the nitrogen

f. $CH_3CH_2NHCH_3$

g. NH_2CH_3

2. Amines are considered weak bases because:

3. Give structures of the products for the following reactions.

a. $CH_3—CH_2—NH_2 + H_2O \longrightarrow$

b. $CH_3—NH—CH_3 + H_2O \longrightarrow$

c. $CH_3CH_2\overset{\overset{\displaystyle O}{\|}}{C}NHCH_3 \quad + \quad H_2O \quad \xrightarrow{\text{enzyme}}$

14

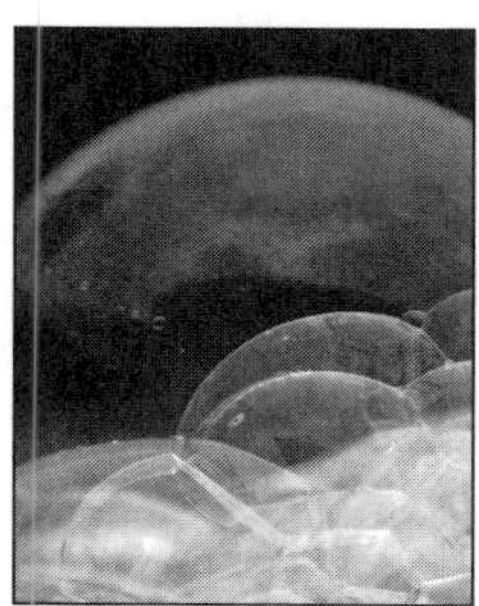

Lipids

Lipids are nonpolar compounds that are essential for living. Fats, oils, and steroids are examples of lipids. The word *lipid* comes from the greek *lipo* meaning fat or lard. Lipids are a class of biomolecules with seemingly unrelated structures. Their common feature, however, is that they are **not soluble in water**. Lipids are soluble in organic solvents but not in water.

I. Lipid Function

Lipids perform several important functions:

a. structural components of membranes

b. energy storage and transport

c. protective coating

d. metabolic regulation

II. Fatty Acids

Fatty acids are long-chain monocarboxylic acids and are a major component of lipids such as fats, oils, and prostaglandins.

Fatty acids have the following characteristics:

a. They are insoluble in water.

b. They contain an even number of carbons (usually 12–20) arranged in a continuous chain.

c. They can be **saturated** (only C–C single bonds) or **unsaturated** (one or more C=C double bonds).

d. Polyunsaturated fatty acids contain more than one double bond. Linoleic and linolenic acids are two polyunsaturated fatty acids.

e. Our bodies can make all the required fatty acids from foods we eat, except for linoleic and linolenic acids; these two acids, called **essential fatty acids**, must be contained in the food we eat. Fish, leafy vegetables, and vegetable oils contain linoleic and linolenic acids.

f. Arachidonic acid is an unsaturated fatty acid containing 20 carbons and is a precursor of **prostaglandins**. Prostaglandins are a group of about 20 lipids which are involved in reproduction and in the inflammatory response to infection and injury. When tissues suffer an injury, arachidonic acid is converted to prostaglandins that produce pain and inflammation in the area. Aspirin, ibuprofen, and naproxen inhibit the production of prostaglandins and therefore decrease pain, inflammation, and fever. Long-term use of these pain relievers may trigger liver, kidney, and gastrointestinal damage.

III. Types of Lipids

Within the lipid family there are various different compounds. Fats, oils, waxes, and glycerophospholipids are **esters** and can be hydrolyzed to produce fatty acids and alcohols. Steroids are also classified as lipids but they do not contain ester groups and do not undergo hydrolysis reactions. Steroids such as cholesterol and sex hormones are characterized by having a steroid nucleus composed of four fused carbon rings.

Lipids Containing Ester Groups	Lipids without Ester Groups
Waxes Triacylglycerols: fats and oils Glycerophospholipids	Steroids

A. Lipids with Ester Groups

Waxes, triacylglycerols (also called triglycerides), and glycerophospholipids are esters and therefore can undergo hydrolysis.

1. **Waxes**

Waxes are esters of fatty acids and long-chain alcohols.

$$CH_3-(CH_2)_{14}-\overset{\overset{\displaystyle O}{\|}}{C}-O-(CH_2)_{29}-CH_3$$

Beeswax

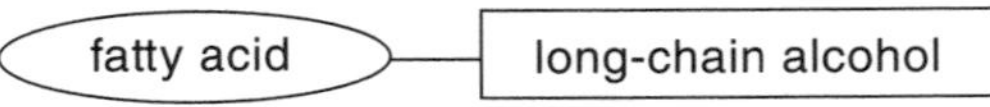

Waxes act as protective coatings for hair, skin, and feathers and to protect plants from dehydration and insects. Lanolin is a wax obtained from wool and is used in lotions and cosmetics. Carnauba wax is obtained from the carnauba palm and is used in car and floor waxes. Spermacetti is the oil of the sperm whale and is used to make candles. Beeswax serves as support for the honeycomb and is used in pharmaceutical products and expensive candles.

2. **Triacylglycerols**

   Triacylglycerols or triglycerides are esters of **glycerol** and **three fatty acids.** If only one fatty acid is present, a monoglyceride is produced. If two fatty acids are present diglyceride is produced. The following is a schematic representation of mono-, di-, and triglycerides.

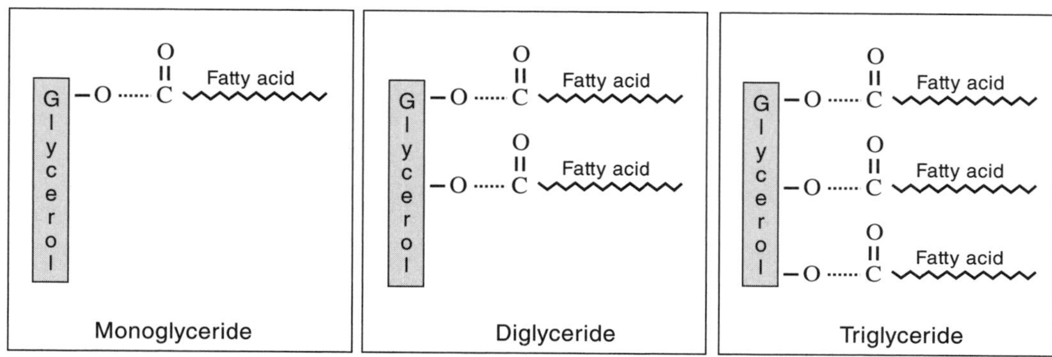

The following example illustrates how a triacylglycerol (triglyceride) is formed:

$$\begin{array}{l} CH_2-O\boxed{H + HO}-\overset{O}{\overset{\|}{C}}-(CH_2)_{16}-CH_3 \\ CH-O\boxed{H + HO}-\overset{O}{\overset{\|}{C}}-(CH_2)_{16}-CH_3 \\ CH_2-O\boxed{H + HO}-\overset{O}{\overset{\|}{C}}-(CH_2)_{16}-CH_3 \end{array} \longrightarrow \begin{array}{l} CH_2-O-\overset{O}{\overset{\|}{C}}-(CH_2)_{16}-CH_3 \\ CH-O-\overset{O}{\overset{\|}{C}}-(CH_2)_{16}-CH_3 \\ CH_2-O-\overset{O}{\overset{\|}{C}}-(CH_2)_{16}-CH_3 \end{array} + 3\,H_2O$$

Glycerol — 3 Stearic Acid Molecules — Tristerin (a triglyceride)

Most fats and oils are mixed triacylglycerols that contain different fatty acids. Fats are solids at room temperature and are usually obtained from animal sources (i.e., lard, butter); oils are liquids and are usually obtained from plant sources (i.e., corn, safflower, canola, and olive oil). Animal fat contains more saturated fatty acids than vegetable oils.

Triacylglycerols can be hydrolyzed in the presence of strong acids or by lipases (enzymes). The products of hydrolysis of the ester bonds are glycerol and three fatty acids. The following reaction illustrates the hydrolysis of a triacylglycerol (triglyceride).

$$\begin{array}{l} CH_2 - O - \overset{O}{\overset{\|}{C}} - (CH_2)_{16}CH_3 \\ | \\ CH - O - \overset{O}{\overset{\|}{C}} - (CH_2)_{16}CH_3 \\ | \\ CH_2 - O - \overset{O}{\overset{\|}{C}} - (CH_2)_{16}CH_3 \end{array} + 3\,H_2O \xrightarrow[\text{lipase}]{H^+ \text{ or}} \begin{array}{l} CH_2 - OH \\ | \\ CH - OH \\ | \\ CH_2 - OH \end{array} + \begin{array}{l} HO - \overset{O}{\overset{\|}{C}} - (CH_2)_{16}CH_3 \\ HO - \overset{O}{\overset{\|}{C}} - (CH_2)_{16}CH_3 \\ HO - \overset{O}{\overset{\|}{C}} - (CH_2)_{16}CH_3 \end{array}$$

Glycerol   3 Fatty acids

Basic hydrolysis (saponification) of a triacylglycerol with a strong base such as sodium hydroxide or potassium hydroxide *produces glycerol and soap*. The term saponification is synonymous with basic hydrolysis and comes from the Latin, *sapo* (soap) and *facare* (to make). The sodium salts are generally solid and can be formed into bars. The potassium salts, called soft soaps, are liquids at room temperature. The following equation describes the saponification of a triacylglycerol.

$$\begin{array}{l} CH_2 - O - \overset{O}{\overset{\|}{C}} - (CH_2)_{16}CH_3 \\ | \\ CH - O - \overset{O}{\overset{\|}{C}} - (CH_2)_{16}CH_3 \\ | \\ CH_2 - O - \overset{O}{\overset{\|}{C}} - (CH_2)_{16}CH_3 \end{array} + 3\,NaOH \xrightarrow{H_2O} \begin{array}{l} CH_2 - OH \\ | \\ CH - OH \\ | \\ CH_2 - OH \end{array} + \begin{array}{l} Na^+ \ {}^-O - \overset{O}{\overset{\|}{C}} - (CH_2)_{16}CH_3 \\ Na^+ \ {}^-O - \overset{O}{\overset{\|}{C}} - (CH_2)_{16}CH_3 \\ Na^+ \ {}^-O - \overset{O}{\overset{\|}{C}} - (CH_2)_{16}CH_3 \end{array}$$

Glycerol   3 Sodium salts of fatty acids (Soap)

The cleaning action of soap is based on simple solubility principles. That is, polar solutes dissolve in polar solvents and nonpolar solutes dissolve in nonpolar solvents. A soap molecule has an ionic polar head which is hydrophilic ("water-loving") and a covalent nonpolar tail which is hydrophobic ("water-fearing"). Dirt contains nonpolar, water-insoluble portions. The hydrophobic end of the soap molecule (nonpolar tail) dissolves the hydrophobic dirt particles and the hydrophilic head of the soap provides the attraction for water molecules. In this way, soap molecules will form an emulsion and will carry the oils and dirt. Soap and detergents have similar mechanisms for cleaning. The scrubbing action associated with cleaning will break up this emulsion into smaller bodies called micelles.

Dual polarity of a soap:

$$\underbrace{CH_3CH_2CH_2CH_2CH_2CH_2CH_2CH_2CH_2CH_2CH_2CH_2CH_2}_{\text{nonpolar tail}}\ \underbrace{\overset{O}{\overset{\|}{C}}\text{-}O^-\ Na^+}_{\text{polar head}}$$

Schematic diagram of soap:

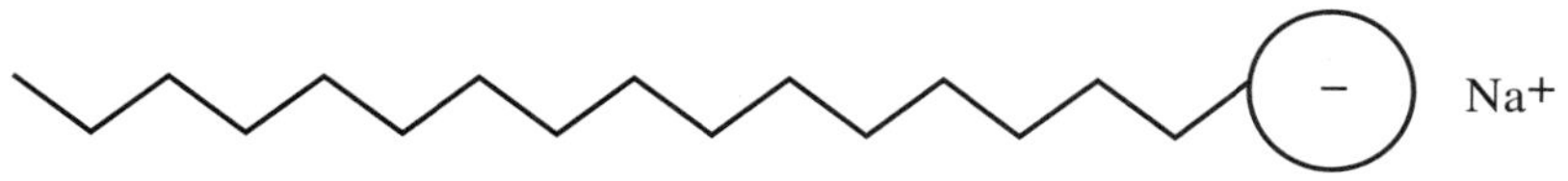

nonpolar tail — polar head (−) Na^+

Hydrogenation of the fatty acid portion of triacylglycerols converts double bonds to single bonds. This occurs by the addition of H_2 in the presence of a catalyst such as Pt, Ni, or Pd. Partially hydrogenated vegetable oil products such as soft margarine and solid shortening are produced by controlling the degree of hydrogenation. Most naturally occurring unsaturated fatty acids contain *cis*-double bonds. In the process of hydrogenation some of the *cis*-double bonds are converted to *trans*-double bonds. Health experts recommend that we limit the total amount of fat (especially saturated fats) in our diets and the amount of trans fatty acids, since these may have an effect similar to saturated fatty acids.

An example of a hydrogenation reaction of an unsaturated triacylglycerol follows.

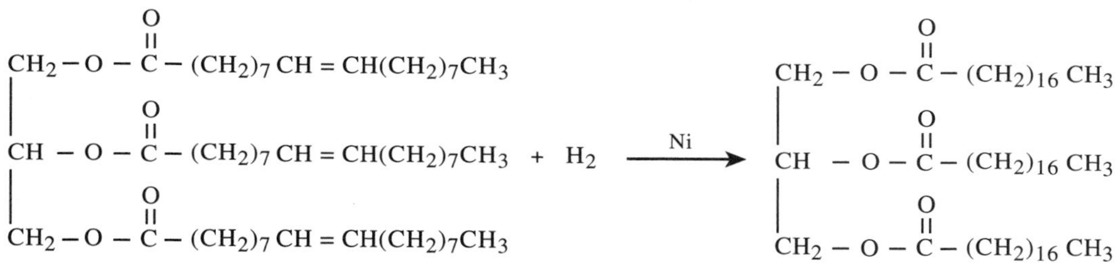

$$\begin{array}{l} CH_2-O-\overset{O}{\overset{\|}{C}}-(CH_2)_7CH=CH(CH_2)_7CH_3 \\ | \\ CH-O-\overset{O}{\overset{\|}{C}}-(CH_2)_7CH=CH(CH_2)_7CH_3 \\ | \\ CH_2-O-\overset{O}{\overset{\|}{C}}-(CH_2)_7CH=CH(CH_2)_7CH_3 \end{array} + H_2 \xrightarrow{Ni} \begin{array}{l} CH_2-O-\overset{O}{\overset{\|}{C}}-(CH_2)_{16}CH_3 \\ | \\ CH-O-\overset{O}{\overset{\|}{C}}-(CH_2)_{16}CH_3 \\ | \\ CH_2-O-\overset{O}{\overset{\|}{C}}-(CH_2)_{16}CH_3 \end{array}$$

Unsaturated Triacylglycerol — Saturated Triacylglycerol

Problem 1. For the following triacylglycerols, show the product(s) obtained from each of the following reactions:

a. hydrogenation　　b. hydrolysis　　c. saponification with NaOH

A.

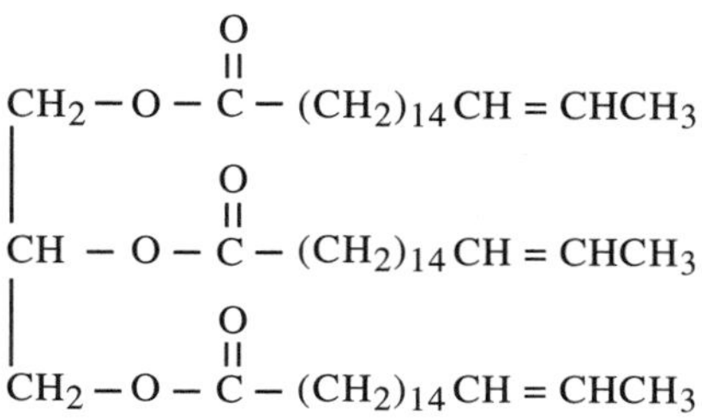

$$\begin{array}{l} CH_2-O-\overset{O}{\overset{\|}{C}}-(CH_2)_{14}CH=CHCH_3 \\ | \\ CH-O-\overset{O}{\overset{\|}{C}}-(CH_2)_{14}CH=CHCH_3 \\ | \\ CH_2-O-\overset{O}{\overset{\|}{C}}-(CH_2)_{14}CH=CHCH_3 \end{array}$$

B.

$$\begin{array}{l} CH_2-O-\overset{O}{\overset{\|}{C}}-(CH_2)_{14}CH=CHCH_3 \\ | \\ CH-O-\overset{O}{\overset{\|}{C}}-(CH_2)_{16}CH_3 \\ | \\ CH_2-O-\overset{O}{\overset{\|}{C}}-(CH_2)_{14}CH_3 \end{array}$$

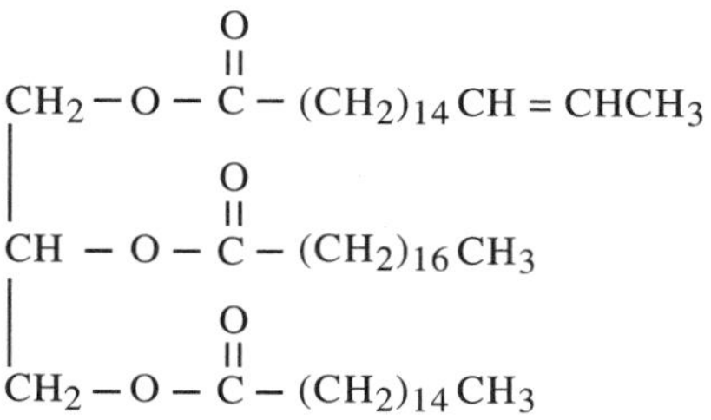

The U.S. Department of Agriculture (USDA) recommends that we use fats and oils, as well as sugars, sparingly. In order to have a healthy diet, the USDA recommends that the My Plate guidelines be used.

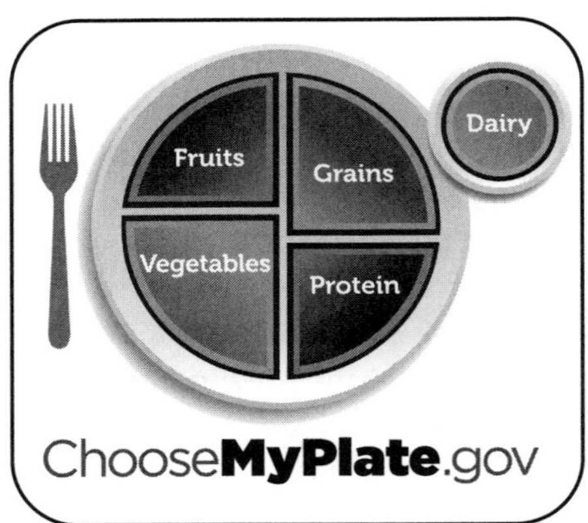

The number of calories in one **gram of fat** or oil **is 9 Calories**, while carbohydrates and proteins each contain 4 Calories per gram. Thus fats and oils have 2.25 times as many calories as do carbohydrates or proteins. It is the high energy content of these lipids that provide us with the main mode of energy storage and usage through the formation and metabolism of body fat. The body converts unused nutrients (i.e., carbohydrates, proteins, and lipids) into small globules of fat that it deposits in adipose tissue. **One pound** of adipose tissue stores and/or provides ~**3500 Calories** of energy. Converting unused nutrients into body fat and then converting this fat into energy when we need it is a very effective means of long-term energy storage. Glycogen, a polysaccharide, is used for short-term energy storage in animals and humans.

Reading Labels and Calculating Percent Fat

Different products list the nutritional information on their labels. The percent fat formula relates the number of fat Calories to the total number of Calories per serving. The number of fat Calories is simply obtained by multiplying the number of grams of fat listed times 9 Calories/gram of fat. Here is an example:

Light *Cream Cheese*

1/3 ***less*** *fat*

serving size	1 oz
Calories	70 Cal
fat	6 g
carbohydrate	1 g
protein	3 g

1. $\text{fat Calories} = \#\text{ g fat} \times \frac{9\text{ Calories}}{1\text{ g}}$

$\text{fat Calories} = 6\text{ g fat} \times \frac{9\text{ Calories}}{1\text{ g}}$

$\text{fat Calories} = \mathbf{54\ Calories}$

2. $\%\text{ fat} = \frac{\text{fat Calories}}{\text{total Calories}} \times 100$

$\%\text{ fat} = \frac{54\text{ Cal}}{70\text{ Cal}} \times 100$

$\%\text{ fat} = 77\%$

3. Glycerophospholipids

In general, the components of glycerophospholipids are two fatty acids, a phosphate group and an amino alcohol. A schematic representation and the structure of a glycerophospholipid follow:

Glycerol
— O ······ C(=O) Fatty acid
— O ······ C(=O) Fatty acid
— Phosphate — Amino Alcohol

$$CH_2-O-\overset{O}{\overset{\|}{C}}-(CH_2)_{14}-CH_3$$
$$CH\ -O-\overset{O}{\overset{\|}{C}}-(CH_2)_{14}-CH_3$$
} nonpolar

$$CH_2-O-\underset{O^-}{\underset{|}{\overset{O}{\overset{\|}{P}}}}-O-CH_2CH_2N^+(CH_3)_3$$
} polar

Glycerophospholipids are the most abundant lipid in cell membranes. One of the important functions of glycerophospholipids in cellular membranes is to separate one fluid compartment from another. Every glycerophospholipid has both a polar and nonpolar portion, which means that one end attracts water while the other end repels water and attracts nonpolar substances. The fluid mosaic model is a current model for the structure of cell membranes. According to this model, cell membranes consist of a double layer of glycerophospholipids called the lipid bilayer. The center of the lipid bilayer contains the nonpolar hydrocarbon tails, while the outer surface is made up of the polar phosphate and amino alcohol groups. The lipid bilayer acts as a barrier that separates the contents inside the cell membrane from the surrounding fluids providing selective permeability to nonpolar molecules. Embedded in the lipid bilayer are proteins that provide tunnels through which polar substances can pass.

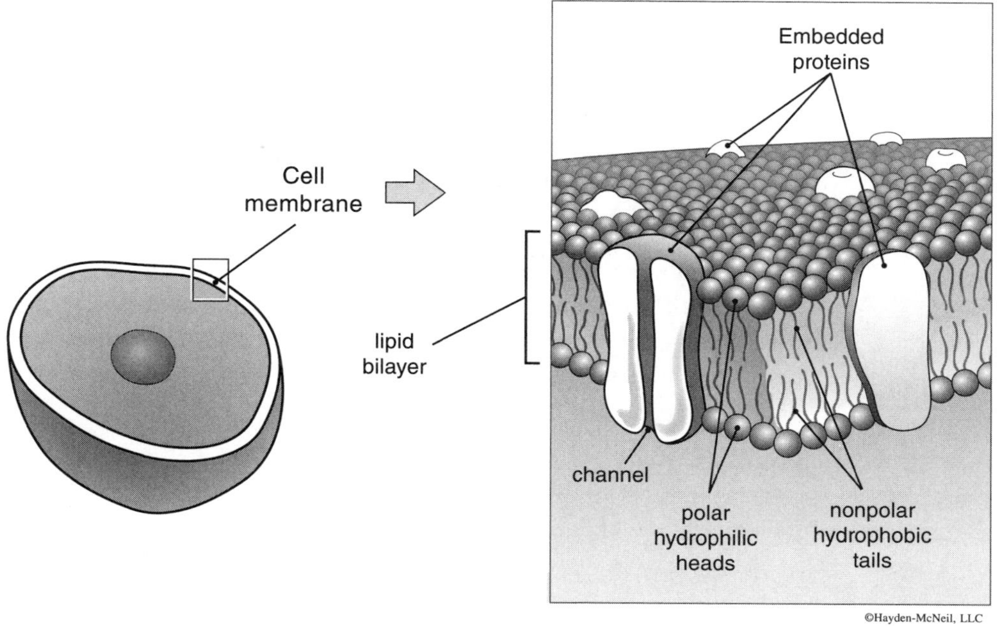

B. Steroids

Cholesterol and *steroid hormones* are lipids without ester groups or amides or fatty acid groups.

All steroids have a fused-ring structure commonly referred to as the steroid nucleus.

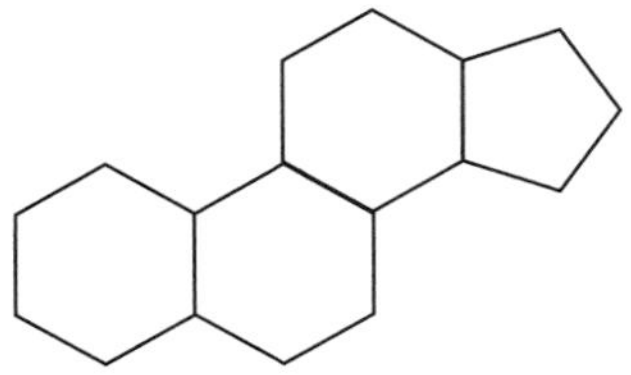

By attaching various groups to the steroid nucleus, a variety of steroids are formed. The most common steroid is cholesterol.

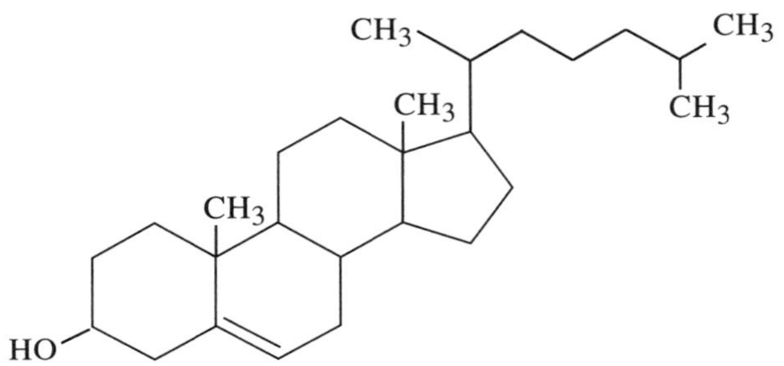

Cholesterol

Cholesterol is essential for the production of hormones, vitamin D, and bile acids. It is a component of brain and nerve tissue, myelin sheath, and cellular membranes. Cholesterol is also found in the liver, where it is synthesized from fats, carbohydrates, and proteins. Cholesterol is also obtained from meats, milk, and eggs. High levels of cholesterol lead to arteriosclerosis, a condition in which lipid material accumulates in the coronary blood vessels narrowing the coronary arteries. Clinically, cholesterol levels are considered elevated if the total plasma cholesterol level exceeds 200–230 mg/dL.

Sex hormones such as estrogen and testosterone are also steroids. Derivatives of testosterone called *anabolic steroids*, which enhance the effects of testosterone, have been synthesized. The use of these steroids by athletes to enhance strength and muscle mass comes with a heavy price—hypertension, fluid retention, liver damage, decreased sperm production, sleep disturbances, acne, etc.

Problem 2. Classify each of the following compounds as a wax, triacylglycerol, glycerophospholipid, or steroid.

a.

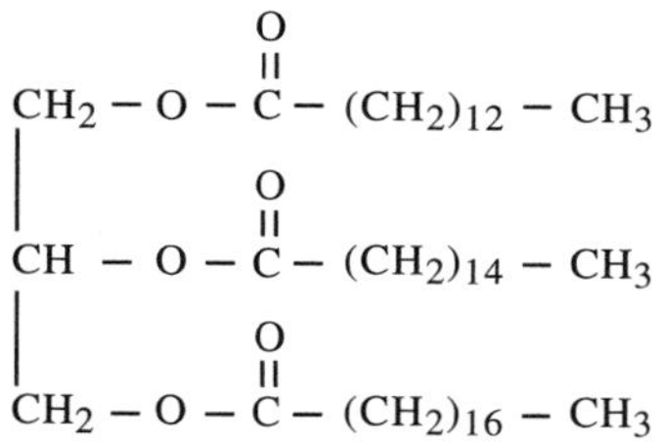

$$\begin{array}{l} CH_2-O-\overset{O}{\overset{\|}{C}}-(CH_2)_{12}-CH_3 \\ | \\ CH-O-\overset{O}{\overset{\|}{C}}-(CH_2)_{14}-CH_3 \\ | \\ CH_2-O-\overset{O}{\overset{\|}{C}}-(CH_2)_{16}-CH_3 \end{array}$$

b.

$$\begin{array}{l} CH_2-O-\overset{O}{\overset{\|}{C}}-(CH_2)_{14}-CH_3 \\ | \\ CH-O-\overset{O}{\overset{\|}{C}}-(CH_2)_{14}-CH_3 \\ | \\ CH_2-O-\overset{O}{\overset{\|}{P}}-O-CH_2CH_2N^{+}H_3 \\ \qquad\qquad\;\; | \\ \qquad\qquad\; O^{-} \end{array}$$

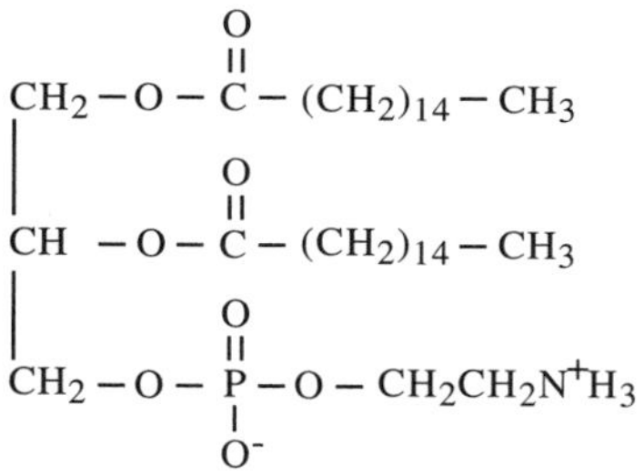

c.

OH
CH_3
CH_3
O

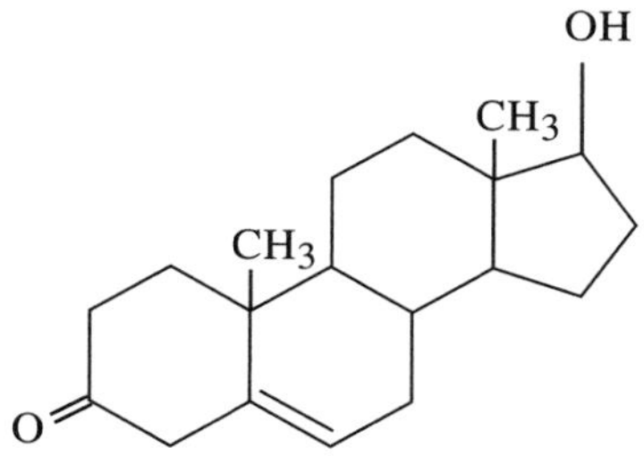

Testosterone

d. $CH_3-(CH_2)_{12}-\overset{O}{\overset{\|}{C}}-O-(CH_3)_{20}-CH_3$

ANSWERS

1. A. a.

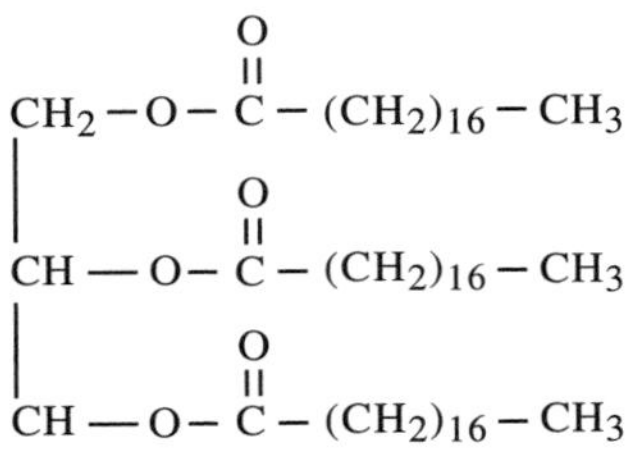

$$\begin{array}{l} CH_2-O-\overset{O}{\overset{\|}{C}}-(CH_2)_{16}-CH_3 \\ | \\ CH-O-\overset{O}{\overset{\|}{C}}-(CH_2)_{16}-CH_3 \\ | \\ CH-O-\overset{O}{\overset{\|}{C}}-(CH_2)_{16}-CH_3 \end{array}$$

b.

$$\begin{array}{l} CH_2-OH \\ | \\ CH-OH \\ | \\ CH_2-OH \end{array} \quad + \quad 3\ HO-\overset{O}{\overset{\|}{C}}-(CH_2)_{14}-CH=CH-CH_3$$

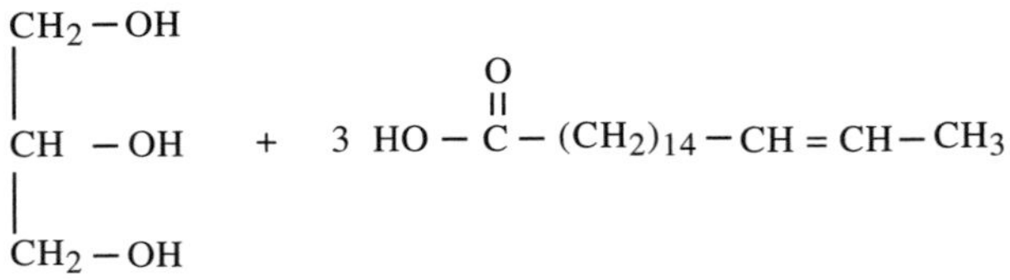

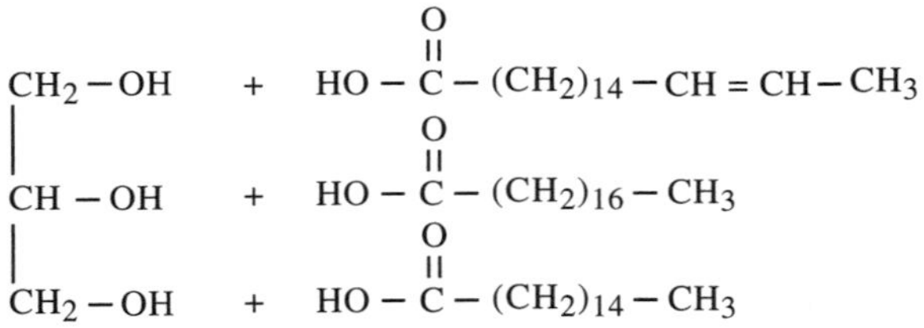

c.

$$\begin{array}{l} CH_2-OH \\ | \\ CH-OH \\ | \\ CH_2-OH \end{array} \quad + \quad 3\ Na^{+}\ {}^{-}O-\overset{O}{\overset{\|}{C}}-(CH_2)_{14}-CH=CH-CH_3$$

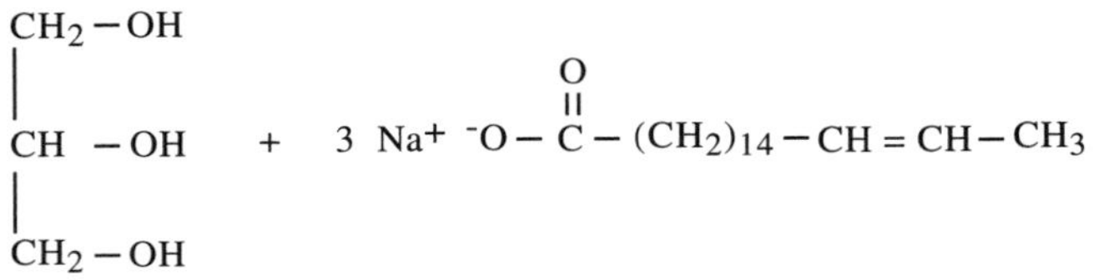

B. a.

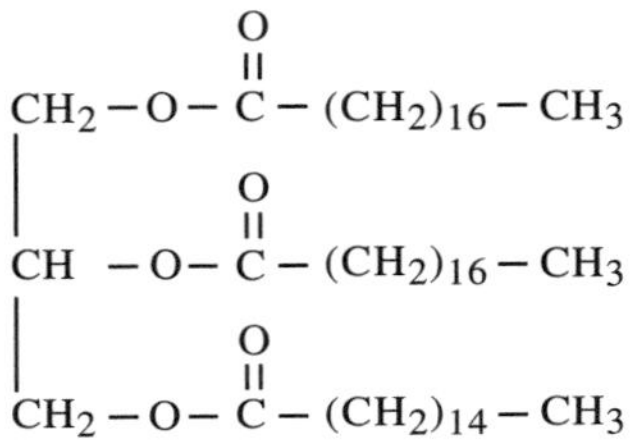

$$\begin{array}{l} CH_2-O-\overset{O}{\overset{\|}{C}}-(CH_2)_{16}-CH_3 \\ | \\ CH-O-\overset{O}{\overset{\|}{C}}-(CH_2)_{16}-CH_3 \\ | \\ CH_2-O-\overset{O}{\overset{\|}{C}}-(CH_2)_{14}-CH_3 \end{array}$$

b.

$$\begin{array}{lll} CH_2-OH & + & HO-\overset{O}{\overset{\|}{C}}-(CH_2)_{14}-CH=CH-CH_3 \\ | & & \\ CH-OH & + & HO-\overset{O}{\overset{\|}{C}}-(CH_2)_{16}-CH_3 \\ | & & \\ CH_2-OH & + & HO-\overset{O}{\overset{\|}{C}}-(CH_2)_{14}-CH_3 \end{array}$$

c.

$$\begin{array}{lll} CH_2-OH & + & Na^{+}\ {}^{-}O-\overset{O}{\overset{\|}{C}}-(CH_2)_{14}-CH=CH-CH_3 \\ | & & \\ CH-OH & + & Na^{+}\ {}^{-}O-\overset{O}{\overset{\|}{C}}-(CH_2)_{16}-CH_3 \\ | & & \\ CH_2-OH & + & Na^{+}\ {}^{-}O-\overset{O}{\overset{\|}{C}}-(CH_2)_{14}-CH_3 \end{array}$$

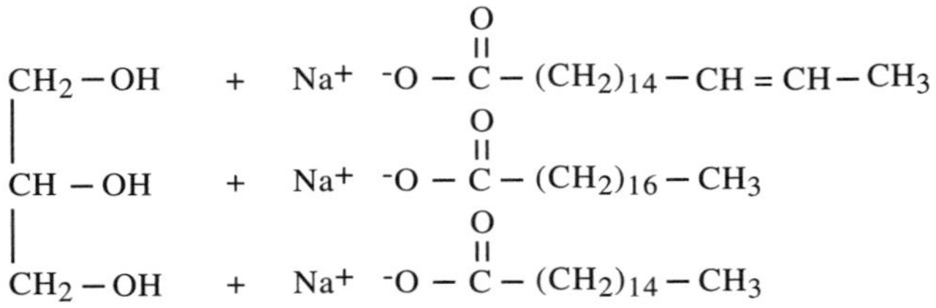

2. a. triacylglycerol b. glycerophospholipid

   c. steroid d. wax

Lipids

14 Assignment

____
Name

____
Student Number

____
Date *Instructor*

1. List three types of compounds that are classified as lipids.

2. Saturated fats come from ____________________ sources, and usually are ____________________ at room temperature.

3. Unsaturated fats come from ____________________ sources, and usually are ____________________ at room temperature.

4. The hydrolysis of a glycerophospholipid in acid usually produces:

5. For the following questions, refer to the structure below.

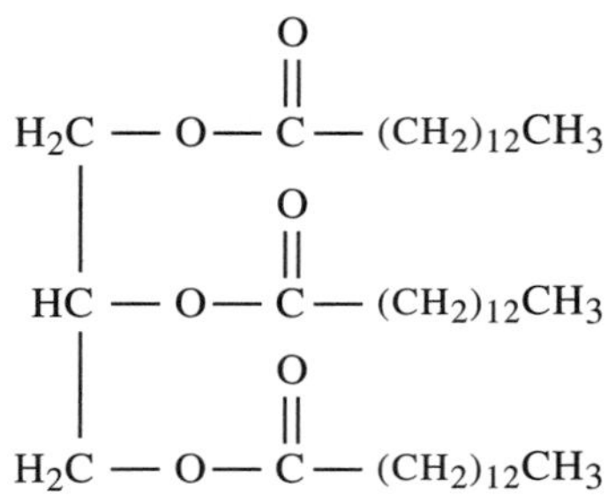

$$\begin{array}{l} H_2C - O - \overset{\overset{\displaystyle O}{\|}}{C} - (CH_2)_{12}CH_3 \\ | \\ HC - O - \overset{\overset{\displaystyle O}{\|}}{C} - (CH_2)_{12}CH_3 \\ | \\ H_2C - O - \overset{\overset{\displaystyle O}{\|}}{C} - (CH_2)_{12}CH_3 \end{array}$$

a. The family or group for this compound is ________________.

b. This molecule was formed by the reaction called________________.

c. To produce three fatty acids and glycerol, this structure would need to react with:

d. What are the products of this compound reacting with a NaOH solution?

6. A sodium or potassium salt of a fatty acid is commonly called ____________________.

7. a. Draw the structure of a triacylglycerol whose hydrolysis products are 1 molecule of glycerol and 3 molecules of

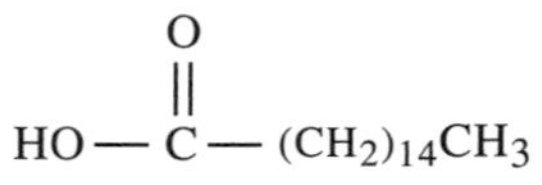

$$HO - \overset{\overset{\displaystyle O}{\|}}{C} - (CH_2)_{14}CH_3$$

b. Is this triacylglycerol saturated or unsaturated?

8. Consider the following triglyceride:

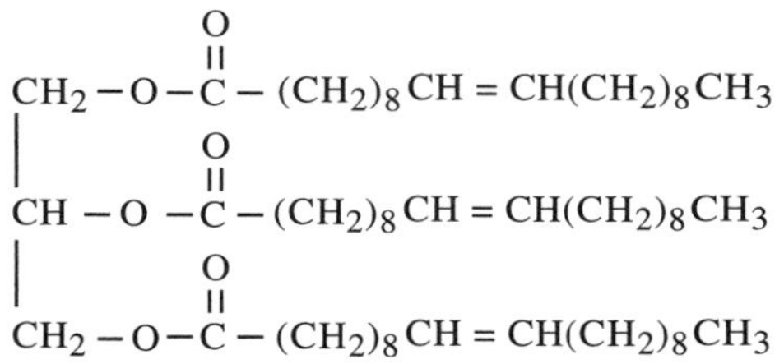

$$\begin{array}{l} \overset{O}{\overset{\|}{}} \\ CH_2-O-C-(CH_2)_8CH=CH(CH_2)_8CH_3 \\ | \overset{O}{\overset{\|}{}} \\ CH-O-C-(CH_2)_8CH=CH(CH_2)_8CH_3 \\ | \overset{O}{\overset{\|}{}} \\ CH_2-O-C-(CH_2)_8CH=CH(CH_2)_8CH_3 \end{array}$$

a. Is this triacylglycerol saturated or unsaturated?

b. Draw the structure of the product when this triacylglycerol undergoes hydrogenation.

c. Draw the structures of the hydrolysis products of this triacylglycerol.

d. Draw the structures of the saponification products of this triacylglycerol.

9. Draw the fused ring structure commonly referred to as the steroid nucleus.

10. Explain the purpose of the lipid bilayer in cell membranes.

11. Which are the fat-soluble vitamins?

12. A jar of baby food indicates in its label that it contains the following:

Carbohydrates	16 grams
Protein	6 grams
Fat	4 grams
Total grams	26 grams

Calculate the total Calories in this jar of baby food.

13. The label for a granola bar gives the following: Fat, 6 grams; carbohydrates, 29 grams; protein, 4 grams. Calculate the total calories. What percentage of the total calories are fat calories?

15

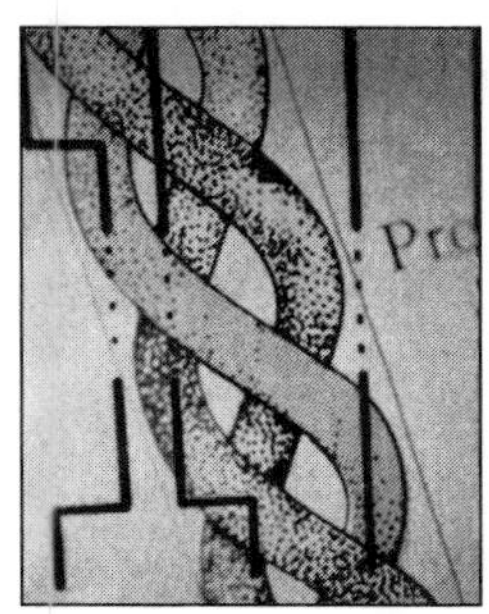

Proteins and Enzymes

The word *protein* comes from the Greek word *proteios*, meaning "first." There are many types of proteins and they perform many different functions. The building blocks of proteins are amino acids. Proteins are large molecules with large molecular weights [e.g., hemoglobin (MW = 64,000) and Tobacco Mosaic Virus (MW = 40,000,000)].

I. Protein Function

Proteins have many important functions in the body:

a. ***Enzymatic Catalysis***. Nearly all biochemical reactions are catalyzed by proteins called *enzymes*.

b. ***Transport and Storage***. Oxygen is transported in the body by a protein called *hemoglobin*. Iron is in the blood plasma and is stored in the liver by the action of a protein called *ferritin*.

c. ***Coordinated Motion***. Muscle expansion and contraction is provided by protein molecules called *actin* and *myosin*.

d. ***Structural***. Proteins like *collagen* and *keratin* are the chief constituents of skin, bones, hair, and fingernails.

e. ***Immune Protection***. *Antibodies* are very specific proteins that protect the body from foreign substances called antigens. Antibodies are used to fight diseases.

f. ***Hormones***. Many hormones are proteins, among them *insulin* and *oxytocin*.

g. ***Generation and Transmission of Nerve Impulses***. The response of nerve cells to specific stimuli is mediated by receptor proteins.

II. Amino Acids

Amino acids are the building blocks of proteins. Their very name implies that they are composed of an amine and a carboxylic acid. All amino acids have the following general structure:

```
     H   H   O
     |   |   ||
 H — N — C — C — OH
         |
        (R)
```

What varies in amino acids is the identity of the group labeled R. Notice also from the structure that the amine group ($-NH_2$) is attached to the carbon which is adjacent to the carboxyl group called the α carbon. Since the amino group is attached to the α carbon these compounds are called α-amino acids.

A. Amino Acids

The table of α-amino acids gives the structure, name, and three letter abbreviation for the 20 amino acids commonly found in proteins. Ten of these twenty amino acids cannot be synthesized by the body and must be obtained from our diets. These ten amino acids are called *essential amino acids* and are marked with an asterisk in the following table. The 20 amino acids have been classified according to the identity of the R group:

a. ***Nonpolar R Group***. Amino acids that contain a nonpolar hydrocarbon side chain which makes them hydrophobic (not soluble in water).

b. ***Alcohol R Group***. Amino acids that contain an alcohol (–OH).

c. ***Thiol (Sulfur) R Group***. Amino acids that contain a sulfur.

d. ***Basic R Group***. Amino acids that contain an amine R group.

e. ***Acidic R Group***. Amino acids that contain a carboxylic acid R group.

f. ***Aromatic R Group***. Amino acids that contain a benzene ring.

g. ***Amide R Group***. Amino acids that contain an amide.

Problem 1. Classify the following amino acids according to their R groups.

a. valine b. glutamic acid c. lysine

d. serine e. tyrosine f. glutamine

B. Properties of Amino Acids

The following are general properties of amino acids:

a. May behave as acids (because of the carboxylic acid group) and as bases (because of the amine group). Since amino acids may act as both acids or bases they are excellent buffers.

b. Are soluble in water.

c. Have high melting points.

d. Migrate when an electric field is applied.

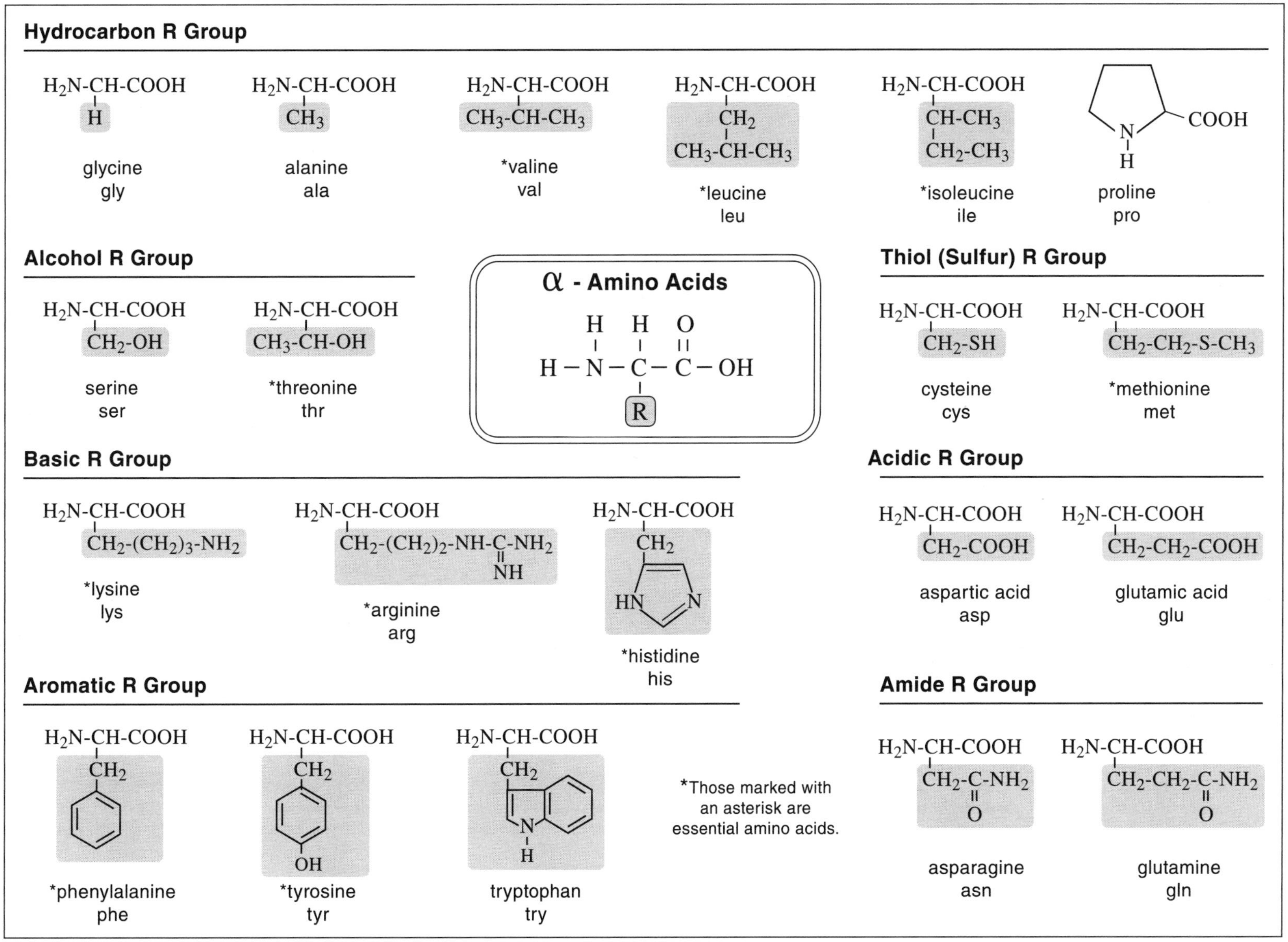
Hydrocarbon R Group
H2N-CH-COOH
H
glycine
gly
H2N-CH-COOH
CH3
alanine
ala
H2N-CH-COOH
CH3-CH-CH3
*valine
val
H2N-CH-COOH
CH2
CH3-CH-CH3
*leucine
leu
H2N-CH-COOH
CH-CH3
CH2-CH3
*isoleucine
ile
COOH
N
H
proline
pro
Alcohol R Group
H2N-CH-COOH
CH2-OH
serine
ser
H2N-CH-COOH
CH3-CH-OH
*threonine
thr
α - Amino Acids
H H O
H – N – C – C – OH
R
Thiol (Sulfur) R Group
H2N-CH-COOH
CH2-SH
cysteine
cys
H2N-CH-COOH
CH2-CH2-S-CH3
*methionine
met
Basic R Group
H2N-CH-COOH
CH2-(CH2)3-NH2
*lysine
lys
H2N-CH-COOH
CH2-(CH2)2-NH-C-NH2
NH
*arginine
arg
H2N-CH-COOH
CH2
HN
N
*histidine
his
Acidic R Group
H2N-CH-COOH
CH2-COOH
aspartic acid
asp
H2N-CH-COOH
CH2-CH2-COOH
glutamic acid
glu
Aromatic R Group
H2N-CH-COOH
CH2
*phenylalanine
phe
H2N-CH-COOH
CH2
OH
*tyrosine
tyr
H2N-CH-COOH
CH2
N
H
tryptophan
try
*Those marked with an asterisk are essential amino acids.
Amide R Group
H2N-CH-COOH
CH2-C-NH2
O
asparagine
asn
H2N-CH-COOH
CH2-CH2-C-NH2
O
glutamine
gln

Properties b, c, and d suggest that amino acids do not exist as uncharged molecules, but rather as highly polar ions, called *zwitterions* ("double-ions"). A zwitterion is an ion that has both a negative and a positive charge within the same structure. The following is the general structure of a zwitterion.

$$H_2\ddot{N}-CHR-C(=O)-O-H \longrightarrow H_3N^+-CHR-C(=O)-O^-$$

Zwitterion

The zwitterionic form of an amino acid exists at a certain pH called the *isoelectric point.* At this pH the amino acid is electrically neutral and will not move during electrophoresis (experiment in which an electric field is applied). No two amino acids have the same isoelectric point, thus this is a characteristic physical property of amino acids.

At pH values below its isoelectric point (i.e., more acidic) an amino acid will exist as a positive ion. This ion will migrate toward the negative pole in an electrophoresis experiment.

$$\underset{\text{Zwitterion}}{H_3N^+-CHR-C(=O)-O^-} \xrightarrow[\text{(lower pH)}]{H^+} \underset{\text{Positive ion}}{H_3N^+-CHR-C(=O)-OH}$$

At pH values above its isoelectric point (i.e., more basic) an amino acid will exist as a negative ion. This ion will migrate toward the positive pole in an electrophoresis experiment.

$$\underset{\text{Zwitterion}}{H_3N^+-CHR-C(=O)-O^-} \xrightarrow[\text{(higher pH)}]{OH^-} \underset{\text{Negative ion}}{H_2\ddot{N}-CHR-C(=O)-O^-}$$

The following is an example of how the amino acid alanine exists at a pH below its isoelectric point, at its isoelectric point, and at a pH above its isoelectric point.

pH < isoelectric point	isoelectric point	pH > isoelectric point
$H_3N^+-CH(CH_3)-C(=O)-OH$	$H_3N^+-CH(CH_3)-C(=O)-O^-$	$H_2N-CH(CH_3)-C(=O)-O^-$

Problem 2. For each of the following amino acids, draw its structure: 1) at a pH below its isoelectric point, 2) at its isoelectric point, and 3) at a pH above its isoelectric point.

a. glycine b. serine c. phenylalanine

III. Peptides

When two or more amino acids combine, they are held together by what is known as a *peptide bond* (amide bond).

```
                                                                    peptide bond
  H   H   O             H   H   O                      H   H   O  |  H   H   O
  |   |   ||            |   |   ||                     |   |   || ↓  |   |   ||
H—N—C—C—[OH + H]—N—C—C—OH  ——→  H—N—C—C—N—C—C—OH
      |                     |                              |              |
     [R]                   [R]                            [R]            [R]

   Amino acid 1    +    Amino acid 2    ——→         Dipeptide
```

Peptides are classified by the number of amino acids that are chemically joined. The sequence of amino acids is written starting with the N-terminal amino acid (amino acid with unreacted or free amino group).

Number of Amino Acids Joined	Name
2	Dipeptide
3	Tripeptide
Many	Polypeptide
> 50	Protein

A. Dipeptides

A dipeptide is formed when two amino acids are chemically joined. These two amino acids are held together by a peptide bond.

The following examples show the formation of two different dipeptides when ala (alanine) and gly (glycine) react.

```
  H   H   O             H   H   O                    H   H   O   H   H   O
  |   |   ||            |   |   ||                   |   |   ||  |   |   ||
H—N—C—C—[OH + H]—N—C—C—OH  ——→  H—N—C—C—N—C—C—OH
      |                     |                            |           |
     CH3                    H                           CH3          H

     ala          +        gly          ——→            ala-gly
```

```
    H   H   O              H   H   O                   H   H   O   H   H   O
    |   |   ||             |   |   ||                  |   |   ||  |   |   ||
H—N—C—C—[OH + H]—N—C—C—OH ——→ H—N—C—C—N—C—C—OH
        |                  |                               |           |
        H                  CH3                             H           CH3
```

gly + ala ⟶ gly-ala

Therefore, if two different amino acids react there are *two* possible products and each of those products contains one peptide bond.

B. Tripeptides

A tripeptide is formed when three amino acids react; as a result two peptide bonds are formed.

```
    H   H   O                  H   H   O                  H   H   O
    |   |   ||                 |   |   ||                 |   |   ||
H—N—C—C—[OH + H]—N—C—C—[OH + H]—N—C—C—OH
        |                          |                          |
       [R]                        [R]                        [R]
                                   |
                                   ↓
        H   H   O   H   H   O   H   H   O
        |   |   ||  |   |   ||  |   |   ||
    H—N—C—C—N—C—C—N—C—C—OH
            |   ↑       |   ↑       |
           [R]  |      [R]  |      [R]
                 peptide bonds
```

When three different amino acids react, there are *six* possible products. Consider the reaction of the following three amino acids: ala, gly, phe.

ala + gly + phe → ala-gly-phe + ala-phe-gly + gly-ala-phe

+ gly-phe-ala + phe-ala-gly + phe-gly-ala

The following example illustrates the tripeptide gly-ala-phe.

```
     H   H   O   H   H   O   H   H   O
     |   |   ||  |   |   ||  |   |   ||
  H—N—C—C—N—C—C—N—C—C—OH
         |           |           |
         H          CH3         CH2
                                 |
                               C6H5
```

gly - ala - phe

Problem 3. Draw structures for each of the following:

a. ala - ala　　b. val - ala

c. phe - ala - gly　　d. val - gly - phe

Problem 4. How many tripeptides can you draw from the following amino acids?

a. 2 alanine and 1 leucine

b. 1 aspartic acid, 1 tyrosine, 1 cysteine

c. 1 serine and 2 valine

IV. Structure of Proteins

Proteins are polypeptides with more than 50 amino acids. There are four levels of protein organization or protein structure:

A. Primary Structure

The sequence of amino acids determines the primary structure of the protein.

Insulin was the first protein for which the amino acid sequence was determined. Insulin contains 51 amino acids. There are slight differences in the sequencing of amino acids from one species to another. Sometimes substituting one or more amino acids in a protein causes very little difference in the protein's function. For example, if there is not enough human insulin to meet demands, often insulin from animals is substituted. The point of difference between the different insulin molecules is illustrated below.

AAs	8 - 9 - 10	30
Human	thr-ser-ile	thr
Hog	thr-ser-ile	ala
Sheep	ala-gly-val	ala
Bovin	ala-ser-val	ala

At other times substituting just one amino acid in a protein causes drastic effects. Hemoglobin is the oxygen carrying molecule in red blood cells and it contains 574 amino acids. Sickle-cell anemia is a serious blood disorder caused by the replacement of *one* amino acid (glutamic acid) with another (valine). This single amino acid change severely affects the structure and function of hemoglobin. This change at a single position is severe enough to cause a high death rate. The following diagram illustrates this point.

	4 5 6 7 8 9
Normal Hb	-Thr-Pro-**Glu**-Glu-Lys-Ala
Sickle-cell Hb	-Thr-Pro-**Val**-Glu-Lys-Ala-

As it was stated earlier, substituting a couple of amino acid in a protein may cause drastic effects. Oxytocin is a small protein containing only 9 amino acids and affects activities related to birth and lactation; it plays a major role in establishing maternal behavior. Oxytocin stimulates uterine contractions during birth and after birth it stimulates the milk ejection (milk letdown). **Oxytocin** differs from **vasopressin**, an antidiuretic hormone, in only **two** of the **nine** amino acids. The most important function of an antidiuretic hormone is to conserve body water by reducing the output of urine. Roughly 60% of the body is water and despite wide variations in the daily water consumption, body water content remains incredibly stable thanks to antidiuretic hormones.

Oxytocin	gly-**leu**-pro-cys-asp-gln-**ile**-tyr-cys
Vasopressin	gly-**arg**-pro-cys-asp-gln-**phe**-tyr-cys

These examples illustrate the relationship between the structure and the function of a protein. The sequence of amino acids in a protein, i.e., its primary structure, is intimately related to the protein function.

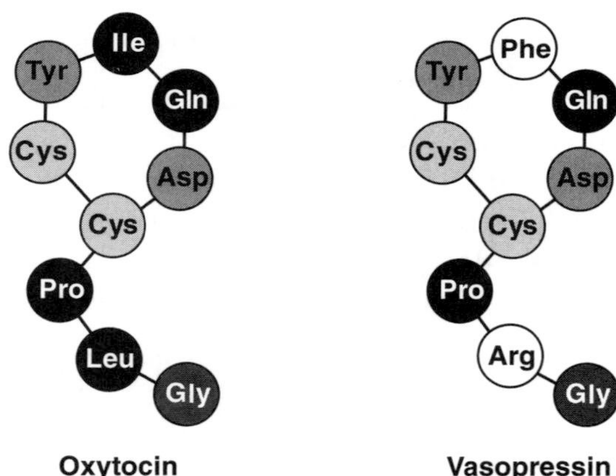

B. Secondary Structure

The folding or aligning of proteins in a repeating pattern is referred to as the 2° structure. The secondary structure of proteins is caused by *hydrogen bonding* within a protein molecule (intramolecular hydrogen bonding) or between several protein molecules (intermolecular hydrogen bonding). Intramolecular hydrogen bonding leads to the protein coiling itself like a telephone cord called an *alpha* (α) *helix*. Intermolecular hydrogen bonding leads to the formation of what is called a β-*pleated sheet.*

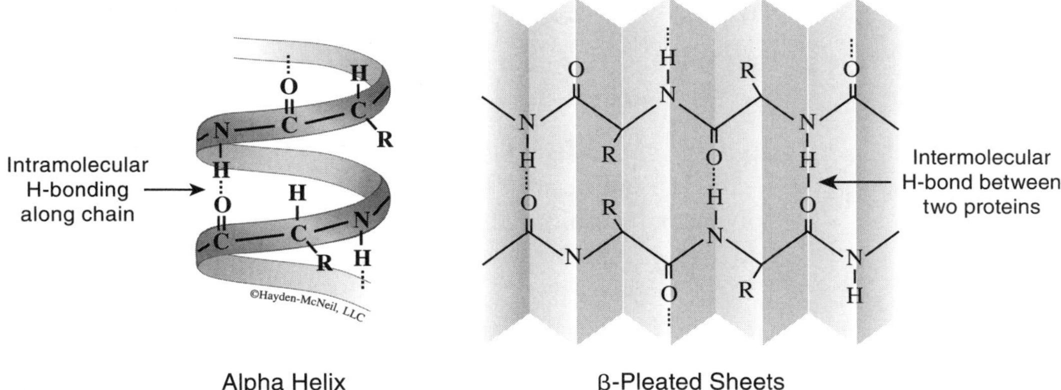

Alpha Helix β-Pleated Sheets

Fibrous proteins called alpha keratins make up the tough fibers of wool, skin, and nails. These proteins consist of three to seven alpha helixes coiled up tightly like a rope. Collagen is an example of a fibrous protein and is made up of a triple helix wound up like a coil.

C. Tertiary Structure

The three-dimensional structure of a protein is called its 3° structure. The tertiary structure of proteins, which is illustrated by the following diagram, is maintained by the following interactions.

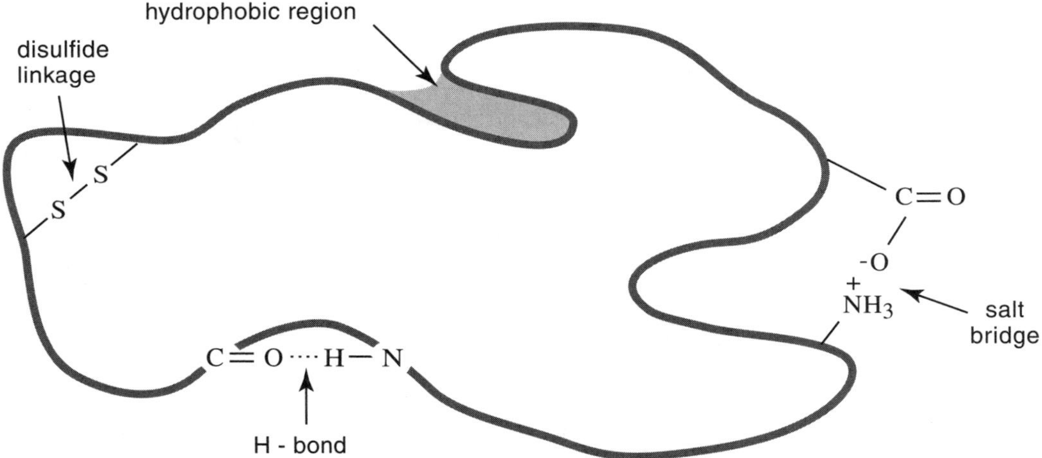

1. **Covalent Cross-linkages.** A covalent cross-linkage (aka disulfide linkage) is formed when two cysteine molecules undergo oxidation.

$$\underset{\text{cys}}{-S-H} + \underset{\text{cys}}{H-S-} \xrightarrow{[O]} \underbrace{-S-S-}_{\text{disulfide linkage}}$$

$\delta^+ \ \delta^-$

2. **Hydrogen Bonding.** The attraction between N-H .... O = C.
3. **Salt Bridges.** This interaction occurs between + and – ions that result from the R groups of amino acids having a charge.
4. **Hydrophobic Interactions.** Hydrophobic interactions occur between the nonpolar R groups of amino acids in the protein. These nonpolar R groups are repulsed by the solvent water molecules thus causing the protein to fold shielding these nonpolar groups from the surrounding water.

D. Quaternary Structure

Some proteins, like hemoglobin and myoglobin, are composed of more than one polypeptide chain. The way these proteins fit together results in the quaternary structure of the protein. The quaternary structure of a protein is maintained by the same linkages described in tertiary structures of proteins. The quaternary structure gives the protein molecule its characteristic shape.

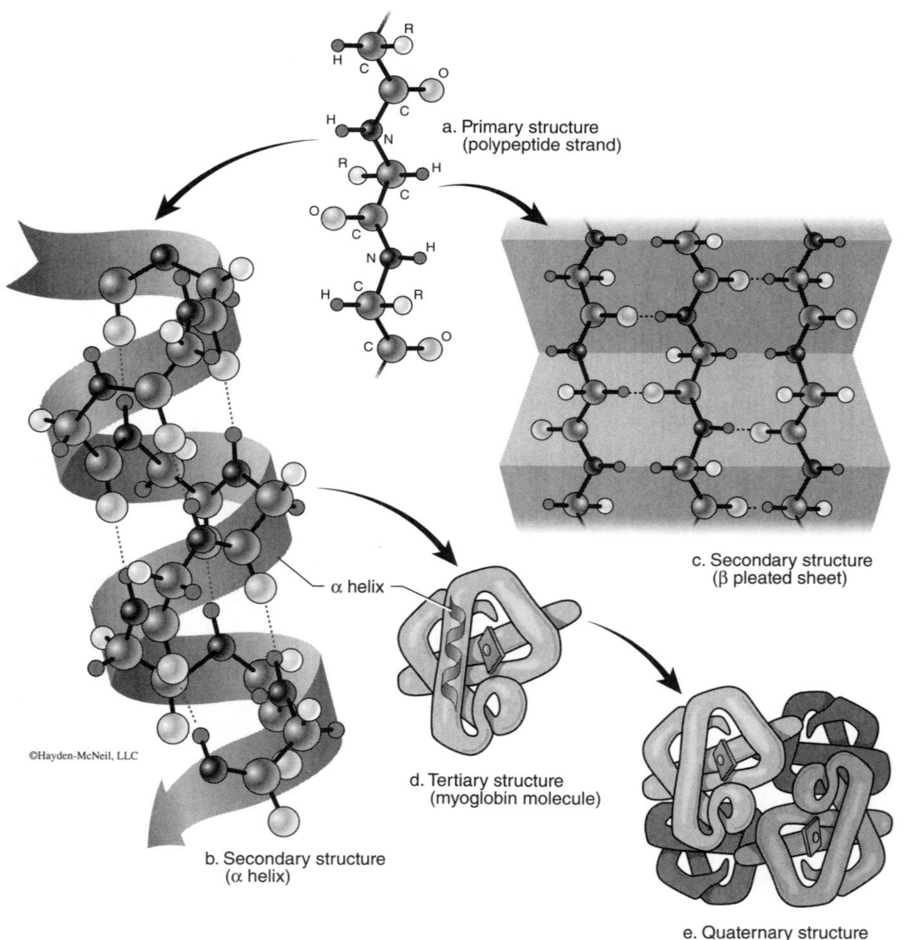

Problem 5. Match the following interactions with the appropriate level of protein structure.

1. Covalent cross-linkage	a. Primary structure
2. Hydrogen bonding	b. Secondary structure
3. Hydrophobic interaction	c. Tertiary structure
4. Peptide linkage	
5. Salt bridges	

V. Denaturation of Proteins

Denaturation occurs when a protein loses its biological activity. Physical or chemical agents which affect the 2°, 3°, and/or 4° structure of a protein will denature it.

Denaturation Agents:

a. ***Heat and Ultraviolet Radiation*** break H-bonding. [The heat applied to surgical instruments denatures the protein in bacteria and destroys the bacteria.]

b. ***Alcohol and Other Organic Solvents*** coagulate proteins. [A 70% isopropyl alcohol solution is applied to a patient's arm before injection because the alcohol penetrates bacteria and destroys them.]

c. ***Reducing Agents*** break disulfide linkages. [The protein keratin makes up human hair. This protein has disulfide linkages, the more of these linkages the curlier the hair is. Permanents are accomplished with the aid of reducing agents.]

d. ***pH Changes*** affect salt bridges and H-bonding. [Stomach acid (~0.5% HCl) both denatures the protein and cleaves peptide linkages (i.e., destroys the primary structure) randomly.]

e. ***Heavy Metals.*** Heavy metal ions (e.g., Ag^+, Pb^{2+}, Hg^{2+}) react with disulfide bonds. A loss of disulfide bonds disturbs its tertiary structure. [A 1% $AgNO_3$ solution placed in a newborn's eyes destroys bacteria such as gonorrhea and chlamydia.]

By carefully reversing any mild conditions that caused denaturation, the protein may be restored to its original shape and biological activity. If the changes are very drastic the denaturation can not be reversed. When this happens, the protein precipitates out of solution.

VI. Hydrolysis of Proteins

The hydrolysis of a protein occurs in the presence of an acid or an enzyme such as trypsin or pepsin. The hydrolysis reaction produces smaller peptides and individual amino acids.

$$\text{Protein} \rightarrow \text{Peptides} \rightarrow \text{Amino Acids}$$

VII. Enzymes

Enzymes are proteins that speed up the rate of biological reactions; they are the **catalysts** present in the body. In the laboratory, proteins, lipids, and carbohydrates can be broken down by using strong acids, bases, heat, and slow reactions. In the body, polysaccharides, fats, and proteins are metabolized (broken down) by cells **very rapidly** and under mild conditions using **enzymes**. Enzymes take a "shortcut" in going from reactants to products and therefore speed up the reaction.

VIII. Enzyme Action

A. Enzyme Specificity and Activation Energy

Activation energy is the energy necessary for a reaction to take place. An enzyme catalyzes a specific reaction by providing an alternative pathway and reducing the **energy of activation**. Enzymes are very **specific catalysts**, and most enzymes react with only one reactant; this is referred to as **enzyme specificity**.

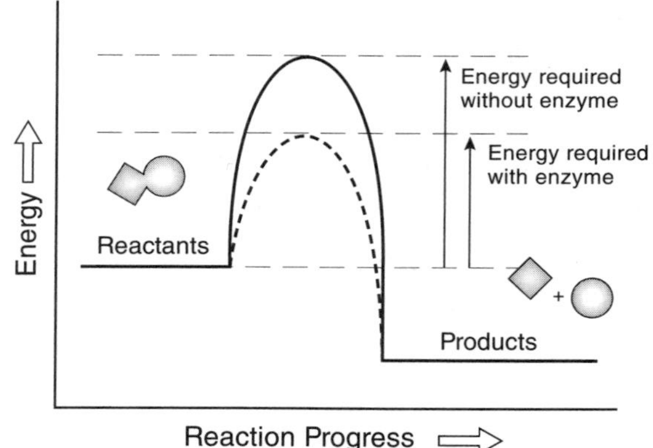

B. Lock and Key Model

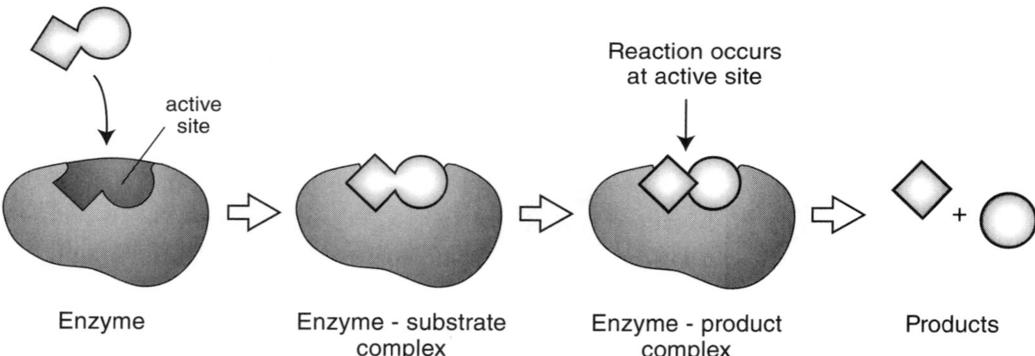

The mechanism of enzyme action can be explained using the lock and key model. The hydrolysis reaction of maltose will be used as an example. The hydrolysis of maltose is catalyzed by the enzyme, maltase. Maltose is called the substrate (reactant); the product of the hydrolysis reaction will be two glucose molecules. Maltase, the enzyme, (E) must first combine with maltose, its substrate (S). The substrate fits tightly into the enzyme just as a key fits into its lock. The active site is the pocket in which the substrate (S) and the enzyme (E) combine. The resulting structure is called the enzyme-substrate complex (E-S).

The model has three steps:

1. First, S combines with E in the active site: E + S → E–S
2. The reaction takes place and products are formed: E–S → E–P
3. The product then dissociates from the enzyme and the enzyme is free to be used again: E–P → E + P

C. *Induced Fit*

The lock and key theory of enzyme action provides a good description of many enzyme-catalyzed reactions. Some enzymes catalyze reactions involving several different substrates. A modification of the lock and key idea is called the induced fit theory. The active site is somewhat flexible and as a substrate enters the active site, it "induces" the enzyme to change shape slightly so the active site "fits" the substrate properly.

IX. Common Names and Classification of Enzymes

In the past, enzymes were usually named according to the substance they act on, called the substrate, or the nature of the reaction being catalyzed. The ending "**ase**" is used. Examples of enzymes that are named for the substrate are urease, which catalyzes the hydrolysis of urea and maltase which acts on maltose. However, some common names were not very informative. Pepsin and trypsin both catalyze the hydrolysis of proteins.

A more systematic classification system groups enzymes into six major classes according to the type of reaction they catalyze. The following is a list of these categories and examples of each type.

1. Oxido-reductases (electron-transfer reactions)
   Dehydrogenases
2. Transferases (transfer of functional groups)
   Transmethylases
   Transaminases
   Transphosphatases
3. Hydrolases (hydrolysis reactions)
   Lipases
   Carbohydrate hydrolases
   Proteases
   Nucleases
4. Lyases (addition or removal of groups from substrate)
   Hydrases—addition of water
   Dehydrase—removal of water
   Decarboxylases—removal of carbon dioxide
5. Isomerases (isomerization reactions)
   Cis-trans isomerases
   Sugar isomerases—converts one sugar to another
6. Ligases (formation of bonds with ATP cleavage)
   Often called synthetases—join two or more molecules to form a larger one

Problem 6: Which of the preceding six categories of enzymes would be involved in the following reactions?

a. triglyceride + 3 H_2O ↔ glycerol + 3 fatty acids

b. pyruvic acid ↔ acetaldehyde + CO_2

c. dipeptide + H_2O ↔ 2 amino acids

d. fructose ↔ glucose

Some enzymes consist of a single polypeptide chain and are called **simple enzymes**. Other enzymes are more complex and are activated by a metal ion or an organic compound. This nonprotein component is called a **cofactor**. These enzymes are called **conjugated proteins**. If the cofactor is an organic compound, like a vitamin, it is called a **coenzyme**.

Protein	+	Cofactor	=	Active enzyme
polypeptide chain		metal ion activator or organic compound		

Problem 7. Classify the following enzymes as simple or conjugated proteins.

a. Pyruvate kinase requires Mg^{2+} for biological activity.

b. This enzyme requires vitamin B_1 (Thiamin) for biological activity.

c. This enzyme consists of protein only.

d. This enzyme is composed of 250 amino acids.

e. This enzyme contains a carbohydrate portion.

X. Factors Affecting Enzyme Activity

Several factors affect the rate at which the enzyme catalyzes reactions:

A. Substrate concentration

B. Enzyme concentration

C. Temperature

D. pH

A. Substrate Concentration

As the amount of substrate present increases, the activity of the enzyme also increases. However, when all the enzyme molecules are combined with substrate, a **maximum activity level** is achieved and after this point there is no further increase in activity even if more substrate is added. At the point of maximum activity the enzyme molecules are "saturated" with substrate.

B. Enzyme Concentration

In general, the concentration of substrate is much higher than that of the enzyme. As the enzyme concentration increases the reaction rate also increases.

C. Temperature

At low temperature there is little energy available for a chemical reaction to take place. In general, as the temperature increases the reaction rate also increases. However, most of the enzymes of the body reach their maximum activity at an **optimum temperature** around 37°C. A decrease in rate occurs if the temperature is increased above this optimum temperature. At temperatures above 60°C, many enzymes denature, destroying the structure of the active site and the enzyme activity drops to zero.

D. pH

Every enzyme has its specific **optimum pH**. The structure and function of the enzyme are very dependent on pH. Since enzymes are proteins, changes in pH will cause changes in the side chains of the amino acid groups resulting in changes in tertiary structure. The optimum pH of the enzyme will vary. Pepsin, a digestive enzyme, has an optimum pH of 2. Trypsin has an optimum pH of 8 and it works in the small intestine.

Problem 8. Describe the effects of the following on the rate of the reaction catalyzed by sucrase in the small intestine if its optimum pH is 6.2 and optimum temperature is 37°C.

$$\text{sucrose} + \text{sucrase} \longrightarrow \text{fructose} + \text{glucose}$$

a. Increase the pH to 8.

b. Increase the sucrose concentration.

c. Decrease the temperature to 15°C.

d. Increase the sucrase concentration.

e. Run the reaction at 55°C.

XI. Enzyme Inhibition

An inhibitor is a compound that slows down or stops the enzyme activity. We will consider two types of enzyme inhibition: competitive and noncompetitive inhibition.

A. Competitive Inhibition

In competitive inhibition, the inhibitor competes with the substrate for the active site on the enzyme. Both substrate and inhibitor are very similar in structure and they both compete for the active site. As long as the inhibitor is binding to the active site, the substrate cannot react. However, addition of large amounts of substrate can reverse the inhibition.

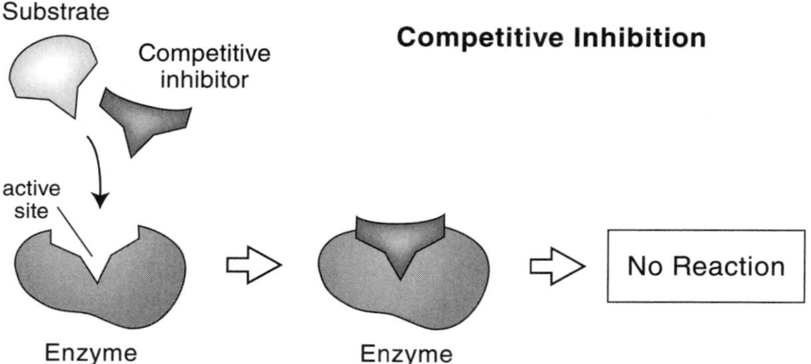

Competitive inhibition is widely used in medicine. For example, certain antibiotics, like penicillin, fight bacterial infection since they interfere with bacterial growth. Penicillin inhibits the formation of bacterial cell membranes and does not interfere with the formation of human cell membranes. When penicillin binds to the active site of the bacterial enzyme, cell membranes are not formed, bacterial growth is stopped, and the infection is controlled.

B. Noncompetitive Inhibition

A noncompetitive inhibitor binds to an enzyme at a site other than its active site. After it binds, it alters the structure of the enzyme and changes the shape of the active site. As a result, the substrate cannot bind and its reaction is inhibited. Since the inhibitor does not bind to the active site, addition of more substrate to the enzyme does not reverse the inhibition.

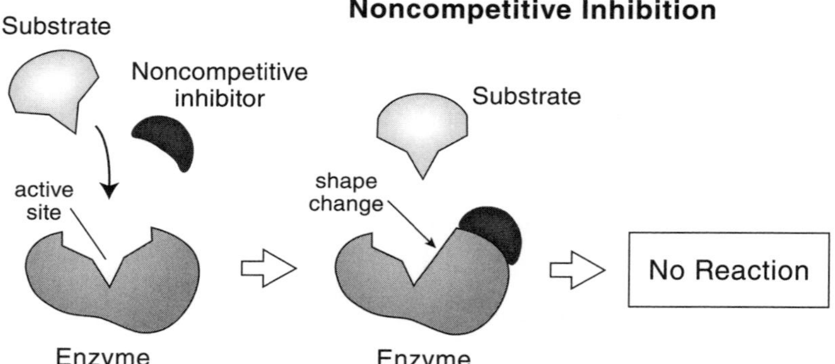

Problem 9. Indicate whether the following describe a competitive or a noncompetitive enzyme inhibitor.

a. has a structure different from the substrate.

b. competes with the substrate for the active site.

c. addition of more substrate reverses inhibition.

d. binds to the enzyme at the same time as the substrate.

e. addition of more substrate cannot reverse inhibition.

XII. Enzymes and Digestion

Digestion, a general term for the breakdown of food into smaller molecules, entails both the physical grinding, softening, and mixing of food, as well as the enzyme-catalyzed hydrolysis of food components. This process begins in the mouth, continues in the stomach, and is completed in the small intestine. This discussion will only be concerned with some of the enzyme-catalyzed reactions.

The partial hydrolysis of starch begins in the mouth and is catalyzed by α-amylase, one of the components of saliva. The optimum pH for this enzyme is 6.8.

In the stomach, which has a pH of 1.5 to 2.5, the salivary amylase is inactivated and there is essentially no further digestion of starch. However, the enzyme pepsin, which is present in the stomach, has an optimum pH in the normal pH range of the stomach. This enzyme accounts for the hydrolysis of some of the peptide bonds in dietary proteins.

The pancreas produces α-amylase, lipase, nucleases, and the proteolytic enzymes trypsin, chymotrypsin, and carboxypeptidase, as well as large quantities of sodium bicarbonate which neutralizes the acid and accounts for the basic pH of the small intestine. Cells in the lining of the small intestine also produce sucrase, lactase, and maltase. The end products of digestion of starch are monosaccharides. Protein is broken down to amino acids, and bile from the gall bladder helps lipase in digesting lipids to fatty acids, glycerol, and monoacylglycerols.

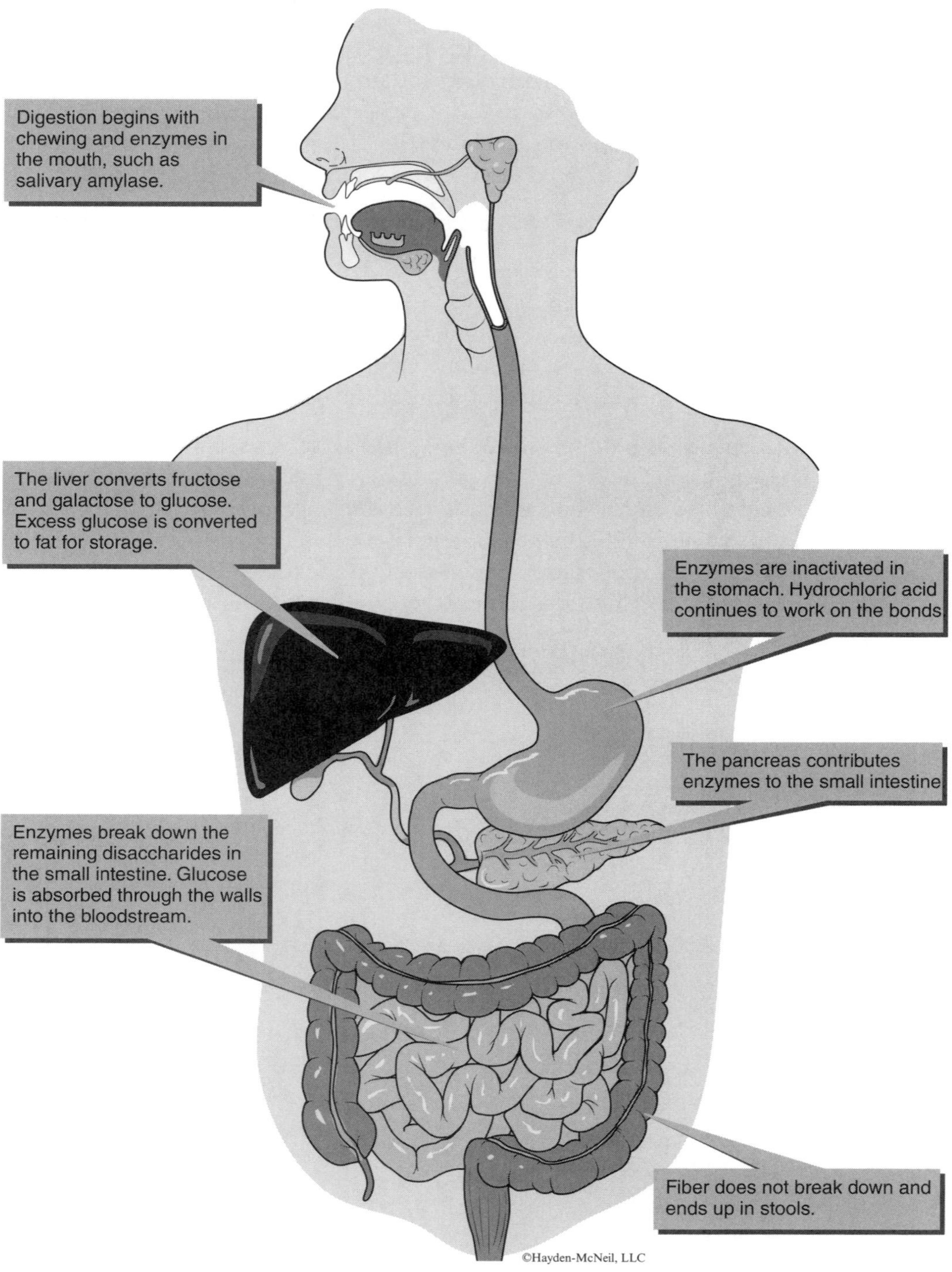
Digestion begins with chewing and enzymes in the mouth, such as salivary amylase.
The liver converts fructose and galactose to glucose. Excess glucose is converted to fat for storage.
Enzymes are inactivated in the stomach. Hydrochloric acid continues to work on the bonds.
The pancreas contributes enzymes to the small intestine.
Enzymes break down the remaining disaccharides in the small intestine. Glucose is absorbed through the walls into the bloodstream.
Fiber does not break down and ends up in stools.
©Hayden-McNeil, LLC

ANSWERS

1. a. Hydrocarbon R group b. Acidic R group c. Basic R group

   d. Alcohol R group e. Aromatic R group f. Amide R group

2.

	pH < Isoelectric Point	Isoelectric Point	pH > Isoelectric Point
a.	$\overset{+}{N}H_3-CH_2-\overset{O}{\overset{\parallel}{C}}-OH$	$\overset{+}{N}H_3-CH_2-\overset{O}{\overset{\parallel}{C}}-O^-$	$NH_2-CH_2-\overset{O}{\overset{\parallel}{C}}-O^-$
b.	$\overset{+}{N}H_3-\underset{CH_2-OH}{\underset{\vert}{CH}}-\overset{O}{\overset{\parallel}{C}}-OH$	$\overset{+}{N}H_3-\underset{CH_2-OH}{\underset{\vert}{CH}}-\overset{O}{\overset{\parallel}{C}}-O^-$	$NH_2-\underset{CH_2-OH}{\underset{\vert}{CH}}-\overset{O}{\overset{\parallel}{C}}-O^-$
c.	$\overset{+}{N}H_3-\underset{CH_2-C_6H_5}{\underset{\vert}{CH}}-\overset{O}{\overset{\parallel}{C}}-OH$	$\overset{+}{N}H_3-\underset{CH_2-C_6H_5}{\underset{\vert}{CH}}-\overset{O}{\overset{\parallel}{C}}-O^-$	$NH_2-\underset{CH_2-C_6H_5}{\underset{\vert}{CH}}-\overset{O}{\overset{\parallel}{C}}-O^-$

3. a. $$NH_2-\underset{CH_3}{\underset{\vert}{CH}}-\overset{O}{\overset{\parallel}{C}}-NH-\underset{CH_3}{\underset{\vert}{CH}}-\overset{O}{\overset{\parallel}{C}}-OH$$

   b. $$NH_2-\underset{CH_3-CH-CH_3}{\underset{\vert}{CH}}-\overset{O}{\overset{\parallel}{C}}-NH-\underset{CH_3}{\underset{\vert}{CH}}-\overset{O}{\overset{\parallel}{C}}-OH$$

   c. $$NH_2-\underset{CH_2-C_6H_5}{\underset{\vert}{CH}}-\overset{O}{\overset{\parallel}{C}}-NH-\underset{CH_3}{\underset{\vert}{CH}}-\overset{O}{\overset{\parallel}{C}}-NH-CH_2-\overset{O}{\overset{\parallel}{C}}-OH$$

   d. $$NH_2-\underset{CH_3-CH-CH_3}{\underset{\vert}{CH}}-\overset{O}{\overset{\parallel}{C}}-NH-CH_2-\overset{O}{\overset{\parallel}{C}}-NH-\underset{CH_2-C_6H_5}{\underset{\vert}{CH}}-\overset{O}{\overset{\parallel}{C}}-OH$$

4. a. 3 different tripeptides
   ala-ala-leu ala-leu-ala leu-ala-ala
   b. 6 different tripeptides
   asp-tyr-cys asp-cys-tyr
   tyr-asp-cys tyr-cys-asp
   cys-asp-tyr cys-tyr-asp
   c. 3 different tripeptides
   ser-val-val val-val-ser val-ser-val

5. a. Primary structure—4
   b. Secondary structure—2
   c. Tertiary structure—1, 2, 3, 5

6. a. hydrolase (lipase)
   b. lyase (decarboxylase)
   c. hydrolase (protease)
   d. isomerase (sugar isomerase)

7. a. conjugated protein
   b. conjugated protein
   c. simple protein
   d. simple protein
   e. conjugated protein

8. a. Decrease the rate
   b. Increase the rate
   c. Decrease the rate
   d. Increase the rate
   e. Decrease the rate

9. a. noncompetitive inhibition
   b. competitive inhibition
   c. competitive inhibition
   d. noncompetitive inhibition
   e. noncompetitive inhibition

Proteins and Enzymes

Name

Student Number

Date Instructor

1. What are five functions of proteins in the human body?

2. Draw the structure of the zwitterion of alanine.

3. What is the structure of cysteine in a solution if the pH of the solution is:

   a. greater than the isoelectric point?

   b. less than the isoelectric point?

   c. equal to the isoelectric point?

4. Draw the structures of the following tripeptides.

   a. leu-lys-ser

   b. asp-val-tyr

5. The ______________ structure of a protein refers to how the protein chain is wound.

6. The way two or more proteins fit together to form a functioning unit is called the __________________ structure.

7. The ______________ structure of a protein is the 3-dimensional structure or the shape of the protein.

8. The ________________ structure of a protein is the sequence and identity of amino acids in the protein.

9. The α-helix and the β-pleated sheet are examples of ____________________ structures of proteins.

10. The __________________ structure of a protein results from hydrogen bonds between the amide H's and the carbonyl O's in the protein.

11. The ________________ structure of a protein is caused by interactions between R-groups of the amino acids in a protein.

12. Give the 4 types of interactions which occur between the R-groups of the amino acids in a protein.

13. Complete hydrolysis of a protein produces ______________________.

14. At a pH higher than its isoelectric pH, an amino acid is _________________.

15. Name one nonpolar amino acid ________________________.

16. Name one polar (not acidic nor basic) amino acid ________________________.

17. What is meant by the "denaturation" of a protein?

18. List 5 denaturation agents.

19. Give the products for the complete hydrolysis of each of the following.

    a. starch
    b. cellulose
    c. a triacylglycerol
    d. a steroid
    e. a protein

20. Give the three steps for the lock and key model of enzyme action on a substrate (S) to produce a product (P). Represent the enzyme with E.

21. Names of enzymes generally end in ______, and often are similar to the ___________ name.

22. Classify the following enzymes as simple or conjugated proteins. If it is conjugated, what is the cofactor?

    a. Pyruvate kinase requires Mg^{+2} to become an active enzyme.

    b. An enzyme that requires vitamin E for biological activity.

    c. This enzyme is composed of 305 amino acids.

    d. This enzyme contains a carbohydrate portion as well as a protein.

23. A nonprotein molecule that collaborates with an enzyme to catalyze a reaction is called a(n) ____________________.

24. Name the type of enzyme which catalyzes the following reactions:

    a. rearrangement of atoms within a molecule: ________________

    b. moves an atom or group of atoms from one molecule to another:

       ____

    c. removes a carbon dioxide from a molecule: _______________

    d. breaks a molecule into two smaller molecules by the addition of water:

       ____

25. Consider a reaction in which the substrate is much more concentrated than the enzyme, so that the enzyme is "saturated."

    a. If the concentration of the substrate is increased, does the reaction rate increase, decrease, or remain the same?

    b. If the concentration of the enzyme is increased, does the reaction rate increase, decrease, or remain the same?

26. Indicate for each of the following whether the inhibitor is a competitive or a noncompetitive inhibitor.

    a. The addition of more substrate does not reverse the inhibition.

    b. The inhibitor has a similar shape as the substrate, and attaches to the active site of the enzyme.

    c. The inhibitor binds to the enzyme at the same time as the substrate.

27. How does a noncompetitive inhibitor slow down the reaction rate?

28. How does a change in body temperature affect the rates of reactions in the body which are catalyzed by enzymes?

16

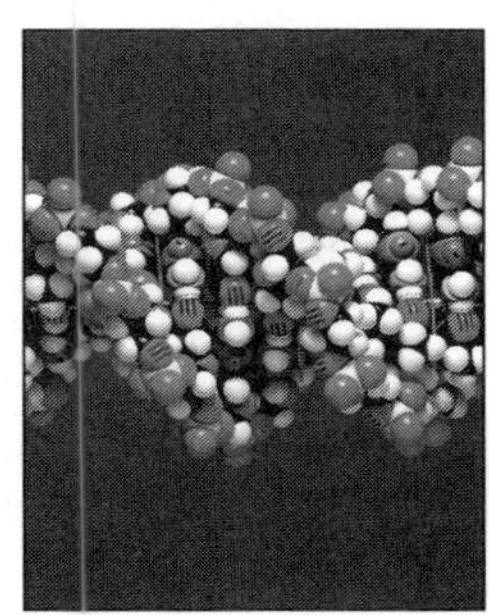

Nucleic Acids—Life's Code

Who we are, why we look the way we look, and how our body works is stored in the genetic material in our cells. Deoxyribonucleic acid (DNA) contains the information, in coded form, to determine each cell's structure and function. A second molecule, ribonucleic acid (RNA), carries the coded information from the nucleus, where DNA resides, to the ribosomes, where protein synthesis occurs..

I. Introduction

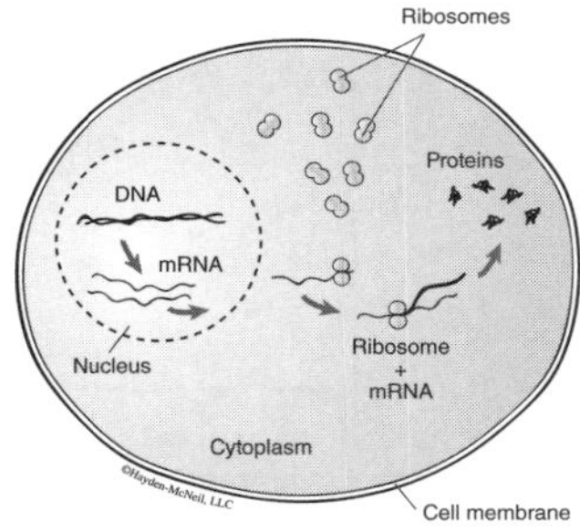

Every cell in our body contains the same genetic material, stored in the DNA molecules, yet different cells will only use part of this information. Only certain proteins will be produced, depending on the type of cell. For example, insulin molecules are only produced in an area of the pancreas, yet *all* cells have the information needed to produce insulin—they just don't.

II. DNA and RNA

A. Composition of DNA

a. **Sugar-phosphate backbone**. A five-carbon sugar—**deoxyribose** —with an ester linkage to a phosphate group (PO_4^{3-}), becomes the backbone for DNA molecules.

b. **Nitrogen bases**. The four nitrogen-containing compounds in DNA are cytosine, thymine (both pyrimidines), adenine, and guanine (these two are purines).

c. Two polynucleotide strands form a double helix.

B. Composition of RNA

a. **Sugar-phosphate backbone.** A five-carbon sugar—**ribose**—with an ester linkage to a phosphate group (PO_4^{3-}), becomes the backbone for RNA molecules.

b. **Nitrogen bases.** The four nitrogen-containing compounds in RNA are cytosine, uracil (both pyrimidines), adenine, and guanine (these two are purines).

c. RNA is composed of only a single strand.

Structural Differences between DNA and RNA

Differences	DNA	RNA
Sugar DNA has one fewer OH group at Carbon-2	Deoxyribose 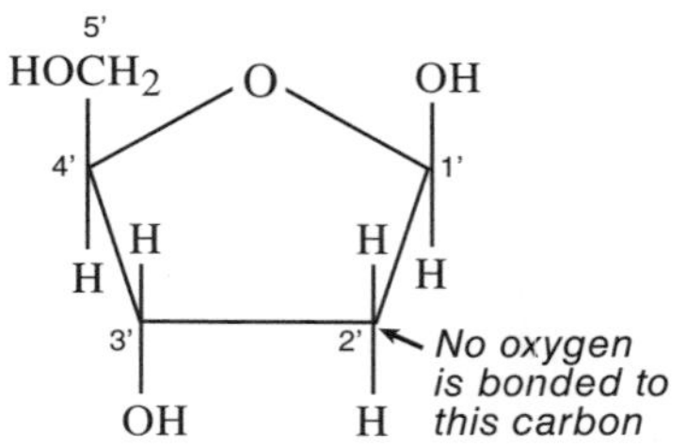 No oxygen is bonded to this carbon	Ribose 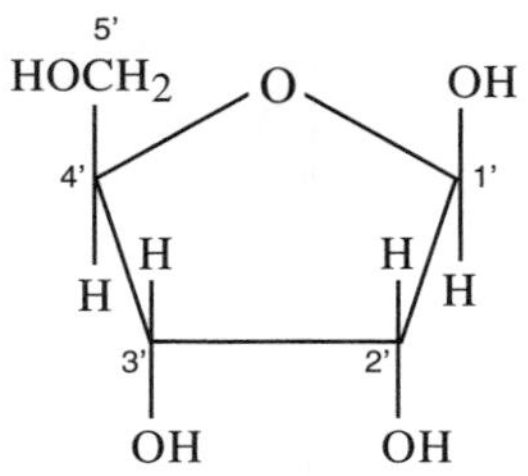
Nitrogen bases DNA contains Cytosine, Thymine, Adenine, and Guanine RNA contains Cytosine, Uracil, Adenine, and Guanine So RNA replaces Thymine with Uracil	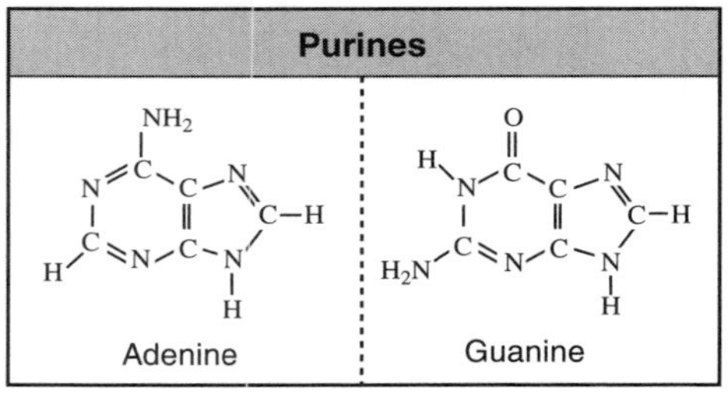 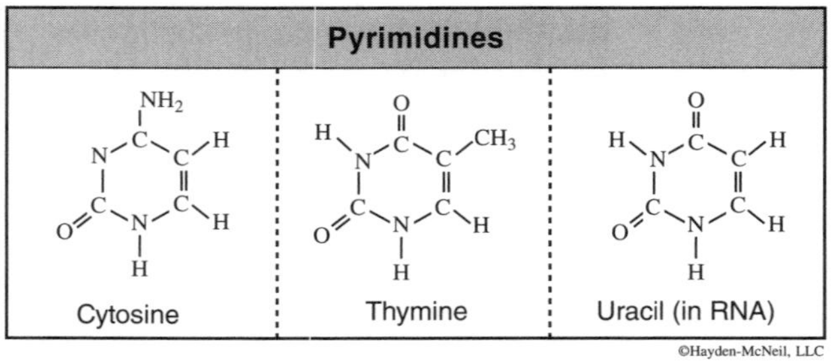 Purines: Adenine, Guanine Pyrimidines: Cytosine, Thymine, Uracil (in RNA) ©Hayden-McNeil, LLC	

Problem 1. Give two structural differences between DNA and RNA:

III. Nucleosides and Nucleotides

When a sugar (deoxyribose) bonds with a nitrogen base via a glycosidic linkage (removal of –OH from Carbon-1 in the sugar and –H from the nitrogen in the base), a **nucleoside** is produced.

For DNA, the nucleosides are: deoxyadenosine, deoxyguanosine, deoxycytidine, and deoxythymidine (remember that DNA uses deoxyribose as the sugar).

For RNA, the nucleosides are: adenosine, guanosine, cytidine, and uridine.

Nucleotides are formed by adding a phosphate group to Carbon-5 of the sugar component of the nucleoside. Nucleotides are named by using the name of the nucleoside and adding 5′-monophosphate, which indicates the position of the phosphate group within the sugar molecule.

The name of the structure below is deoxyadenosine-5′-monophosphate, abbreviated (thankfully!) to dAMP.

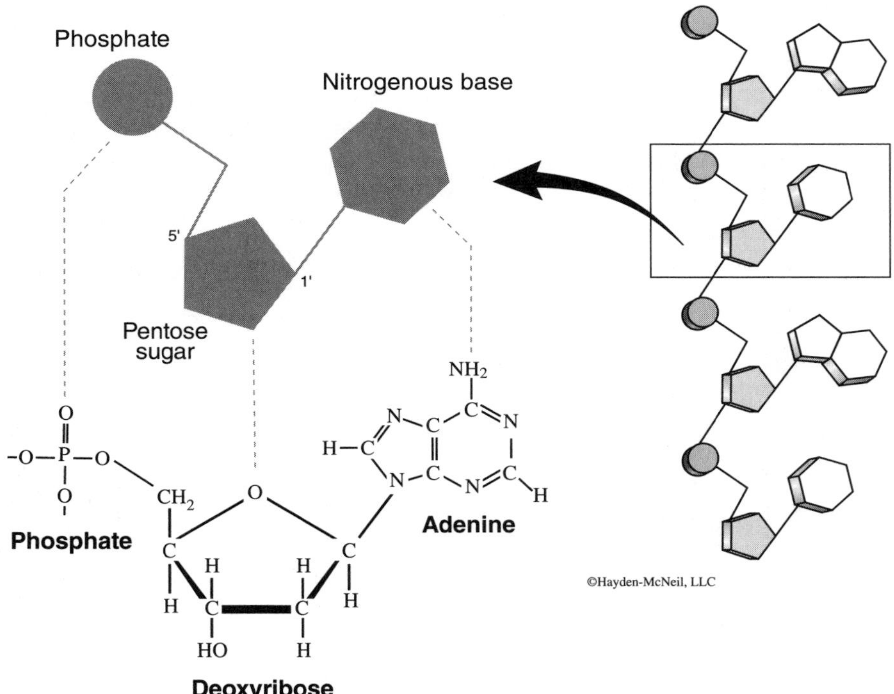

Problem 2. List the components of a nucleoside:

Problem 3. List the components of a nucleotide:

IV. Nucleic Acids

When many nucleotides are linked together, a nucleic acid is formed. This linkage occurs between the phosphate group of one nucleotide and the carbon-3–OH group of the sugar in a second nucleotide. The primary structure of this nucleic acid is described by the sequence of the nitrogen bases, starting from the free phosphate group. This structure has the sequence ATA.

RNA is a single-stranded nucleic acid, while DNA has a double strand—two nucleic acids linked by hydrogen bonding between the nitrogen bases. These two strands in DNA exist in a double helical structure (like a spiral staircase) held together by hydrogen bonds between the bases. The two strands in DNA are complementary to each other. This means that the base adenine in one strand can only hydrogen bond with thymine in the second strand and similarly, cytosine can only hydrogen bond with guanine. Notice that Adenine and guanine (the purines) both have two rings fused together, while thymine and cytosine (both pyrimidines) have only one ring. So the match is always of a purine with a pyrimidine. Therefore, adenine always pairs with thymine (AT) and cytosine always pairs with guanine (CG).

V. Replication of DNA

DNA molecules must copy themselves *exactly* in order to preserve the information coded within. To do so, the double helix must unwind and start separating by breaking the hydrogen bonds in order to expose each nitrogen base sequence. This is similar to opening a zipper. Now that there are single strands, they become templates to produce new complementary strands.

Every time there is an adenine in the single strand, the new strand that is being produced will have a thymine at the matching position. The new strand that was synthesized has the same configuration as the former complementary strand that was unwound.

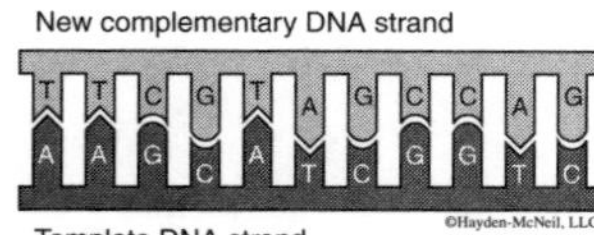

Problem 4. Draw the complementary strand (DNA replication):

T—A—G—C—A—A—C—G—T

VI. RNA

A. **Messenger RNA (mRNA)** is formed in the nucleus of the cell. The sequence of bases in the mRNA is determined by the complementary sequence in a portion of the DNA strand (a gene). This single-stranded molecule then travels from the nucleus to the ribosomes, which is the site of protein synthesis in the cell.

B. **Transfer RNA (tRNA)** is the carrier of amino acids for protein synthesis. A given tRNA will only transfer one specific amino acid from the cytoplasm to the ribosomes.

C. **Ribosomal RNA (rRNA)** combines with proteins to form the ribosomes.

Problem 5. For each of the following RNA molecules, state where it is found within the cell:

a. rRNA b. tRNA c. mRNA

Problem 6. Describe the function for:

a. tRNA b. mRNA

VII. Protein Synthesis

There are several steps involved in protein synthesis. The information originally stored in the nucleus must travel to the ribosomes, the protein factory of the cell. This process involves DNA, mRNA, and tRNA and has three defined steps: transcription, translation, and finally, termination.

A. ***Transcription***, which means "to copy," involves the formation of the mRNA in the nucleus of the cell. This mRNA is complementary to a portion of the DNA molecule. Remember that RNA molecules have uracil instead of thymine. So, when the DNA portion contains an adenine base, the mRNA produced will contain uracil.

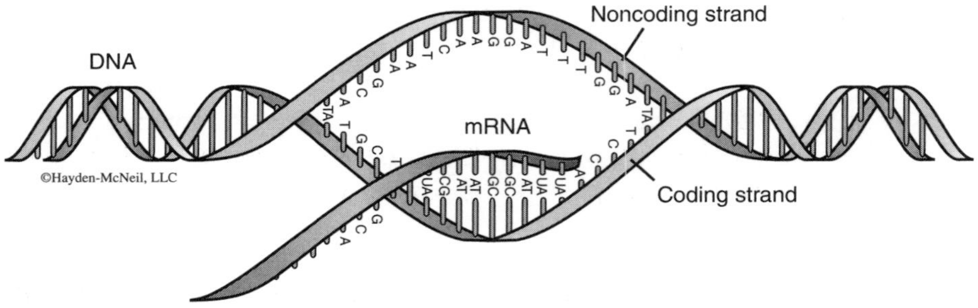

B. **Translation** is the process by which the information contained in nucleic acids is converted into a specific protein. Each three-base sequence in a mRNA is called a **codon**, and indirectly specifies one particular amino acid, thereby determining the primary sequence of amino acids within a protein molecule being synthesized.

This mRNA, which is now attached to the ribosomes, then directs a tRNA to place its amino acid in the proper location. Just like the mRNA had a three-base sequence (codon), the tRNA has the complementary three-base sequence, called an **anticodon**, to match. Repeated placements of different amino acids brought by separate, different tRNA molecules, creates the protein molecule.

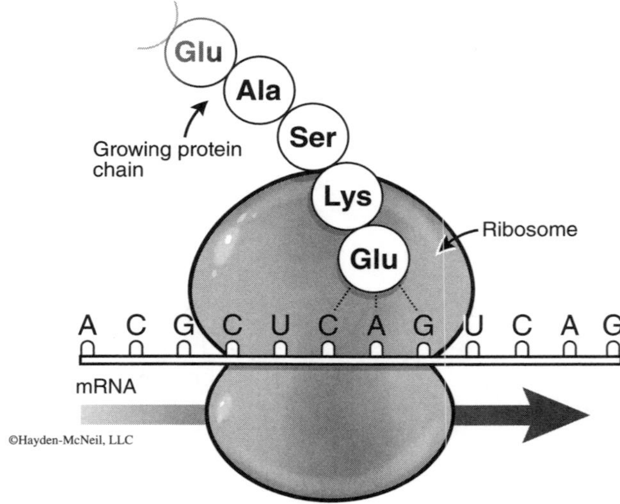

C. ***Termination***, as the term implies, is the completion of a protein molecule. Certain codons in mRNA indicate the end of a particular protein. There are no tRNA molecules with the matching anticodon, so the process stops and the completed protein molecule separates from the ribosome.

Problem 7. What is the name of the step within protein synthesis that ends the production of a protein molecule?

Problem 8. What is the name of the step within protein synthesis that creates the template for the amino acid sequence in a protein molecule?

Problem 9. What is the name of the step within protein synthesis where the tRNA matches a codon in the mRNA that specifies a particular amino acid?

Problem 10. Draw the complementary mRNA strand for following DNA segment:

T—A—G—C—A—A—C—G—T

Problem 11. Give the appropriate anticodon found in tRNA for each of the following 3-base codons in mRNA:

a. C—G—A   b. U—A—G   c. G—A—C

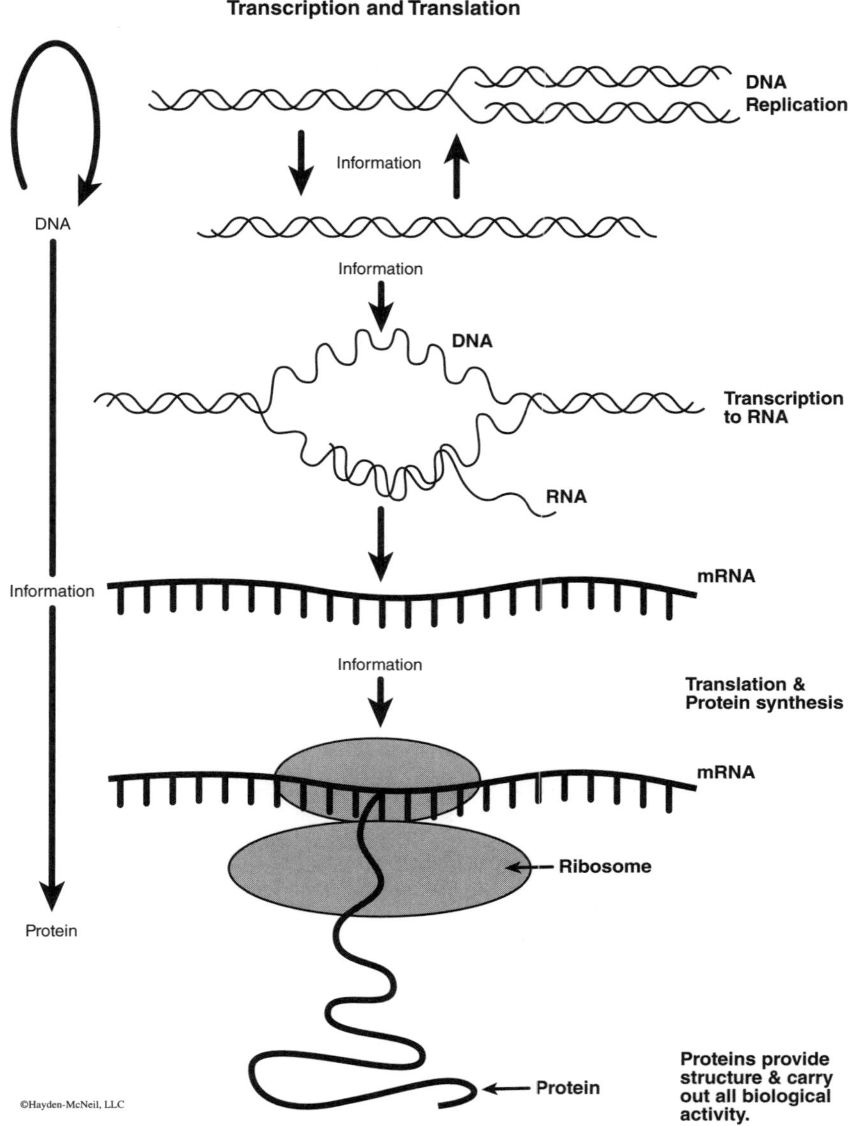

VIII. Mutations

Any change in the sequence of bases in DNA is considered a mutation. This mutation may cause a change in the amino acid sequence of a particular protein molecule, and that change may be detrimental to the organism. For example, sickle-cell anemia is caused by one amino acid change in the β-chain of the hemoglobin molecule, resulting in a different shape. Now the hemoglobin is less efficient in its ability to carry oxygen and, in addition, it can cause hemoglobin molecules to clump together, affecting blood circulation.

Many other diseases are also genetic in nature, all based on defects in the DNA. Among these are cystic fibrosis, PKU, muscular dystrophy, and hemophilia.

ANSWERS

1. Two differences between DNA and RNA

   a. the sugar used—deoxyribose in DNA and ribose in RNA

   b. the bases used—DNA has thymine while RNA has uracil

   c. DNA has a double strand while RNA is only single-stranded

2. The components of a nucleoside are a sugar (ribose or deoxyribose) and a nitrogen base (adenine, thymine, uracil, cytosine, or guanine).

3. The components of a nucleotide are a nucleoside (sugar and nitrogen base) and a phosphate group.

4. The complementary DNA strand is:

   T—A—G—C—A—A—C—G—T

   A—T—C—G—T—T—G—C—A

5. a. rRNA ribosomes

   b. tRNA cytoplasm AND ribosomes

   c. mRNA nucleus and ribosomes

6. a. tRNA brings amino acids from the cytoplasm to the ribosomes

   b. mRNA carries the genetic code—in the form of a codon—from the DNA molecule in the nucleus, to the ribosomes for protein synthesis.

7. Termination

8. Transcription

9. Translation

10. The complementary mRNA strand for DNA is

    T—A—G—C—A—A—C—G—T

    A—U—C—G—U—U—G—C—A

11. a. C—G—A b. U—A—G c. G—A—C

    G—C—U **A—U—C** **C—U—G**

Nucleic Acids— Life's Code

Name

Student Number

Date Instructor

1. Identify the following as pertaining to DNA, RNA, or both.
   a. deoxyribose
   b. uracil
   c. ribose
   d. adenine
   e. thymine
   f. single-stranded

2. Give the components of:
   a. deoxyguanosine
   b. cytidine
   c. deoxythymidine-5′-monophosphate
   d. uridine-5′-monophosphate
   e. d-TMP

3. Indicate the nitrogenous base that pairs with each of the following:

   a. thymine

   b. cytosine

   c. uracil

   d. guanine

4. Draw the complementary strand (DNA replication):

   a. T—A—A—T—C—G—C—G—A

   b. C—T—T—G—A—C—C—G—T

   c. G—T—G—A—C—T—C—C—G

5. Select the location where each of the following starts its function in protein synthesis.

a. mRNA	1. ribosomes
b. tRNA	2. nucleus
c. rRNA	3. cytoplasm

6. Select the function for each of the following in protein synthesis.

a. mRNA	1. carries amino acid into ribosome
b. tRNA	2. structural component of ribosome
c. rRNA	3. carries information from nucleus

7. Provide a short description for each of these steps in protein synthesis.

   a. transcription

   b. translation

   c. termination

8. Draw the complementary mRNA strand given the following DNA strand.

   a. G—A—C—T—C—A—C—G—C

   b. C—T—G—G—A—T—C—A—T

   c. G—A—C—A—C—G—C—C—G

9. Give the appropriate anticodon found in tRNA for each of the following 3-base codons in mRNA.

   a. U—G—G   b. A—C—G   c. G—U—C

NOTES

Rounding Off Numbers and Scientific Notation

I. Recommendations on the Purchase of a Calculator

It is recommended that you get a low-priced scientific calculator. The calculator should have at least the following functions:

$\times$, $\div$, $+$, $-$, EXP or EE (scientific notation)

II. Rounding Off Numbers

The following are examples of numbers that have been rounded off to the second decimal place. The answer depends on the identity of the "next" digit (i.e., the digit after the cut off point).

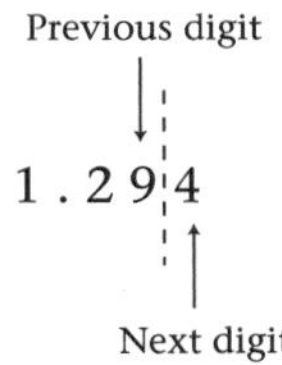

Example A: The Rules

	Answer		Rules
1.294	1.29	1.	If the next digit is less than 5, then the previous digit remains the same.
0.9946	0.99		
0.999	1.00	2.	If the next digit is equal to or greater than 5, then the previous digit is increased by one.
1.2950	1.30		

Problem 1. Round off each of the following numbers to the first decimal place:

a.	0.123	b.	25.151
c.	3.950	d.	7.100
e.	6.7501	f.	7.745

III. Scientific Notation and Powers of Ten

When numbers are very small or large, it is more convenient to write those numbers in scientific notation. Regardless of a numbers magnitude, all numbers can be expressed in scientific notation, whose general form is as follows:

Any number from 1-9 → $\boxed{N}. \times 10^{x}$ ← Exponent (Power of Ten)

For example, $\mathbf{3}.21 \times 10^{3}$, $\mathbf{9}.9 \times 10^{-4}$, and $\mathbf{1}. \times 10^{0}$.

The following are examples that illustrate what a number raised to a power of ten means:

Positive Exponents	Negative Exponents
$10^0 = 1$	
$10^1 = 10$	$10^{-1} = \frac{1}{10} = 0.1$
$10^2 = 10 \times 10 = 100$	$10^{-2} = \frac{1}{10 \times 10} = 0.01$
$10^3 = 10 \times 10 \times 10 = 1000$	$10^{-3} = \frac{1}{10 \times 10 \times 10} = 0.001$

To convert numbers into scientific notation, use the following guidelines:

a. As you move the decimal place to the left (i.e., make the number *smaller*), the power of ten (i.e., exponent) must *increase* by the same amount. For example,

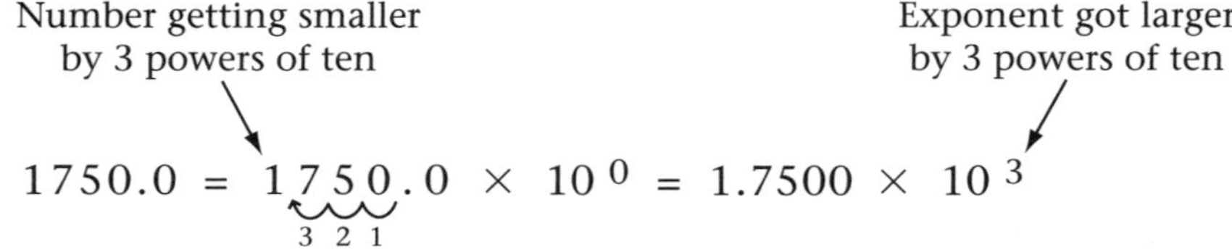

b. As you move the decimal place to the right (i.e., make the number *larger*), the power of ten (i.e., exponent) must *decrease* by the same amount. For example,

Number getting larger by 2 powers of ten — Exponent got smaller by 2 powers of ten

$$0.050 = 0.050 \times 10^{0} = 5.0 \times 10^{-2}$$

(decimal moved 1, 2 places to the right)

Problem 2. Write each of the following numbers in scientific notation:

a. 22,400. b. 0.007

c. 8,000. d. 22.4

e. 1.9 f. 0.00035

g. 0.00905 h. 0.273

IV. Inputting Numbers Written in Scientific Notation into a Calculator

Scientific Notation key employed by most calculators → [EXP] or [EE].

Example of how to input numbers written in scientific notation into a typical calculator:

Number	Keys to Press	Calculator Display
2.0×10^{3}	[2] [.] [0] [EXP] [3]	2.0 ^{03}
2.0×10^{-3}	[2] [.] [0] [EXP] [+/−] [3]	2.0 $^{-03}$

V. Converting Numbers Written in Scientific Notation to Numbers without a Power of Ten

In converting a number written in scientific notation to a number without a power of ten, one actually converts the number in question to a number with a power of 10^0.

Example B: Write the following numbers without a power of ten:

a. 1.601×10^{-1} b. 3.063×10^{2}

c. 3.16×10^{-3} d. 6.0×10^{2}

a. $1.601 \times 10^{-1} = 0.1601 \times 10^{0} = 0.1601$ (decimal moved 1 place)

b. $3.063 \times 10^{2} = 306.3 \times 10^{0} = 306.3$ (decimal moved 1 2)

c. $3.16 \times 10^{-3} = 0.00316 \times 10^{0} = 0.00316$ (decimal moved 3 2 1)

d. $6.0 \times 10^{2} = 600 \times 10^{0} = 600$ (decimal moved 1 2)

Problem 3. Write the following numbers without a power of ten:

a. 1.601×10^{-2} b. 3.063×10^{4}

c. 3.16×10^{-3} d. 6.0×10^{5}

e. 9.300×10^{2} f. 0.600×10^{-1}

ANSWERS

1. a. 0.1 b. 25.2 c. 4.0 d. 7.1
   e. 6.8 f. 7.7

2. a. 2.2400×10^{4} b. $7. \times 10^{-3}$ c. 8.000×10^{3} d. 2.24×10^{1}
   e. 1.9×10^{0} f. 3.5×10^{-4} g. 9.05×10^{-3} h. 2.73×10^{-1}

3. a. 0.01601 b. 30,630 c. 0.00316 d. 600,000
   e. 930.0 f. 0.0600

NOTES

B

Significant Figures

I. Significant Figures (SF)

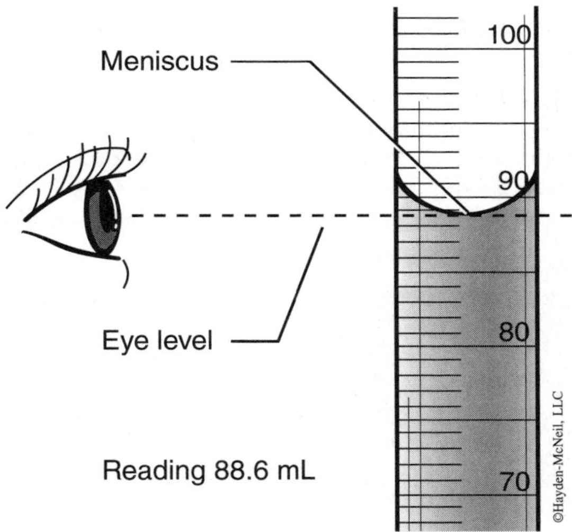

The volume of the solution measured with the graduated cylinder shown above is recorded to one decimal place, **88.6 mL.** The last digit is an estimated value and it is a significant figure. This measurement, 88.6 mL, has 3 significant figures. The number of significant figures given in a measured quantity will depend on the instrumentation used. The value 80.0 mL also has 3 significant figures.

Significant figures indicate how accurately measurements have been made. The rules for counting significant figures apply only to numbers that have been obtained from a measurement.

To find how many significant figures a number has:

1. First, locate the first nonzero digit (start from left → right).

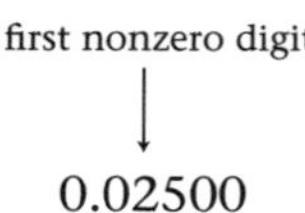

2. Second, starting with the first nonzero digit, count the number of digits the number has.

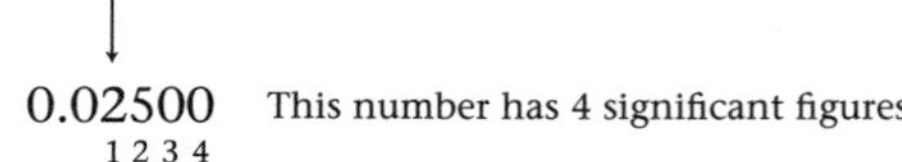

Zeros at the end of a number that has no decimal point may or may not be significant. For example, the number 300 may have 1, 2, or 3 significant figures. It is for this reason that decimal points should be included if zeros are significant.

Numbers that are exact have an infinite number of significant figures. For example, numbers that have been counted are exact; if you have 30 pennies, that means you have exactly 30 pennies, no measuring tool is needed to determine this amount. Exact numbers are not measured. Defining 1 ft = 12 in is also an exact quantity. Exact numbers do not affect the number of significant figures in a calculated answer.

Problem 1. How many significant figures are in each of the following numbers?

a. 700.0 b. 0.006

c. 20.001 d. 0.0500

e. 700 f. 60.0

II. Determining the Number of Significant Figures in Multiplication and Division Problems

In multiplication and division, the final answer has the same number of significant figures as the number with the least number of significant figures. For example,

Final answer rounded off to the correct number of significant figures

$$2.5670 \times 4.5 = 11.5515 = 12$$

5 SF (under 2.5670); 2 SF (circled, under 4.5); Calculator Results (under 11.5515)

When a number obtained from a mathematical operation is very large and the number of significant figures that should be reported is small, then the answer should be written in scientific notation. For example, if the calculated answer is 5,924,532.57 and it needs to be reported to **two** significant figures then the final answer is 5.9×10^6.

Problem 2. Perform the following operations, and give the answers with the correct number of significant figures.

a. 0.0065×46.00 b. 27.05×0.003

c. 2.00×45.00 d. $61.0/0.0020$

e. $\dfrac{3.61 \times 9.6}{0.8}$ f. $\dfrac{3.61 \times 9.6}{0.8 \times 6.3}$

g. $\dfrac{10.00 \times 100.0}{0.008 \times 6.3}$ h. $\dfrac{9.0 \times 0.800}{1.06 \times 9.0}$

ANSWERS

1. a. 4 b. 1 c. 5
   d. 3 e. 1, 2, or 3 f. 3

2. a. 0.30 b. 0.08 c. 90.0 d. 3.1×10^4
   e. 4×10^1 f. 7 g. 2×10^4 h. 0.75

C

Answers to Module Assignments

Module 1

1. a. 5.5×10^5 b. 6.43×10^{-4}
2. a. 0.00000173 b. 4,810
3. grams
4. 100 cm / 1 m
5. a. 0.525 L b. 19.7 cg
   c. 43.7 cm d. 2.23 in
   e. 59,600 mL f. 49.3 oz
6. 96.6 miles/hr or 97.2 miles/hr
7. 6.0 g/mL
8. 27.6 mL
9. 3.36 kg
10. a. 86.0 °F b. 10.0 °C
11. 211 cm
12. 6,810 g; 6.81 kg
13. 13.6 g/mL
14. 54.5 g
15. 3 tablets
16. −260 °F
18. a. 8 tsp/day b. 2 tsp/dose
19. 4 tsp
20. 15 mL

Module 2

1. solution
2. compound
3. heterogeneous

4. liquid
5. a definite, a definite
6. sublimation
7. condensation
8. a. K potassium b. Ag silver c. Sn tin
   d. Hg mercury e. Mn manganese f. Se selenium
9. a. gold Au b. iron Fe c. sodium Na
   d. xenon Xe e. fluorine F
10. a. Si metalloid b. Ga metal c. Se nonmetal
11. helium, *nitrogen*, boron, carbon, *hydrogen*, lithium, iron, arsenic, *iodine*, tin, beryllium
12.

Isotope	Protons	Neutrons	Electrons
C–14	6	8	6
Cr–53	24	29	24
Mg–24	12	12	12
Cl–37	17	20	17
P–31	15	16	15
K–41	19	22	19
I–131	53	78	53
^{60}Co	27	33	27

13. a. Cs, Ba, Ge, Br, Kr, Be, Li, F, S, Sn, Al
    b. Ce, U
    c. Al
    d. V, Zn, Kr, Fe, Ge, Br
    e. V, Zn, Fe
    f. Br, F
    g. Kr
    h. Li, Cs
    i. Ba, Be

14. a. S <u>6</u> b. Al <u>3</u> c. Mg <u>2</u> d. Si <u>4</u> e. Cl <u>7</u>

15.

Symbol for Element	Electronic Configuration
N	2-5
Si	2-8-4
Li	2-1
Ca	2-8-8-2
Mg	2-8-2
K	2-8-8-1
P	2-8-5
O	2-6
Ne	2-8
Cl	2-8-7

16. a. Na 1 e^- lost b. Al 3 e^- lost c. P 3 e^- gained
    d. S 2 e^- gained e. Ba 2 e^- lost f. Br 1 e^- gained

Module 3

1. 18
2. 2
3. gains
4. ionic
5. −1
6. +2
7. :S̤̈: Mg· ·P̈· $[:\ddot{O}:]^{2-}$ Al^{3+} $[:\ddot{Cl}:]^{-}$

8. a. K_2O ionic b. CCl_4 covalent c. $BaCl_2$ ionic d. SO_2 covalent

9. a. Li & O Li_2O b. Al & Cl $AlCl_3$
   c. Ca & N Ca_3N_2 d. Mg & S MgS

10. a. :C̤̈l : P̤̈ : C̤̈l: with :C̤̈l: below P b. H : Si : H with H above and below Si c. :N:::N: d. :F̤̈ : Ö̤ : F̤̈: e. :Ö̤ : S̤̈ :: Ö with :Ö̤: below S

11. a. ammonium sulfate b. aluminum bicarbonate
    c. magnesium chloride d. carbon dioxide
    e. sodium phosphate f. potassium nitride
    g. dichlorine pentoxide h. calcium nitrate

12. a. $Be(CN)_2$ b. NF_3
    c. Ba_3P_2 d. $Ca(HCO_3)_2$
    e. Li_2S f. $(NH_4)_2CO_3$
    g. $Sr(OH)_2$ h. SF_6

13. a. K & $\underline{Cl}$ b. Ca & $\underline{Mg}$ c. S & $\underline{Cl}$ d. O & $\underline{F}$ e. Sb & $\underline{Br}$ f. H & $\underline{F}$

14. H-S H-Se $\underline{\text{H-O}}$ H-Te

15.

	Cl^{1-}	PO_4^{3-}	NO_3^{1-}	CO_3^{2-}
K^{1+}	KCl Potassium chloride	K_3PO_4 Potassium phosphate	KNO_3 Potassium nitrate	K_2CO_3 Potassium carbonate
Be^{2+}	$BeCl_2$ Beryllium chloride	$Be_3(PO_4)_2$ Beryllium phosphate	$Be(NO_3)_2$ Beryllium nitrate	$BeCO_3$ Beryllium carbonate
Co^{3+}	$CoCl_3$ Cobalt(III) chloride	$CoPO_4$ Cobalt(III) phosphate	$Co(NO_3)_3$ Cobalt(III) nitrate	$Co_2(CO_3)_3$ Cobalt(III) carbonate
Ca^{2+}	$CaCl_2$ Calcium chloride	$Ca_3(PO_4)_2$ Calcium phosphate	$Ca(NO_3)_2$ Calcium nitrate	$CaCO_3$ Calcium carbonate
Fe^{2+}	$FeCl_2$ Iron(II) chloride	$Fe_3(PO_4)_2$ Iron(II) phosphate	$Fe(NO_3)_2$ Iron(II) nitrate	$FeCO_3$ Iron(II) carbonate

Module 4

1. a. 30 g/mole b. 148.3 g/mole c. 174 g/mole d. 58 g/mole

2. 0.142 moles C_2H_6

3. 3.71 g $Mg(NO_3)_2$

4. 0.856 moles K_2SO_4

5. 5.17 moles C_4H_{10}

6. a. $C_4H_{10}O + \underline{6}\ O_2 \rightarrow \underline{4}\ CO_2 + \underline{5}\ H_2O$

   b. $\underline{3}\ Mg + N_2 \rightarrow Mg_3N_2$

   c. $2\ Na + Cl_2 \rightarrow 2\ NaCl$

   d. $4\ K + O_2 \rightarrow 2\ K_2O$

   e. $2\ Al + 3\ F_2 \rightarrow 2\ AlF_3$

   f. $BaO + H_2O \rightarrow Ba(OH)_2$

   g. $Fe_2O_3 + 3\ CO_2 \rightarrow Fe_2(CO_3)_3$

   h. $P_4O_{10} + 6\ H_2O \rightarrow 4\ H_3PO_4$

7. a. 5.8 moles O_2

   b. 0.977 moles CO_2

   c. 237 g O_2

Module 5

1. polar ionic

2. I_2 <u>KCl</u> <u>HBr</u> C_6H_6 Kr Cl_2 <u>Na_2SO_4</u>

3. a. $C_6H_{12}O_6$ nonelectrolyte b. $MgCl_2$ electrolyte c. CH_3OH nonelectrolyte

4. a. A supersaturated sugar solution. The sugar crystal will cause the excess sugar to precipitate out of solution.

   b. An unsaturated sugar solution. The additional sugar crystal will dissolve.

   c. A saturated sugar solution. The additional sugar crystal will precipitate out of solution.

5. 4.80%

6. 200 mL

7a. [(50.0g)/(400.mL)] × 100 = 12.5%

7b. First convert the 50.0 g $C_6H_{12}O_6$ to moles.

50.0 g $C_6H_{12}O_6$ × (1 mole / 180 g $C_6H_{12}O_6$) = 0.278 moles $C_6H_{12}O_6$

Then convert the 400 mL of solution to liters

400 mL × (1 L / 1000 mL) = 0.400 L

Divide moles by liters of solution.

0.278 moles $C_6H_{12}O_6$ / 0.400 L solution = 0.694 M

8. 0.900 mole

9. 79.8 grams

10. 0.500%

11. 250 mL solution × (6.0 mL alcohol / 100 mL solution) = 15 mL alcohol

12. 25.0 mL + 50.0 mL = 75.0 mL final volume

    $V_1C_1 = V_2C_2$

    (50.0 mL) (6.00 M) = (75.0 mL)(C_2)

    4.0 M = C_2

13. 12.0%

14. colloids solutions <u>suspensions</u>

15. hypotonic hemolyse

16. a. 5% glucose isotonic b. 2% NaCl hypertonic c. 1% glucose hypotonic

17. cannot

18. water

Module 6

1. a. base
   b. acids and bases
   c. base
   d. acid
   e. acid
   f. acid
   g. base

2. a. weak acid
   b. weak base
   c. strong acid
   d. strong base
   e. strong acid
   f. weak acid
   g. weak base
   h. strong base
   i. strong acid
   j. weak base

3.

pH	pOH	$[H^+]$	$[OH^-]$	Acidic, Basic, or Neutral
6	8	1×10^{-6} M	1×10^{-8} M	acidic
4	10	1×10^{-4} M	1×10^{-10} M	acidic
9	5	1×10^{-9} M	1×10^{-5} M	basic
11	3	1×10^{-11} M	1×10^{-3} M	basic
5	9	1×10^{-5} M	1×10^{-9} M	acidic
2	12	1×10^{-2} M	1×10^{-12} M	acidic
7	7	1×10^{-7} M	1×10^{-7} M	neutral
12	2	1×10^{-12} M	1×10^{-2} M	basic

4. a. $HBr + NaOH \rightarrow NaBr + HOH$ already balanced
   b. $H_2SO_4 + 2\ NH_4OH \rightarrow (NH_4)_2SO_4 + 2\ HOH$
   c. $Mg(OH)_2 + 2\ HCl \rightarrow MgCl_2 + 2\ HOH$
   d. $Al(OH)_3 + 3\ HCl \rightarrow AlCl_3 + 3\ HOH$

5. a. $HCl + KOH \rightarrow KCl + HOH$ already balanced

   b. $H_3PO_4 + 3\ NaOH \rightarrow Na_3PO_4 + 3\ HOH$

   c. $Ba(OH)_2 + 2\ HNO_3 \rightarrow Ba(NO_3)_2 + 2\ HOH$

   d. $3\ H_2SO_4 + 2\ Mn(OH)_3 \rightarrow Mn_2(SO_4)_3 + 6\ HOH$

6. A weak acid and its salt or a weak base and its salt. A buffer system works by neutralizing both added acid and added base.

7. b, c, and d

8. b

9. a

10. e

11. d

Module 7

1. Least penetrating is alpha, then beta, and gamma radiation is the most penetrating.

2. electrons

3. helium nuclei

4. a. α-radiation <u>paper or clothing</u>

   b. β-radiation <u>heavy clothing</u>

   c. γ-radiation <u>lead or concrete</u>

5. 16 times

6. a. $^{28}Al \rightarrow {}^{28}Si + \beta$

   b. $^{238}U \rightarrow {}^{234}Th + \alpha$

   c. $^{210}Bi \rightarrow {}^{206}Tl + \alpha$

   d. $^{35}S \rightarrow {}^{35}Cl + \beta$

7. $^{226}Ra \rightarrow {}^{222}Rn + \alpha$

8. $^{60}Co \rightarrow {}^{60}Ni + \beta + \gamma$

9. 15 grams Sr remains

10. 32 days

11. 128 hours; 5.3 days

12. 3.13 mg

Module 8

1. a. decreases
   b. increases
   c. increases
   d. doubled
   e. increase, two
   f. faster, increases

2. 0.395 atm

3. 570 mmHg

4. 250 torr

5. a. higher
   b. lower
   c. higher

6. Treatment for carbon dioxide poisonings, burns, cancer treatments, the bends (nitrogen narcosis).

7. higher

8. increase

9. higher, lower

Module 9

1. a. 3-methylhexane

   b. 5-ethyl-3,3-dimethylnonane

   c. 3-bromo-5,5-dimethyloctane

   d. 1,1,3-trimethylcylopentane

   e. 1,1-dichloro-3-isopropylcyclohexane

   f. *trans*-4-methyl-2-pentene

   g. 3-methyl-1-propylcyclohexene

   h. 1,3-dichlorobenzene or *m*-dichlorobenzene

   i. 4-isopropyltoluene or *p*-isopropyltoluene

   j. 5,5-dimethyl-1-heptene

   k. 4-bromo-1-chloro-2-ethylbenzene

   l. 5-methyl-2-hexyne

   m. 3-methylcyclopentene

   n. 1-ethyl-3-methylcyclopentane

   o. 3-isopropyl-4-methyl-2-pentene

2.

a. 2,3,5-trimethyloctane	b. o-dibromobenzene
$H_3C-CH(CH_3)-C(H)(CH_3)-C(H)(H)-CH(CH_3)-CH_2CH_2CH_3$	Br, Br
c. 3-ethyl-1-isopropyl-1-methylcyclohexane	**d. *trans*-5,6,7-trimethyl-3-nonene**
CH_3, HC(CH_3)(CH_3), CH_2CH_3	$H_3C-CH_2(H)C=C(H)-CH(CH_3)-C(H)(CH_3)-C(H)(CH_3)-CH_2CH_3$

e. 2,2-dimethyl-4-propyldecane 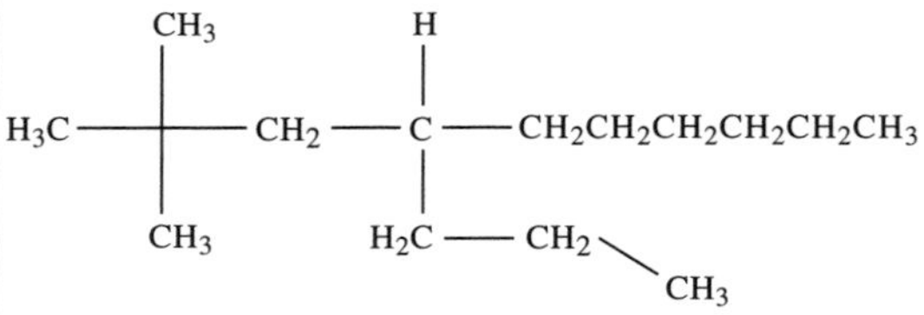 CH_3 H H_3C — C — CH_2 — C — $CH_2CH_2CH_2CH_2CH_2CH_3$ CH_3 H_2C — CH_2 — CH_3	f. 2,4,7-trichloro-1-heptene 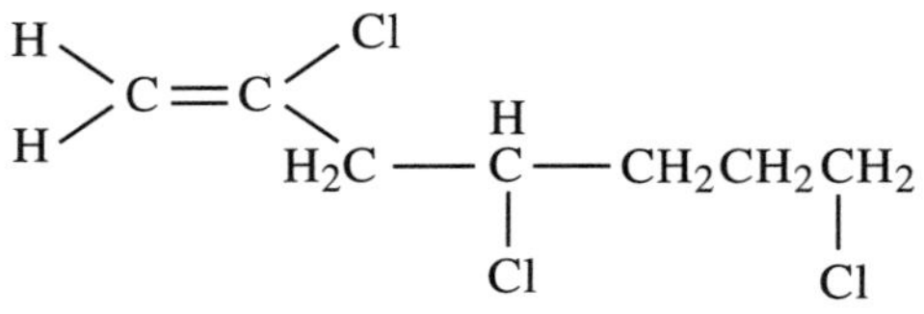 H, H >C=C< Cl H_2C — C(H)(Cl) — $CH_2CH_2CH_2$ — Cl
g. 3,4,4-trimethylcyclohexene 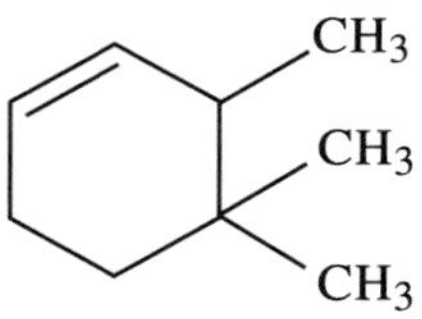 CH_3 CH_3 CH_3	h. 3-ethyl-1-hexyne 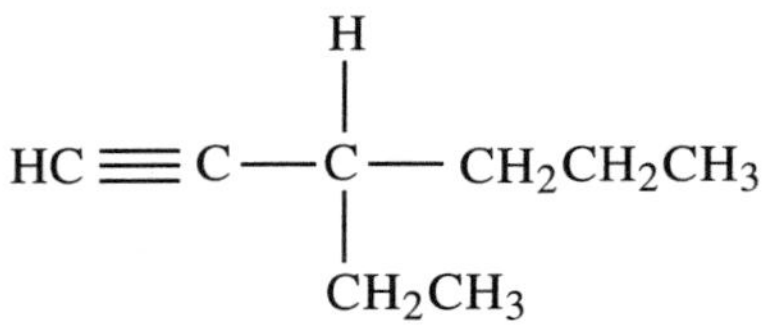 H HC ≡ C — C — $CH_2CH_2CH_3$ CH_2CH_3
i. 1,2,4-trimethylbenzene 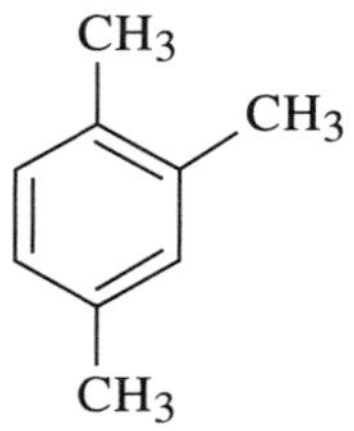 CH_3 CH_3 CH_3	j. p-bromoisopropylbenzene 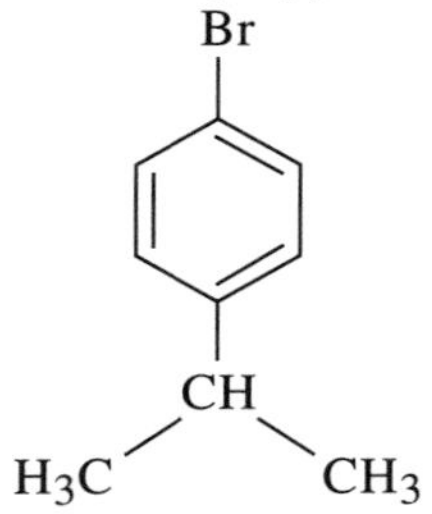 Br CH H_3C CH_3
k. 4-chloro-1-butyne 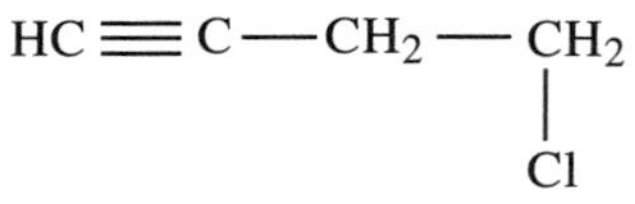 HC ≡ C — CH_2 — CH_2 Cl	l. *cis*-1-chloro-2,3-dimethyl-2-pentene 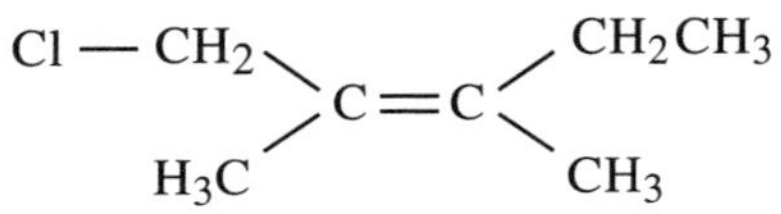 Cl — CH_2 >C=C< CH_2CH_3 H_3C CH_3

3. Structure # 3, this structure has only 5 carbon atoms

4.

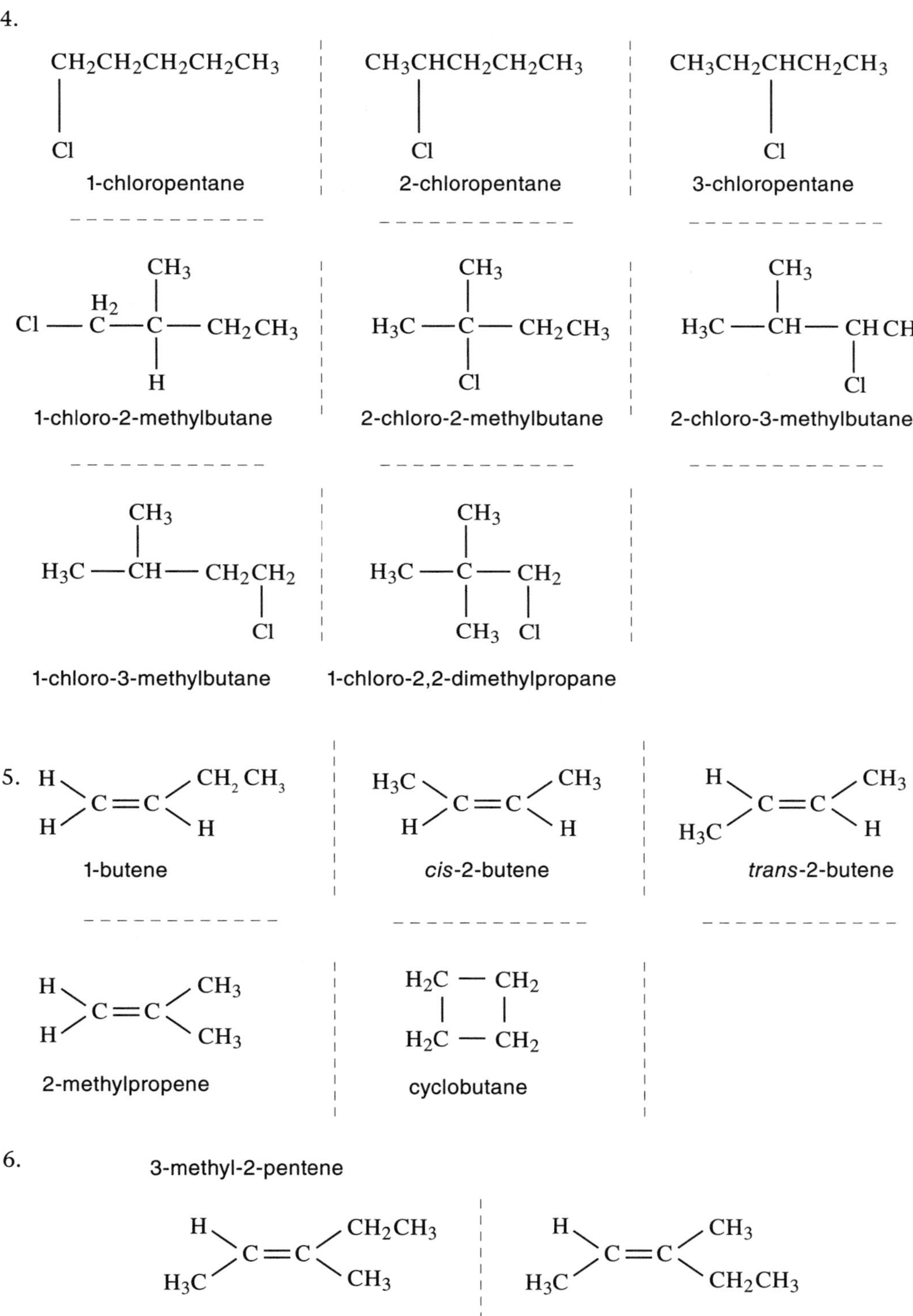

6. 3-methyl-2-pentene

7. a hydration (addition across the double bond)

8. a. cyclohexane + Br_2 $\xrightarrow{\text{light}}$ bromocyclohexane + HBr

b. $CH_3CH_3 + Cl_2 \xrightarrow{\text{light}} CH_3CH_2Cl + HCl$

c. $CH_2{=}CHCH_2CH_3 + HI \longrightarrow H_2C(H){-}CH(I)CH_2CH_3$

d. cyclopentene + $Br_2 \longrightarrow$ 1,2-dibromocyclopentane

e. $CH_2{=}CHCH_2CH_2CH_3 + HBr \longrightarrow H_2C(H){-}CH(Br)CH_2CH_2CH_3$

f. $CH_3C(CH_3){=}CHCH_3 + H_2O \xrightarrow{H^+} CH_3C(OH)(CH_3){-}CH(H)CH_3$

g. 1-methylcyclohexene + $HCl \longrightarrow$ 1-chloro-1-methylcyclohexane (Cl, CH_3; H, H)

h. $CH_2{=}C(CH_3)CH_2CH_3 + H_2 \xrightarrow{Pt} CH_3CH(CH_3)CH_2CH_3$

9. Product: chlorocyclobutane

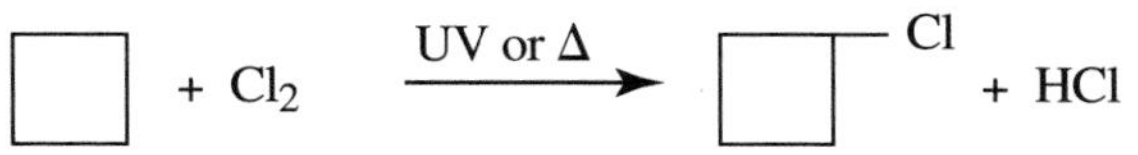

$$\square + Cl_2 \xrightarrow{\text{UV or } \Delta} \square\!-\!Cl + HCl$$

10. Product: 1-methylcyclopentanol

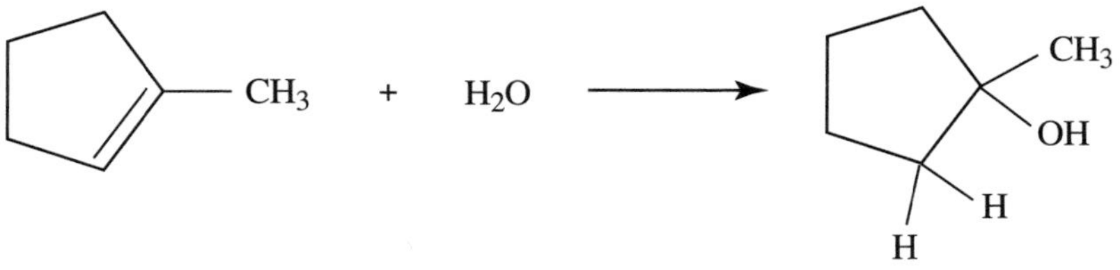

$$\text{1-methylcyclopentene}-CH_3 + H_2O \longrightarrow \text{cyclopentane ring with } CH_3,\ OH \text{ on C1 and } H,\ H \text{ on C2}$$

Module 10

1. a. ketone b. 3° alcohol c. 3° alcohol
   d. 2° alcohol e. aldehyde f. 3° alcohol
   g. aldehyde h. 2° alcohol i. ketone
   j. 1° alcohol k. aldehyde l. 1° alcohol
   m. 2° alcohol n. ketone

2. a. cyclopentanone b. 1-methylcyclohexanol
   c. 2-methyl-2-pentanol d. cyclopentanol
   e. pentanal f. 2,4-dimethyl-2-pentanol
   g. propanal h. 2-propanol
   i. propanone j. 1-propanol
   k. 5-chloro-3,5-dimethylhexanal l. 2,2-dimethyl-1-propanol
   m. 2-butanol n. 2-methylcyclohexanone

3. ketone
4. carboxylic acid
5. primary alcohol
6. tertiary alcohol or ketone
7. $$CH_3CH_2-CH(CH_3)-CH_2-OH \xrightarrow{[O]} CH_3CH_2-CH(CH_3)-C(H)=O$$

   2-methylbutanal

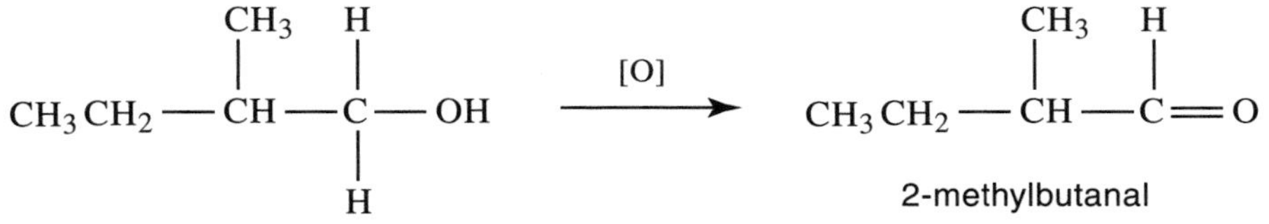

8. $CH_3CH_2OCH_2CH_3$, same type of compounds (ethers)

9. a. $CH_3CH(OH)CH_3 \xrightarrow[\text{high temp.}]{H^+} CH_3-CH=CH_2 + HOH$

b. $CH_3CH_2CH_2OH \xrightarrow[\text{high temp.}]{H^+} CH_3-CH=CH_2 + HOH$

c. $CH_3CH_2OH \xrightarrow[\text{high temp.}]{H^+} H_2C=CH_2 + HOH$

d. $CH_3CH(OH)CH_2CH_3 \xrightarrow[\text{high temp.}]{H^+} CH_3-CH=CH-CH_3 + HOH$

e. $CH_3CH_2C(=O)\text{-}OH \xrightarrow{[H]} CH_3CH_2CH(=O)$

f. cyclohexanone $\xrightarrow{[H]}$ cyclohexanol (C bearing H and OH)

g. $CH_3CH(OH)CH_2CH_3 \xrightarrow{[O]} CH_3C(=O)CH_2CH_3$

h. 1-methylcyclopentanol (ring C bearing CH_3 and OH) $\xrightarrow{[O]}$ No Reaction

i. $CH_3CH_2C(CH_3)_2\text{-}OH \xrightarrow{[O]}$ No Reaction

j. cyclohexanol (ring C bearing OH) $\xrightarrow{[O]}$ cyclohexanone (ring C=O)

k. $CH_3CH_2CH_2OH \xrightarrow{[O]} CH_3CH_2C(H)=O$

Module 11

1. tetrose

2. a.

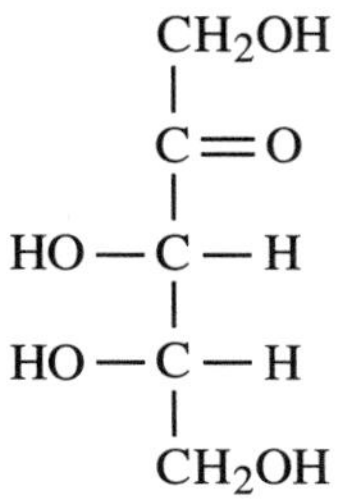

$$\begin{array}{c} CH_2OH \\ | \\ C{=}O \\ | \\ HO-C-H \\ | \\ HO-C-H \\ | \\ CH_2OH \end{array}$$

b.

$$\begin{array}{c} H-C{=}O \\ | \\ HO-C-H \\ | \\ CH_2OH \end{array}$$

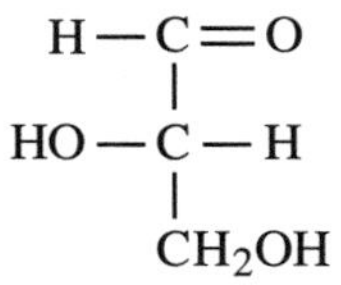

3. aldotetrose

4. Haworth

5. a.

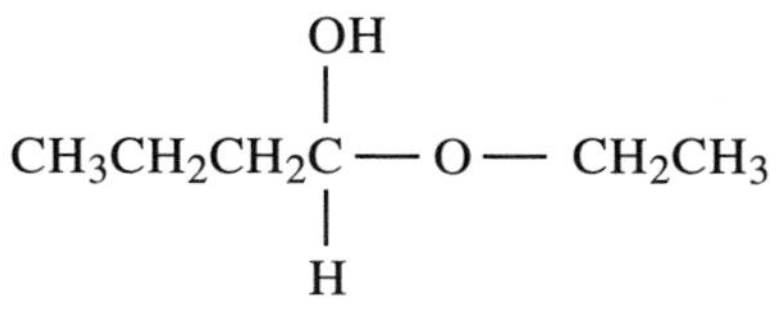

$$\begin{array}{c} OH \\ | \\ CH_3CH_2CH_2C-O-CH_2CH_3 \\ | \\ H \end{array}$$

b.

$$\begin{array}{c} OH \\ | \\ CH_3CH_2C-CH_3 \\ | \\ O-CH_3 \end{array}$$

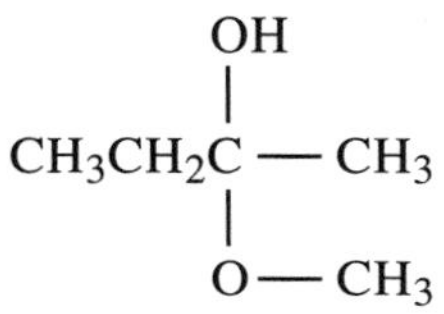

6. glucose

7. D isomer, the –OH group in C-5 is on the right side.

8.

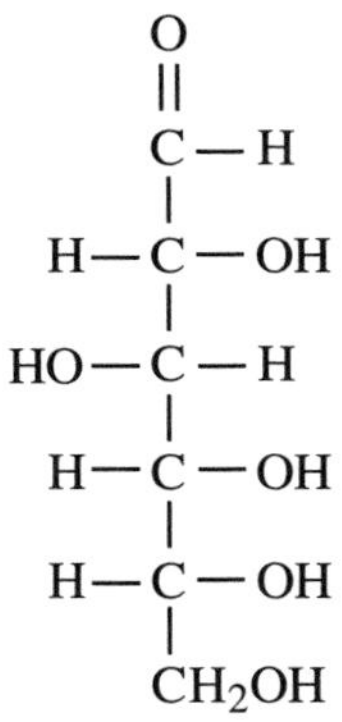

$$\begin{array}{c} O \\ \| \\ C-H \\ | \\ H-C-OH \\ | \\ HO-C-H \\ | \\ H-C-OH \\ | \\ H-C-OH \\ | \\ CH_2OH \end{array}$$

a. D-glucose

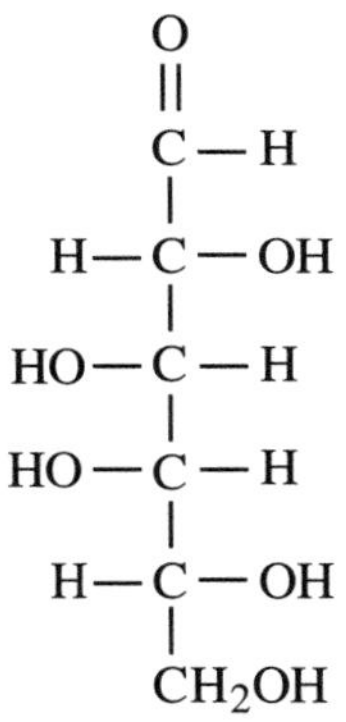

$$\begin{array}{c} O \\ \| \\ C-H \\ | \\ H-C-OH \\ | \\ HO-C-H \\ | \\ HO-C-H \\ | \\ H-C-OH \\ | \\ CH_2OH \end{array}$$

b. D-galactose

$$\begin{array}{c} CH_2OH \\ | \\ C{=}O \\ | \\ HO-C-H \\ | \\ H-C-OH \\ | \\ H-C-OH \\ | \\ CH_2OH \end{array}$$

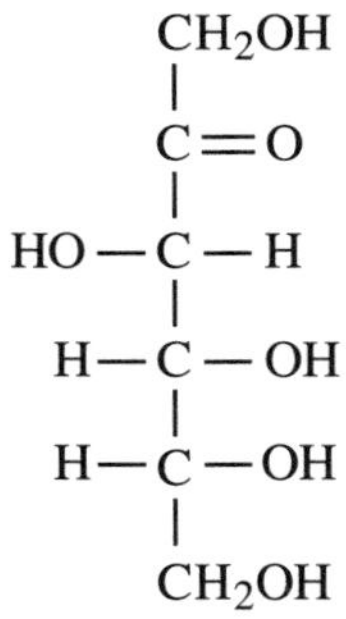

c. D-fructose

9.

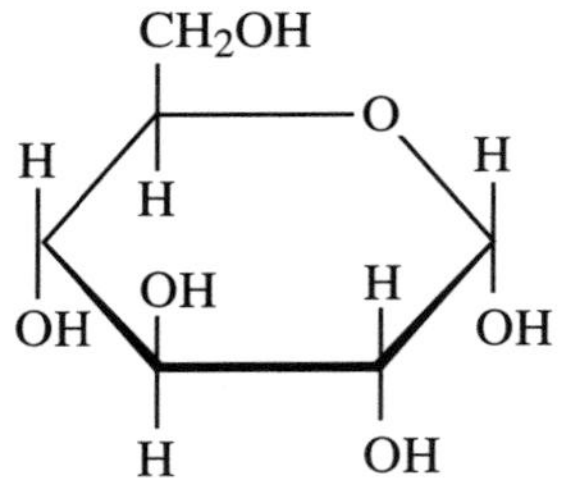

a. α-D-glucose

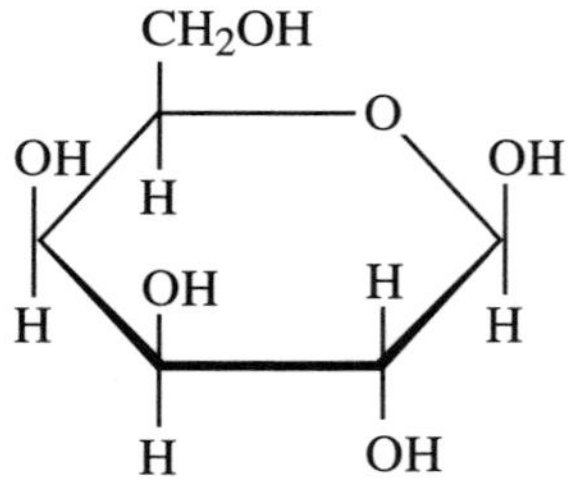

b. β-D-galactose

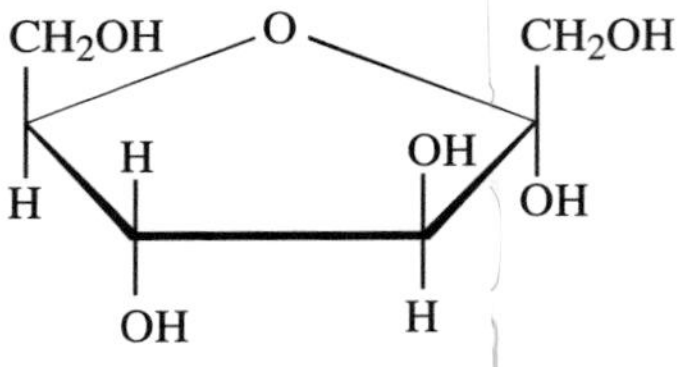

c. α-D-fructose

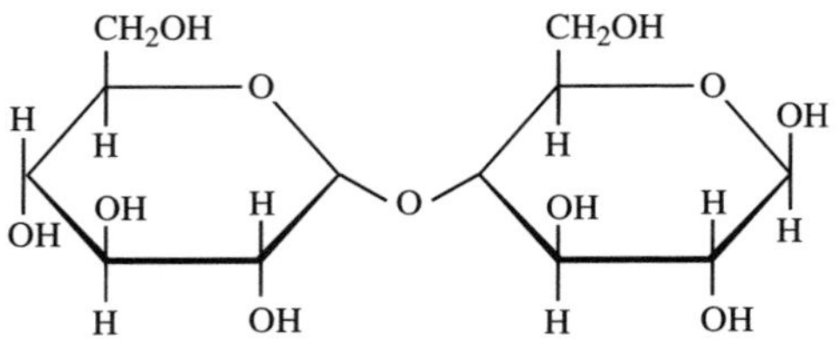

d. β-maltose

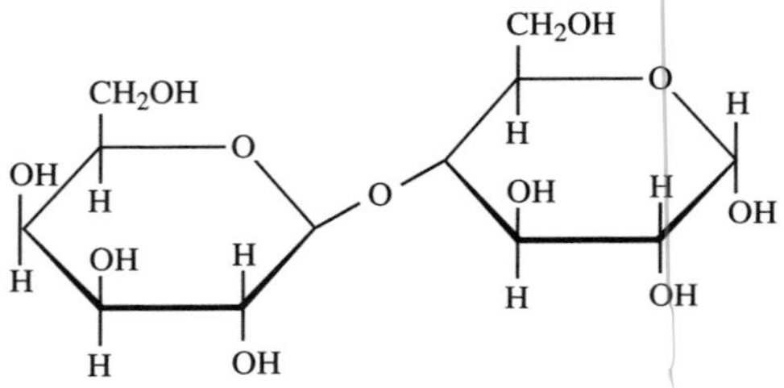

e. α-lactose

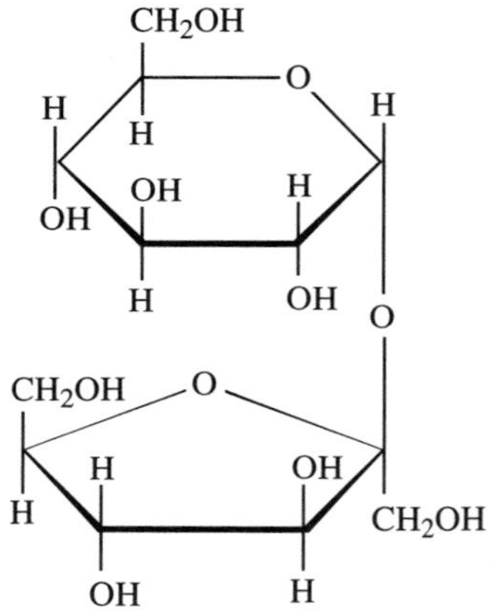

f. sucrose

10. two glucose molecules

11. mutarotation

12. glycogen

13. a. amylose and cellulose

    Both are polysaccharides (polymers of glucose). Amylose has α-1,4-glycosidic linkages while cellulose has β-1,4-glycosidic linkages. They are both straight chains—not branched and both are from plants.

    b. amylose and amylopectin

    Both are polysaccharides (polymers of glucose) connected by α-1,4-glycosidic linkages. Both are present in starch. Amylopectin has α-1,6- branch points while amylose has no branching.

    c. amylopectin and glycogen

    Both are polysaccharides (polymers of glucose) connected by α-1,4-glycosidic linkages. Amylopectin is found in plants and glycogen is the polysaccharide found in animals to store excess glucose. Both have α-1,6- branch points, but there is more branching in glycogen.

14. a. The blue solution (Cu^{2+} ions) changes to a brick orange precipitate (Cu_2O).

    b. A blue-black iodine/starch complex is produced.

    c. For each of the following carbohydrates, indicate whether the Benedict's test is positive or negative and whether the iodine test is positive or negative.

Sugar	Benedict's Test	Iodine Test
sucrose	negative	negative
glucose	positive	negative
fructose	positive	negative
lactose	positive	negative
starch	negative	positive
glycogen	negative	positive

Module 12

1. Classify each of the following as a/an aldehyde, alcohol, carboxylic acid, ester, ether, or ketone.

   a. ketone b. ether c. ester

   d. aldehyde e. carboxylic acid f. ether

   g. ester h. alcohol

2. 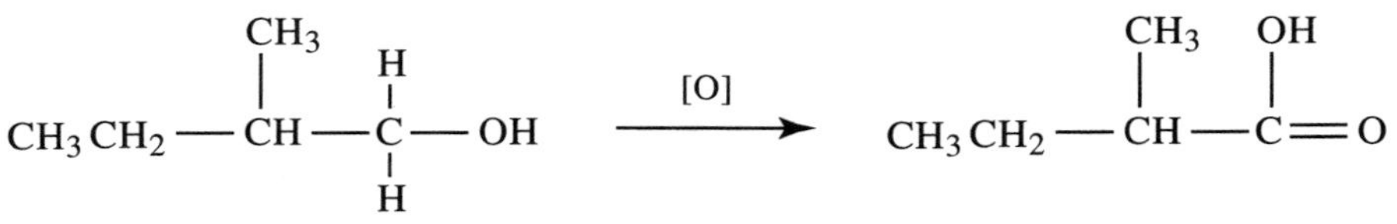 $$CH_3CH_2-\underset{\displaystyle CH_3}{CH}-\underset{H}{\overset{H}{C}}-OH \xrightarrow{[O]} CH_3CH_2-\underset{\displaystyle CH_3}{CH}-\overset{\displaystyle OH}{C}=O$$

3. ester

4. carboxylate salt and alcohol

5. a. neutralization $CH_3CH_2CH_2-\overset{O}{\overset{\|}{C}}-O^{\ominus}\ Na^{+}\ +\ HOH$

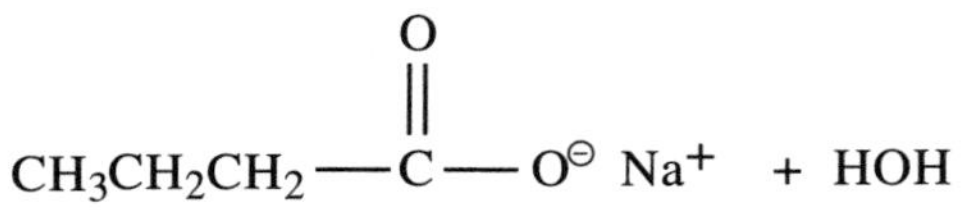

   b. esterification $CH_3CH_2CH_2-\overset{O}{\overset{\|}{C}}-O-\underset{CH_3}{\overset{H}{C}}-CH_2CH_3\ +\ HOH$

   c. esterification $CH_3CH_2\underset{CH_3}{CH}-\overset{O}{\overset{\|}{C}}-O-\underset{H}{\overset{H}{C}}-CH_3\ +\ HOH$

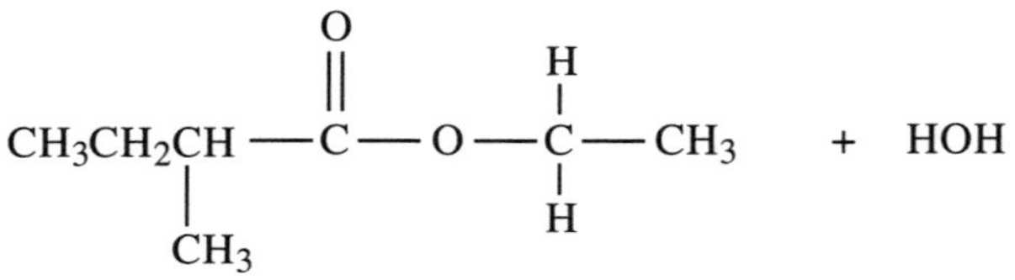

   d. acid hydrolysis $CH_3-\overset{O}{\overset{\|}{C}}-OH\ +\ HO-CH_2CH_2CH_2CH_3$

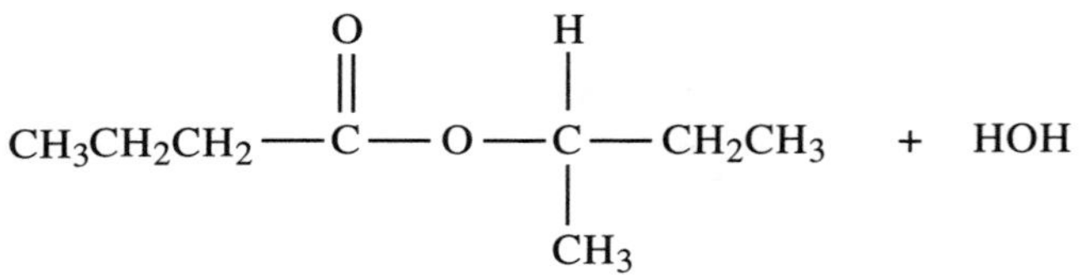

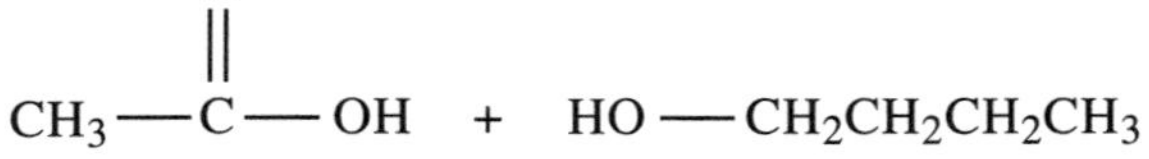

   e. basic hydrolysis $CH_3CH_2CH_2-\overset{O}{\overset{\|}{C}}-O^{\ominus}\ Na^{+}\ +\ HO-CH_2CH_2CH_3$

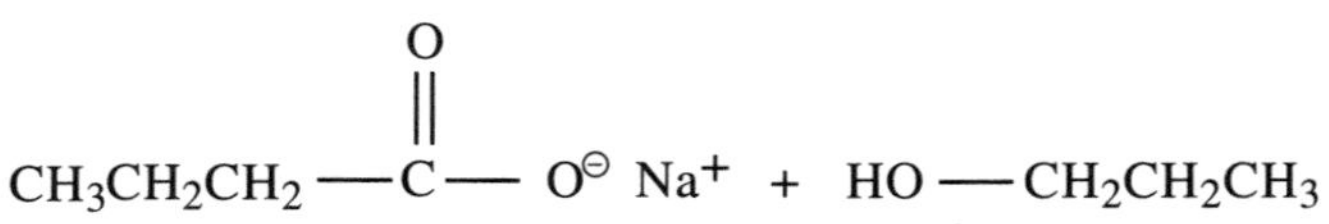

   f. esterification $CH_3CH_2-\overset{O}{\overset{\|}{C}}-O-\underset{H}{\overset{H}{C}}-CH_3\ +\ HOH$

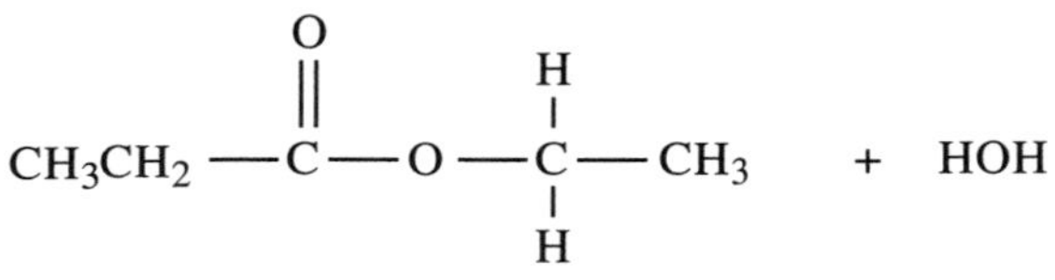

g. basic hydrolysis (cyclohexanol) $C_6H_{11}OH$ + $Na^+ \ ^-O{-}C(=O){-}CH_2CH_2CH_2CH_3$

h. neutralization $CH_3CH_2{-}C(=O){-}O^- \ K^+$ + HOH

i. basic hydrolysis $H_3C{-}C(=O){-}O^- \ Na^+$ + $HO{-}CH_2CH_3$

6. The following compound is produced from the reaction of (draw structures)

$$C_6H_{11}{-}C(=O){-}OH \; + \; HO{-}CH(CH_3){-}CH_3$$

Module 13

1. a. amide b. primary amine c. secondary amine
   d. primary amine e. tertiary amine f. secondary amine
   g. primary amine

2. Amines react with water to produce hydroxide ions.

3. a. $CH_3{-}CH_2{-}NH_2 + H_2O \longrightarrow CH_3{-}CH_2{-}NH_3^+ + OH^-$

   b. $CH_3{-}NH{-}CH_3 + H_2O \longrightarrow CH_3{-}N^+H_2{-}CH_3 + OH^-$

   c. $CH_3{-}CH_2{-}C(=O){-}OH \; + \; H{-}N(H){-}CH_3$

Module 14

1. Waxes, triacylglycerides, glycerophospholipid, and steroids.

2. Saturated fats come from <u>animal</u> sources, and usually are <u>solids</u> at room temperature.

3. Unsaturated fats come from <u>plant</u> sources, and usually are <u>liquid</u> at room temperature.

4. Glycerol, fatty acids, phosphate group and amino alcohol.

5. a. Triacylglycerol
   b. Esterification
   c. Water in the presence of acid
   d. Carboxylate salts (soaps) and glycerol

6. A sodium or potassium salt of a fatty acid is commonly called <u>soap</u>.

7. a.

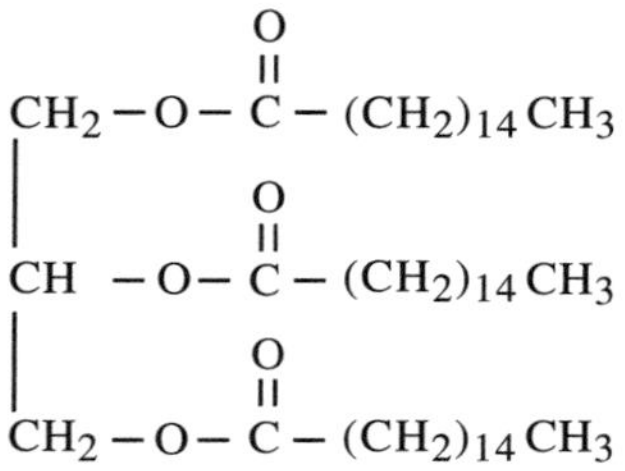

$$
\begin{array}{l}
CH_2-O-\overset{\overset{\displaystyle O}{\|}}{C}-(CH_2)_{14}CH_3 \\
| \\
CH\ -O-\overset{\overset{\displaystyle O}{\|}}{C}-(CH_2)_{14}CH_3 \\
| \\
CH_2-O-\overset{\overset{\displaystyle O}{\|}}{C}-(CH_2)_{14}CH_3
\end{array}
$$

   b. saturated

8. a. unsaturated

   b. hydrogenation product

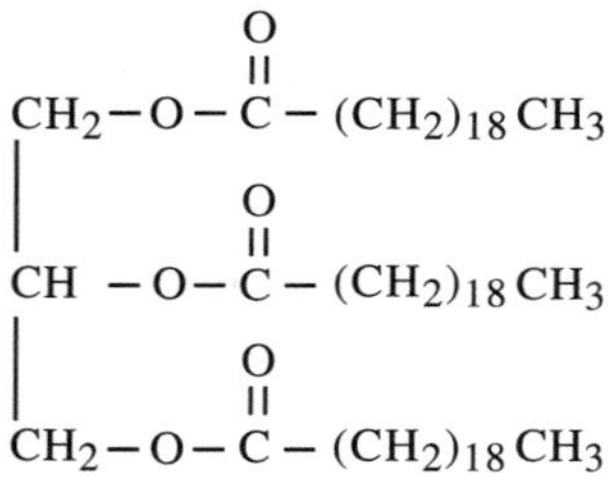

$$
\begin{array}{l}
CH_2-O-\overset{\overset{\displaystyle O}{\|}}{C}-(CH_2)_{18}CH_3 \\
| \\
CH\ -O-\overset{\overset{\displaystyle O}{\|}}{C}-(CH_2)_{18}CH_3 \\
| \\
CH_2-O-\overset{\overset{\displaystyle O}{\|}}{C}-(CH_2)_{18}CH_3
\end{array}
$$

c. hydrolysis products

$$
\begin{array}{llll}
CH_2-OH & + & HO-\overset{\displaystyle O}{\overset{\|}{C}}-(CH_2)_8CH{=}CH(CH_2)_8CH_3 \\
| & & \\
CH-OH & + & HO-\overset{\displaystyle O}{\overset{\|}{C}}-(CH_2)_8CH{=}CH(CH_2)_8CH_3 \\
| & & \\
CH_2-OH & + & HO-\overset{\displaystyle O}{\overset{\|}{C}}-(CH_2)_8CH{=}CH(CH_2)_8CH_3
\end{array}
$$

d. saponification products

$$
\begin{array}{llll}
CH_2-OH & + & Na^+\ {}^-O-\overset{\displaystyle O}{\overset{\|}{C}}-(CH_2)_8CH{=}CH(CH_2)_8CH_3 \\
| & & \\
CH-OH & + & Na^+\ {}^-O-\overset{\displaystyle O}{\overset{\|}{C}}-(CH_2)_8CH{=}CH(CH_2)_8CH_3 \\
| & & \\
CH_2-OH & + & Na^+\ {}^-O-\overset{\displaystyle O}{\overset{\|}{C}}-(CH_2)_8CH{=}CH(CH_2)_8CH_3
\end{array}
$$

9. steroid nucleus.

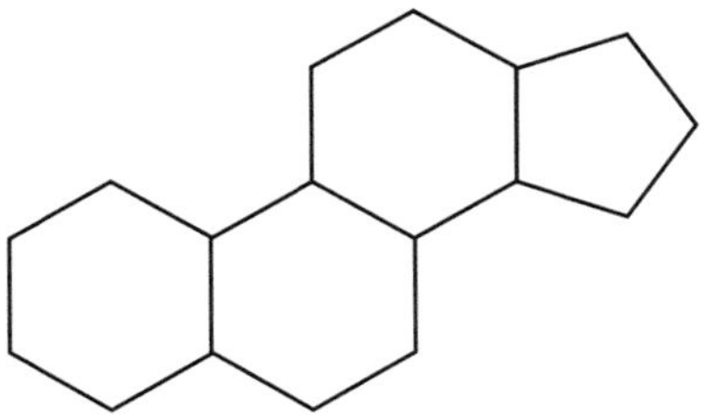

10. Controls the movement of particles in and out of the cell.
11. Vitamins A, D, E, and K.
12. 124 Calories

16 g carbohydrate × 4 Cal/g	=	64 Cal from carbohydrates
6 g proteins × 4 Cal/g	=	24 Cal from proteins
4 g fat × 9 Cal/g	=	36 Cal from fat
Total Calories	=	124 Calories

13. The label for a granola bar gives the following: Fat, 6 grams; carbohydrates, 29 grams; protein, 4 grams. Calculate the total Calories. What percentage of the total Calories are fat Calories?

6 g fat × 9 Cal/g	=	54 Cal from fat
29 g carbohydrate × 4 Cal/g	=	116 Cal from carbohydrates
4 g proteins × 4 Cal/g	=	16 Cal
Total Calories	=	186 Cal

% Cal from fat = 54/186 × 100 = 29.0%

Module 15

1. Enzymatic catalysis; transport and storage; coordinated motion; structural; immune protection; hormones; generation and transmission of nerve impulses.

2. $H—N^{+}H_2—CH(CH_3)—C(=O)—O^-$

3. a. $H—NH—CH(CH_2SH)—C(=O)—O^-$ b. $H—N^{+}H_2—CH(CH_2SH)—C(=O)—OH$ c. $H—N^{+}H_2—CH(CH_2SH)—C(=O)—O^-$

4. a. $H_2N—CH(CH_2—CH(CH_3)—CH_3)—C(=O)—NH—CH(CH_2—CH_2—CH_2—CH_2—NH_2)—C(=O)—NH—CH(CH_2—OH)—C(=O)—OH$

b. $H_2N-CH(CH_2-C(=O)-OH)-C(=O)-N(H)-CH(CH(CH_3)-CH_3)-C(=O)-N(H)-CH(CH_2-C_6H_4-OH)-C(=O)-OH$

5. secondary

6. quaternary

7. tertiary

8. primary

9. secondary

10. secondary

11. tertiary

12. H-bond; disulfide linkage; hydrophobic region; salt bridge

13. amino acids

14. negatively charged

15. glycine; alanine; valine; leucine; isoleucine; phenylalanine; methionine; praline; tryptophan

16. serine; threonine; tyrosine; cysteine; asparagines; glutamine

17. The loss of biological activity

18. Heat and ultraviolet radiation; alcohol and other organic solvents; reducing agents; pH changes; heavy metals

19. a. glucose b. glucose c. glycerol + 3 fatty acids
    d. no change e. amino acids

20. E + S → E-S → E-P → E + P

21. "ase," substrate

22. a. conjugated, Mg^{2+}
    b. conjugated, vitamin E
    c. simple
    d. conjugated, carbohydrate

23. cofactor

24. a. isomerase b. transferase
    c. decarboxylase d. hydrolase

25. a. remain the same b. increase

26. a. noncompetitive
    b. competitive
    c. noncompetitive

27. Changes the overall shape of the enzyme, thereby changing the shape of the active site.

28. An increase in temperature will generally speed up the rate of an enzyme-catalyzed reaction; however, if the temperature increase starts to denature the enzyme, then the reaction is slowed down.

Module 16

1. a. DNA
   b. RNA
   c. RNA
   d. Both RNA and DNA
   e. DNA
   f. RNA

2. a. deoxyribose and guanine
   b. ribose and cytosine
   c. deoxyribose, adenine, and phosphate
   d. ribose, uracil, and phosphate
   e. deoxyribose, thymine, and phosphate

3. a. adenine
   b. guanine
   c. adenine
   d. cytosine

4. a. A—T—T—A—G—C—G—C—T

   b. G—A—A—C—T—G—G—C—A

   c. C—A—C—T—G—A—G—G—C

5. a. 2
   b. 3
   c. 1

6. a. 3
   b. 1
   c. 2

7. a. The step within protein synthesis creates the template for the amino acid sequence in a protein molecule.
   b. The step within protein synthesis where the tRNA matches a codon in the mRNA that specifies a particular amino acid.
   c. The step within protein synthesis that ends the production of a protein molecule.

8. a. C—U—G—A—G—U—G—C—G
   b. G—A—C—C—U—A—G—U—A
   c. C—U—G—U—G—C—G—G—C

9. a. A—C—C   b. U—G—C   c. C—A—G

D

Extra Learning Resources: Practice Quizzes

Practice Quiz #1—Modules 1–3

1. What is the mass, in grams, of 50.0 mL of ethyl alcohol, which has a density of 0.790 g/mL?
   a. 0.0158 g
   b. 63.3 g
   c. 49.2 g
   d. 39.5 g
   e. 63,300 g
2. Convert 61.0 degrees Fahrenheit to degrees Celsius.
   a. 1.89°C
   b. 118.6°C
   c. 16.1°C
   d. 51.7°C
   e. 52.2°C
3. An injured person is losing blood at a rate of 0.430 mL/sec. If it takes 16.0 minutes to transport the person to the hospital, and blood loss continues at the same rate, how many liters of blood will be lost by the time the person reaches the hospital?
   a. 1.61 L
   b. 37.2 L
   c. 0.413 L
   d. 24.8 L
   e. 413 L

4. How many liters are there in 4.45 qt?
   a. 2.23 L
   b. 9.41 L
   c. 8.42 L
   d. 4.70 L
   e. 4.21 L
5. Which is the basic unit of length in the metric system?
   a. liter
   b. gram
   c. kilogram
   d. meter
   e. centimeter
6. 38.2 mL is a measure of:
   a. density
   b. distance
   c. mass
   d. volume
   e. temperature
7. 6.75 grams are equivalent to:
   a. 0.675 kg
   b. 67.5 cg
   c. 675 dg
   d. 0.0675 kg
   e. 6750 mg
8. A slice of cake contains 8 grams protein, 15 grams fat and 22 grams carbohydrate. What is the total number of Calories in this slice, if the caloric values of proteins, fats, and carbohydrates are 4 kcal/g, 9 kcal/g, and 4 kcal/g, respectively?
   a. 255 Cal
   b. 295 Cal
   c. 135 Cal
   d. 180 Cal
   e. 365 Cal
9. Consider a neutral atom with 28 protons, 28 electrons and 32 neutrons. The mass number for this atom is:
   a. 28
   b. 32
   c. 56
   d. 60
   e. 88

10. Which of the following elements is a metal?
    a. phosphorus
    b. fluorine
    c. argon
    d. nitrogen
    e. strontium
11. Which of the following elements is a noble gas?
    a. bromine
    b. nitrogen
    c. sodium
    d. strontium
    e. argon
12. Conversion from solid to gas is:
    a. freezing
    b. sublimation
    c. deposition
    d. evaporation
    e. condensation
13. What is the electron shell arrangement (shorthand notation) for the aluminum atom?
    a. 2,8,8
    b. 2,8,5
    c. 2,8,7
    d. 2,8,3
    e. 2,8,10
14. The symbol for the element sulfur is:
    a. S
    b. Si
    c. Sc
    d. Su
    e. Sf
15. Elements in group 5A of the periodic table form ions with a charge of:
    a. 0
    b. 3^+
    c. 1^-
    d. 3^-
    e. 1^+

16. What is the symbol for the ion with 19 protons and 18 electrons?
    a. K^-
    b. F^+
    c. F^-
    d. K^+
    e. Ar^+
17. How many valence electrons are in the electron-dot structures for the elements in group 2A?
    a. 1
    b. 2
    c. 3
    d. 4
    e. 5
18. What is the name for $FeSO_4$?
    a. iron (I) sulfate
    b. iron (III) sulfate
    c. iron sulfite
    d. iron (II) sulfide
    e. iron (II) sulfate
19. What is the formula of silicon tetrachloride?
    a. Si_2Cl_4
    b. SiCl
    c. $SiCl_3$
    d. $SiCl_5$
    e. $SiCl_4$
20. How many electrons will sulfur gain or lose when it forms an ion?
    a. lose 2
    b. gain 6
    c. lose 1
    d. gain 1
    e. gain 2

Practice Quiz #2—Modules 4–8

1. Calculate the number of grams present in 0.507 moles of NaCl:
   a. 23.5 grams
   b. 115.4 grams
   c. 18.0 grams
   d. 29.7 grams
   e. 58.5 grams
2. 0.270 mole of magnesium weighs:
   a. 90.0 g
   b. 5.40 g
   c. 0.270 g
   d. 6.56 g
   e. 0.243 g
3. Calculate the formula weight of $Cr_2(SO_4)_3$
   a. 328 grams/mole
   b. 248 grams/mole
   c. 212 grams/mole
   d. 348 grams/mole
   e. 392 grams/mole
4. OPTIONAL

   In the reaction of nitrogen gas with hydrogen gas to form ammonia gas, NH_3, how many moles of hydrogen are needed to react to produce four moles of ammonia?

   $N_2 + 3\ H_2 \rightarrow 2\ NH_3$
   a. 4 moles
   b. 8 moles
   c. 6 moles
   d. 12 moles
   e. 3 moles
5. Balance the following combustion reaction with the smallest whole number coefficient possible, and choose the number that is the SUM of the coefficients in the balanced equation. Don't forget coefficients of "one."

   $\_\ C_5H_{12} + \_\ O_2 \rightarrow \_\ CO_2 + \_\ H_2O$
   a. 13
   b. 18
   c. 19
   d. 20
   e. None of these

6. The atomic mass of a copper atom is:
   a. 63.55 g.
   b. 29.0 amu.
   c. 6.02×10^{23} grams.
   d. 63.55 amu.
   e. 127.1 amu.
7. OPTIONAL
   Consider the equation for the combustion of propane in a camping stove.
   $$C_3H_8 + 5\ O_2 \rightarrow 3\ CO_2 + 4\ H_2O$$
   How many moles of H_2O are formed if 0.385 moles of C_3H_8 are completely burned?
   a. 1.54 moles
   b. 5.01 moles
   c. 1.16 moles
   d. 2.70 moles
   e. 0.0963 moles
8. A red blood cell will undergo hemolysis in:
   a. pure water
   b. 5% NaCl
   c. 10% glucose
   d. 0.9% NaCl
   e. 5% glucose
9. When a small amount of sugar is added to warm tea and it dissolves completely, and even more sugar may be added and dissolved, the solution is:
   a. saturated.
   b. supersaturated.
   c. polar.
   d. unsaturated.
   e. nonpolar.
10. Water is a polar solvent and benzene C_6H_6 is a nonpolar solvent. Which of the following correctly describes the solubility of the solute?
   a. CCl_4, soluble in benzene
   b. mineral oil, soluble in water
   c. olive oil, soluble in water
   d. sodium carbonate, soluble in benzene
   e. octane, soluble in water

11. Which of the following is a strong electrolyte?
    a. HCl
    b. $C_6H_{12}O_6$
    c. KBr
    d. none of these
    e. two of these
12. When water moves through a semipermeable membrane from an area of higher concentration of water to one of lower concentration of water, this process is called:
    a. osmosis
    b. dialysis
    c. ionization
    d. neutralization
    e. electrolysis
13. How many mL of a 30% solution of isopropyl alcohol would you need to make 150 mL of a 20% solution of isopropyl alcohol?
    a. 20.0 mL
    b. 150 mL
    c. 30.0 mL
    d. 225 mL
    e. 100 mL
14. What is the molarity of a solution that contains 48.0 g of sulfuric acid, H_2SO_4, in 250 mL of solution?
    a. 1.96 M
    b. 0.490 M
    c. 0.00196 M
    d. 0.122 M
    e. none of these
15. The function of a buffer is to:
    a. maintain the pH of a solution.
    b. change color at the end point of a titration.
    c. act as a strong acid.
    d. be a strong base.
    e. maintain a neutral pH.

16. In hyperventilation, the blood more rapidly:
    a. loses H^+
    b. loses Na
    c. loses CO_2
    d. loses both CO_2 and H^+
    e. none of these are correct
17. When HCl reacts with NaOH to produce NaCl and H_2O, this is a ______ reaction.
    a. dissociation
    b. reduction
    c. oxidation
    d. neutralization
    e. ionization
18. Consider a solution with a hydrogen ion concentration of 10^{-3} M. The pOH of this solution is:
    a. 1.0
    b. 3.0
    c. 7.0
    d. 11.0
    e. 14.0
19. A solution with a pH of 2 is:
    a. slightly basic.
    b. extremely acidic.
    c. slightly acidic.
    d. neutral.
    e. extremely basic.
20. Which of the following groups of formulas represent only weak acids?
    a. HNO_2, HCl, HI
    b. H_2SO_4, $HClO^4$, HCl
    c. H_3PO_4, HI, HNO_3
    d. HCl, HI, HF
    e. H_2CO_3, HF, HClO
21. Which one of the following is characteristic of a base?
    a. is insoluble in water
    b. produces hydrogen ions in water
    c. neutralizes bases
    d. has a sour taste
    e. turns red litmus blue

22. A nuclear emission that is equivalent to a helium nucleus is:
    a. gamma ray
    b. neutron
    c. beta particle
    d. proton
    e. alpha particle
23. Strontium-85 is an isotope containing:
    a. 47 protons and 38 neutrons.
    b. 38 protons and 47 neutrons.
    c. 38 protons and 85 neutrons.
    d. 85 protons and 47 neutrons.
    e. 85 protons and 38 neutrons.
24. Krypton-79 has a half-life of 35 hours. How many half-lives have passed after 140 hours?
    a. 5 half-lives
    b. 1 half-life
    c. 4 half-lives
    d. 2 half-lives
    e. 3 half-lives
25. What is the name of the missing product?

    W-159 → Hf-155 + ?
    a. alpha particle
    b. neutron
    c. proton
    d. beta particle
    e. gamma ray
26. The air that humans exhale consists primarily of nitrogen, oxygen, carbon dioxide and water vapor. Under a total pressure of 745 torr, the partial pressures for nitrogen, oxygen and carbon dioxide are respectively: 567 torr, 105 torr and 35 torr. What is the value for the partial pressure of water vapor?
    a. 1207 torr
    b. 38 torr
    c. 1452 torr
    d. 73 torr
    e. it depends on the weather

27. The speed of gas particles is directly related to the ______ of the gas.
    a. quantity of gas
    b. density
    c. volume
    d. pressure.
    e. temperature

Practice Quiz #3—Modules 9–11

1. Some alkenes have geometric (cis-trans) isomers because:
    a. each of the carbon atoms in the double bond has four different groups attached to it.
    b. the carbon atoms in the double bond are free to rotate.
    c. all of the carbon atoms in the compound are rigid and cannot rotate.
    d. the carbon atoms in the double bond cannot rotate.
    e. one of the carbon atoms in the double bond has two identical groups attached to it.
2. A formula that shows the arrangement of all bonds in a molecule is called a(n):
    a. isomeric formula.
    b. structural formula.
    c. molecular formula.
    d. condensed structural formula.
3. Hydrocarbons that contain only single bonds are:
    a. aromatic
    b. alkanes
    c. haloalkanes
    d. alkenes
    e. alkynes
4. Hydrogen atoms always have how many covalent bonds?
    a. one
    b. four
    c. three
    d. two
    e. five
5. The compounds CH_3-CH_2-OH and CH_3-O-CH_3 are:
    a. alcohols
    b. ethers
    c. isosteres
    d. isotopes
    e. isomers

6. The reaction of Cl_2 with $CH_3CH = CHCH_3$:
   a. is a combustion reaction
   b. produces 2,3-dichlorobutane
   c. is an oxidation reaction
   d. TWO of the previous choices are correct
   e. NONE of the above choices are correct
7. An alkane with a continuous chain of five carbon atoms is?
   a. pentane
   b. propane
   c. hexane
   d. heptane
   e. butane
8. The structural formula of benzene is often represented as a:
   a. cycloalkane.
   b. ring of five carbon atoms.
   c. cycloalkyne.
   d. ring of six carbon atoms with a circle in the center.
   e. ring of six carbon atoms with six double bonds.
9. The correct name for this structure is:

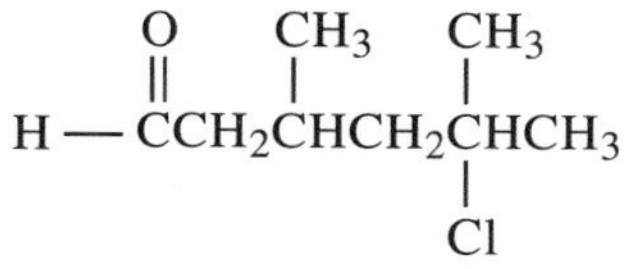

   $$H-\overset{\overset{\displaystyle O}{\|}}{C}CH_2\overset{\overset{\displaystyle CH_3}{|}}{C}HCH_2\underset{\underset{\displaystyle Cl}{|}}{\overset{\overset{\displaystyle CH_3}{|}}{C}}HCH_3$$

   a. 2-chloro-2,4-dimethyl-6-hexanal
   b. 5-chloro-3,5-dimethyl-1-hexanal
   c. 5-chloro-3,5-dimethylhexanal
   d. 2-chloro-2,4-dimethyl-6-hexanone
   e. 5-chloro-3,5-dimethylhexanone
10. Which of the following alcohols is the *most* soluble in water?
    a. 1-pentanol.
    b. ethanol.
    c. 1-hexanol.
    d. 1-heptanol.
    e. 1-butanol.
11. The oxidation of a tertiary alcohol produces:
    a. no reaction
    b. a secondary alcohol
    c. a ketone
    d. a tertiary alcohol
    e. an aldehyde

12. Which type of alcohol can normally be oxidized?
    a. both primary and secondary alcohols
    b. all classes of alcohols
    c. tertiary alcohol
    d. secondary alcohol
    e. primary alcohol
13. Identify the product of the following reaction:

    a. 1-butene
    b. 2-butanol
    c. 2-butene
    d. butanone
    e. butanal
14. What kind of bonds do alcohols form *between* individual molecules?
    a. hydrogen bonds
    b. carbon bonds
    c. ionic bonds
    d. oxygen bonds
    e. single bonds
15. A monosaccharide that consists of 4 carbon atoms, one of which is in a ketone group, is classified as a(n):
    a. ketotetrose.
    b. aldopentose.
    c. ketopentose.
    d. aldotetrose.
    e. aldohexose.
16. An example of a polyaccharide is(are): I. sucrose II. fructose III. galactose IV. amylose
    a. I and II
    b. II and IV
    c. IV only
    d. II and III
    e. None of these
17. Which sugar is NOT a reducing sugar?
    a. maltose
    b. lactose
    c. galactose
    d. glucose
    e. sucrose

18. A polypeptide with α-1,4 AND α-1,6 glycosidic linkages is:
    a. lactose
    b. cellulose
    c. amylose
    d. amylopectin
    e. maltose
19. Lactose can be hydrolyzed to:
    a. glucose and glucose
    b. glucose and fructose
    c. fructose and galactose
    d. galactose and glucose
    e. galactose and galactose
20. How many chiral carbons are there in this structure?

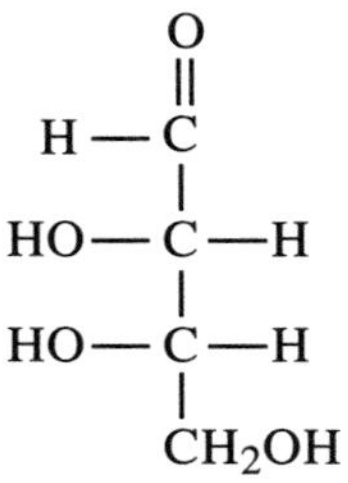

$$\begin{array}{c} \mathrm{O} \\ \| \\ \mathrm{H-C} \\ | \\ \mathrm{HO-C-H} \\ | \\ \mathrm{HO-C-H} \\ | \\ \mathrm{CH_2OH} \end{array}$$

    a. 1
    b. 2
    c. 3
    d. 4
    e. 5
21. In the cyclic structures of D-glucose, the β -isomer has the –OH group:
    a. pointing upwards
    b. pointing either up or down depending on how the ring closes
    c. pointing downwards
    d. reacting to form the ether ring structure
    e. None of these

Practice Quiz #4—Modules 12–16

1. The reactants that will form an ester in the presence of an acid catalyst are:
   a. a carboxylic acid and an alcohol.
   b. an aldehyde and an alcohol.
   c. two carboxylic acids.
   d. two aldehydes.
   e. two alcohols.
2. Commercially, liquid vegetable oils are converted to solid fats such as margarine by:
   a. oxidation.
   b. hydrogenation.
   c. saponification.
   d. hydration.
   e. hydrolysis.
3. Amides are derivatives of _____ and _____.
   a. acids, alcohols
   b. amines, esters
   c. amines, acids
   d. alkanes, amines
   e. alcohols, acids
4. What is the method of preparing carboxylic acids from alcohols or aldehydes?
   a. reduction
   b. hydrolysis
   c. hydration
   d. oxidation
   e. saponification
5. In what kind of amine is the nitrogen bonded to three carbon atoms?
   a. primary
   b. secondary
   c. tertiary
   d. quaternary
   e. amide
6. The reaction of an ester with NaOH is known as:
   a. saponification.
   b. neutralization.
   c. oxidation.
   d. esterification.
   e. reduction

7. The products of the base catalyzed hydrolysis of a triacylglycerol are:
   a. fatty acids and glycerol.
   b. salts of fatty acids.
   c. phospholipids.
   d. the esters of fatty acids.
   e. salts of fatty acids and glycerol.
8. Lipids may be:
   a. components of cell membranes
   b. used for storage of energy
   c. hormones for metabolic regulation
   d. used as protective coating for hair, skin and feathers
   e. All of the above
9. A compound which contains three fatty acid molecules and glycerol may be:
   a. steroid
   b. triacylglycerols
   c. wax
   d. petroleum
   e. glycerophospholipid
10. The complete oxidation of 2-methyl-1-butanol results in:
   a. 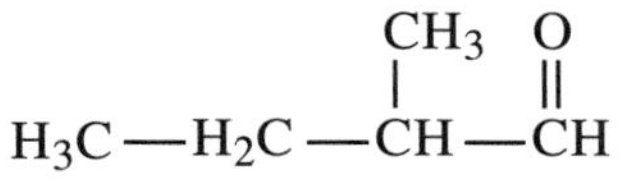 $H_3C—H_2C—\underset{\displaystyle CH}{\overset{\displaystyle CH_3}{|}}—\underset{\displaystyle CH}{\overset{\displaystyle O}{\|}}$
   b. 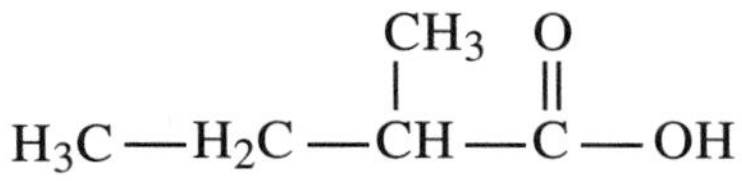 $H_3C—H_2C—\underset{\displaystyle CH}{\overset{\displaystyle CH_3}{|}}—\underset{\displaystyle C}{\overset{\displaystyle O}{\|}}—OH$
   c. $H_3C—H_2C—\underset{\displaystyle CH}{\overset{\displaystyle OH}{|}}—\underset{\displaystyle C}{\overset{\displaystyle O}{\|}}—H$
   d. 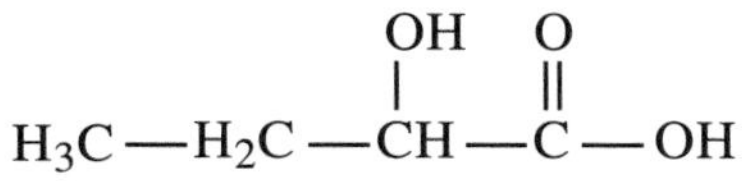 $H_3C—H_2C—\underset{\displaystyle CH}{\overset{\displaystyle OH}{|}}—\underset{\displaystyle C}{\overset{\displaystyle O}{\|}}—OH$
11. Name the following compound?

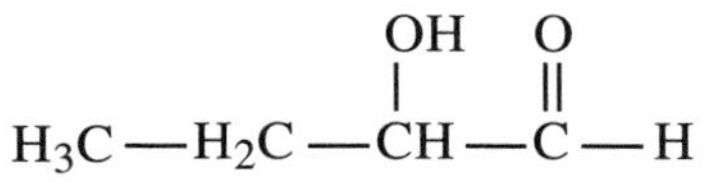

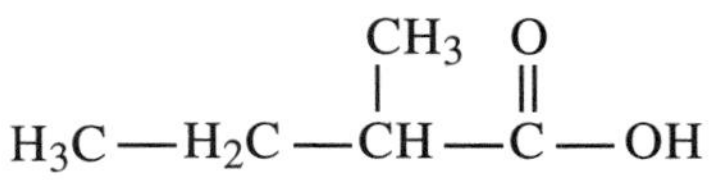

$$H_3C—H_2C—\underset{\displaystyle CH}{\overset{\displaystyle CH_3}{|}}—\underset{\displaystyle C}{\overset{\displaystyle O}{\|}}—OH$$

   a. 2-methyl butanoic acid
   b. pentanoic acid
   c. 2-methylbutanal
   d. 3-methyl - 4-butanoic acid
   e. pentanone

12. The main lipid components in cellular membranes are:
    a. triacylglycerols.
    b. glycerolphospholipids.
    c. steroids.
    d. fatty acids.
    e. waxes.
13. Collagen, a protein found in tendons and cartilage, would be classified as a ______ protein.
    a. hormone
    b. structural
    c. catalytic
    d. transport
    e. storage
14. The tertiary structure of proteins is held together by:
    a. ionic attraction
    b. cross-linkages
    c. peptide bonds
    d. two of the above
    e. all of the above
15. Which of the following is NOT a function of proteins?
    a. stores the genetic information of a living organism
    b. provide structural components
    c. transport substances through the bloodstream
    d. catalyze reactions in the cells
    e. movement of muscles
16. Denaturation involves:
    a. the breaking of the peptide bonds.
    b. destruction of the primary structure.
    c. the return of a protein to its native conformation.
    d. destruction of the secondary and tertiary structure.
    e. None of the above.
17. Glycerophospholipids can interact both with other lipids and water because they contain:
    a. cholesterol
    b. polar regions and nonpolar regions
    c. saturated fatty acids
    d. glycerol
    e. double bonds

18. At a pH equal to its isoelectric pH an amino acid is:
    a. negatively charged
    b. very insoluble
    c. frustrated
    d. uncharged
    e. positively charged
19. A biological catalyst is called a(n) _____.
    a. coenzyme
    b. enzyme
    c. lipid
    d. cofactor
    e. substrate
20. The general function of an enzyme in the body is to:
    a. maintain homeostasis.
    b. eliminate waste products from the blood.
    c. maintain a neutral pH.
    d. catalyze chemical reactions.
    e. act as a reactant in carbohydrate storage.
21. How many different tripeptide molecules can be made from one molecule of glycine and two molecules of alanine?
    a. 1
    b. 2
    c. 3
    d. 4
    e. 5
22. A dipeptide has:
    a. many peptide bonds
    b. 2 peptide bonds
    c. 4 peptide bonds
    d. 3 peptide bonds
    e. 1 peptide bond
23. Which of the following is NOT true for a competitive inhibitor?
    a. Increasing the substrate concentration can reverse competitive inhibition.
    b. It binds to the enzyme at a site remote from the active site.
    c. It occupies the active site.
    d. It has a structure similar to the substrate.
    e. It cannot be converted to products.

24. The process of making RNA from DNA:
    a. transcription
    b. translation
    c. conjunction
    d. peptide synthesis
    e. this process cannot happen
25. Which of the following is not one of the bases in a DNA molecule?
    a. adenine
    b. cytosine
    c. uracil
    d. thymine
    e. guanine
26. What is a nucleotide?
    a. a phosphate, five-carbon sugar, and a nitrogen base
    b. a group of linked amino acids
    c. one half of a DNA molecule
    d. a protein, a sugar, and a phosphate
    e. a phosphate, a six-carbon sugar, and a nitrogen base
27. What is the role of ribosomes in protein synthesis?
    a. they provide a source of amino acids
    b. they provide a site for transfer RNA's to link to messenger RNA's
    c. they translate the basic DNA code using transfer RNA
    d. they carry proteins to their site of action
    e. they have no function in protein synthesis

ANSWERS Quiz 1:

1	2	3	4	5	6	7	8	9	10	11	12	13	14	15
D	C	C	E	D	D	E	A	D	E	E	B	D	A	D
16	**17**	**18**	**19**	**20**										
D	B	E	E	E										

ANSWERS Quiz 2:

1	2	3	4	5	6	7	8	9	10	11	12	13	14	15
D	D	E	C	D	D	A	A	D	A	E	A	E	A	A
16	**17**	**18**	**19**	**20**	**21**	**22**	**23**	**24**	**25**	**26**	**27**			
D	D	D	B	E	E	E	B	C	A	B	E			

ANSWERS Quiz 3:

1	2	3	4	5	6	7	8	9	10	11	12	13	14	15
D	B	B	A	E	B	A	D	C	B	A	A	D	A	A
16	**17**	**18**	**19**	**20**	**21**									
C	E	D	D	B	A									

ANSWERS Quiz 4:

1	2	3	4	5	6	7	8	9	10	11	12	13	14	15
A	B	C	D	C	A	E	E	B	B	A	B	B	D	A
16	**17**	**18**	**19**	**20**	**21**	**22**	**23**	**24**	**25**	**26**	**27**			
D	B	D	B	D	C	E	B	A	C	A	B